GUIDE TO THE REPTILES, AMPHIBIANS, AND FRESH-WATER FISHES OF FLORIDA

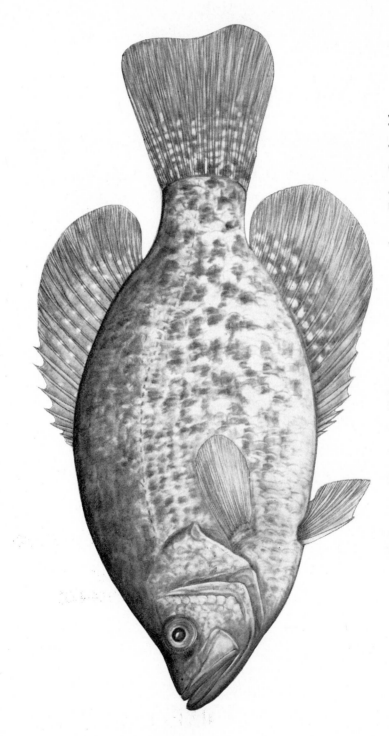

A popular Florida game fish—the Speckled Perch, *Pomoxis nigromaculatus*. Esther Coogle, *del.*

GUIDE to the

REPTILES, AMPHIBIANS

and FRESH-WATER FISHES

of FLORIDA

BY

ARCHIE CARR

GRADUATE RESEARCH PROFESSOR OF BIOLOGY,
UNIVERSITY OF FLORIDA, AND RESEARCH ASSOCIATE,
THE AMERICAN MUSEUM OF NATURAL HISTORY

AND

COLEMAN J. GOIN

PROFESSOR OF BIOLOGICAL SCIENCES,
UNIVERSITY OF FLORIDA, AND RESEARCH ASSOCIATE,
THE CARNEGIE MUSEUM

UNIVERSITY OF FLORIDA PRESS

Gainesville — 1959

To
the memory of
J. SPEED ROGERS

A UNIVERSITY OF FLORIDA PRESS BOOK

PREFACE

THIS IS A BOOK about the backboned animals of the classes Reptilia, Amphibia, and Pisces that are known to occur in Florida. These animals are often referred to collectively as "cold-blooded vertebrates" to contrast them with the mammals and birds, the so-called "warm-blooded vertebrates." This terminology is not very appropriate. A cold-blooded vertebrate sitting in the sun is likely to be pretty hot-blooded. No matter what we say, though, people will probably go right on using figures of speech like "a cold fish" or "cold as a frog," and probably no real harm will come of it.

However, there is another name for the group of animals we are concerned with, and in spite of our determination to avoid unnecessary technical terms we may use it from time to time. That name is exothermal. It is a good term for the creatures you will find in this book because it shows that you recognize the important fact that a lizard, say, is not always cold. With anything like a decent break a lizard can keep its temperature very stable; the word "exothermal" (*exo*—outside; *therm*—heat) means that the lizard does this by taking heat from, or losing it to, the environment, by moving back and forth between warm and cool—usually sunny and shady—places. This sounds like an annoying responsibility, but the lizard doesn't seem to mind. It doesn't have much else to do.

So in spite of the sort of professorial sound of the word, it's a handy one to have, and, as we say, we'll use it occasionally. We'll start off by saying that the state of Florida has more of these exotherms than any other equal area in the world. There are, in fact, 333 kinds of them here, and it is a mystery to us why nothing is made of this in the Chamber of Commerce advertising program. There is no use trying to hide the humiliating fact that, counting reptiles alone, California is better off than we are. But taking all the exotherms together—reptiles, amphibians, and fishes—Florida tops the whole world. If this should seem to you like a questionable sort of blessing that only a zoologist could find any advantage in, you ought to find out how many people pass Ross Allen's turnstiles each year just to look at snakes, or come to Florida because of the fishing, or say after they get here that they would go home content if they could only see a wild alligator. Once in a blue moon a snake hurts somebody, or the fishing lags, or the frogs wake up the baby; but on the whole our exotherms are a blessing—one of the real, marketable assets of the state and one deeply involved in our appeal to visitors from the outside.

We may not be able to hold on to the asset forever. Some way to do this may be worked out but so far the way has not been found. With people flocking in so fast, the day is not far off when the frog ponds will all be dry and still, and the bass fishing will all be in managed water, and the only alligators will be under fence. But for the time at least, we have a wonderful remnant of unfenced nature to color the Florida scene and we ought to enjoy it. Not just the zoologists, but everybody able to see the good in it. It is the purpose of this book to help people see the good in it.

The compiling of this guide has taken a scandalously long time and has involved us in indebtedness to a great many people. Most of these, including the continuous stream of graduate students of the Department of Biology, University of Florida, who have given their time or information, must remain anonymous except in our private memories. Besides them, there have been individuals whose contributions so materially advanced the growth of the book that they should be separately acknowledged.

The section of the text involving the greatest technical difficulties was that on the fishes. Here we encroached on the field of special interest of our colleague, Dr. John Kilby, and his knowledge, forbearance, and critical interest have been a comfort and a boon. Assistance with special ichthyological problems was furnished by Dr. Reeve Bailey, University of Michigan Museum of Zoology, whose help with the keys to the darters and minnows was indispensable; by Mr. John F. Dequine of Tallahassee; by Dr. Earl Herald of the Steinhart Aquarium; by Dr. William McLane of the Florida Game and Fresh Water Fish Commission, whose array of new records for Florida, and for marine fishes in fresh water, swelled our faunal list conspicuously; by Dr. Luis Rivas, University of Miami, who advised us on the classification of Centropomus and Gambusia; by Mr. Stewart Springer, United States Fish and Wildlife Service, who furnished information on fresh-water sharks and rays; by Dr. Royal Suttkus, Tulane University, who helped with the difficult genus Notropis; and by Dr. Ralph Yerger, Florida

State University, who gave us a number of new state records and has maintained a constant interest in the slow course of the project.

The frontispiece, all the line drawings, and the fine series of wash sketches illustrating the fish section are the work of Esther Coogle, Staff Artist of the Department of Biology, University of Florida. She made these a long time ago and has remained amazingly cheerful through the years that they never saw the light.

Mr. Ross Allen of Silver Springs has been an unfailing source of information, encouragement, and material. He and his associate, Mr. Wilfred Neill, have made repeated contributions from the resources of the Silver Springs establishment and from their own broad knowledge of Florida herpetology. Dr. James Oliver, New York Zoological Society, counselled us concerning Florida anoles. We are indebted to Mr. Robert Hellman, New York City, for providing specimens from which illustrations were prepared, and to Mr. Walter Auffenberg, University of Florida, for help in constructing keys. Dr. C. B. Pollard, Department of Chemistry, University of Florida, furnished information on the latest method of treating snake bite.

To our old friend Leonard Giovannoli, of the Florida State Museum, we are grateful for long hours spent compiling reptile characters and descriptions and for assistance in a great many other aspects of the project.

A chief factor in our willingness to undertake the task of composing this book was the early offer by Roger and Isabelle Conant of the Philadelphia Zoological Garden to furnish photographs of reptiles and amphibians for illustrations. At the time we started our project the Conants were beginning work on their forthcoming book, A Field Guide to the Reptiles and Amphibians, a work profusely illustrated in color, to be published next year by Houghton Mifflin Company; and they agreed to make separate photographs of the Florida species for our use. The privilege of publishing these magnificent pictures lent heart to the undertaking at a time when it seemed in prospect a dreary and long one.

Of all our debts, the greatest is the one we owe Olive Bown Goin. There is no real justice in her exclusion from co-authorship, unless it be the already overlong citation our title will impose on bibliographers of the future. Mrs. Goin has typed every part of the manuscript through at least two stages of development, copying at times from atrocious hand script, and screening the whole thing for errors and inconsistency, and has had a hand in nearly every phase of the assembling and tending of the manuscript through the press. Mrs. Carr has been helpful too, but her services have been pretty much what you expect of a wife; indexing, testing keys, making coffee—things like that. We are grateful to them both, but we really must apologize to Mrs. Goin for leaving her name off the title page.

TABLE OF CONTENTS

GUIDE TO THE REPTILES, AMPHIBIANS, AND FRESH-WATER FISHES OF FLORIDA

INTRODUCTION

IN USING THIS BOOK to identify an animal the first step is to make sure the specimen you have is a reptile, amphibian, or fish. In most cases this will be easy. After that, it will be necessary to decide which of the three groups—reptile, amphibian, or fish—your animal belongs to. This presents no real problems either, if a few facts and generalizations are kept in mind.

Reptiles have scales and no paired fins. One Florida lizard lives in the ground, is blind, and resembles an earthworm; but it has jaws with teeth in them, a short tail that extends beyond the anal opening and, of course, a backbone inside. Another one of our lizards, the so-called glass snake, lacks legs, and to the casual observer looks like a snake; but a more careful appraisal shows that it can blink its eyes and has jaws hinged behind like your own; neither of these things is true of snakes. Apart from these two exceptional lizards, there is clear sailing among the reptiles. All the rest of them are pretty obviously snakes, lizards, turtles, crocodiles, or alligators.

Amphibians are frogs or salamanders. They got the name "amphibian," not because they go in and out of the water like an "amphibian" airplane, but because most of them begin life as aquatic larvae or tadpoles and later change shape and go out on land to live. They have no scales, and the skin is usually soft and damp. Toads, it is true, are pretty dry but the chances are you were raised among toads and won't be really misled by their not being damp. "Toad" after all is simply the name given to the kinds of frogs that have dry skins. One group of salamanders called newts has dry skin, too, and many people mistake newts for lizards—in fact one of the writers grew up calling them spring lizards. There is no real excuse for this though— newts can always be distinguished from lizards by a simple rule-of-thumb: poke the creature you are doubtful about and see how it walks. Newts walk slowly. Any Florida lizard able to walk at all walks fast.

Mature Florida amphibians have legs and lack paired fins. Aside from the dry newts, the only possible cause of confusion among them is a handful that have unorthodox life histories. All of these are salamanders, and the odd thing about them is that they never get to be

3

land animals at all, but stay in the water where they were born and become sexually mature and breed there. They belong to four different types, as follows:

Amphiuma.—This is a long, gray-black salamander with legs so small you have to hunt for them. Amphiuma is almost universally mistaken for an eel, and since an eel is a fish, a lot of people might try to identify an amphiuma in the fish section of the book if we failed to warn them in time. No matter how long and slick the creature you have may be, if it has legs—any legs at all—it is not an eel and should be looked for in the amphibian key.

Siren and Pseudobranchus.—These also look like eels, and in a way are even worse traps for the unwary than amphiuma, because they have no hind legs at all but only a single pair of pitiful little arms up behind the head. But even this is good evidence that they are not fish. Sirens are fat and either black or mottled; Pseudobranchus is slim and striped, and in some places is used as bass bait—mostly by people who are sure they are using eels. Both these salamanders have gills and are helpless on land.

Necturus.—This is a more typical looking salamander; its only eccentricity is its failure to emerge from the water. It keeps its gills throughout life and breeds where it passed its larval life.

So much for the potentially puzzling amphibians. As far as the Florida fauna is concerned, you can cling to these two generalizations about them: they never have scales and they always have legs.

We also ought to go over a few rough spots among the fishes. As we implied above, fishes never have legs. They usually are covered with scales, but a few—eels, catfish, sting rays—are naked. None of the naked ones should give any real trouble, however, provided the superficial resemblance between eels and the eel-like salamanders is kept in mind. A sting ray is easily known by its flat body and long round tail armed at the base with a poisonous spine. Of the catfishes, the madtom looks something like a tadpole and might get a beginner off the track, but not for long, because madtoms have chin whiskers and poisoned fin rays. Another fish that sometimes causes uncertainty is the pipefish. The trouble with the pipefish is, it doesn't look like *anything*. It sometimes reminds you of a twig or a stem of seaweed, but not always. It has curious habits, too. The females have figured out a way of getting the males pregnant. During the breeding season you can tell pipefishes by the pregnant males. Other times they may puzzle you for a while.

Once you are sure the animal you want to identify is a fish, an amphibian, or a reptile, and have made up your mind which of the three it is, turn to the appropriate key, and if zoological keys are new to you, look this one over to see how it works. It is composed of a series of couplets, each of which is made up of a pair of contrasting statements. The couplets are numbered in order. Primed numbers indicate the alternative choice in each couplet, and the number in parentheses tells what couplet it was that referred you to the present one.

After feeling your way around the key for a while pick up your specimen and try keying it out. Read couplet number one. No matter how appealing the first statement may seem, reserve your judgment until you have read the second too—you may like it even better. When you have decided which of the two descriptions best fits the animal at hand, read the number at the extreme right and go directly to the couplet with that number. Keep this up, in each couplet you are sent to choosing the more appropriate of the two descriptions, until finally you come to a name at the right instead of a number. This ought to be the name of your animal; and the page number beside it refers you to the place in the text where you can find out more about it.

Since we are praying for a wide and diversified audience for this book, it might be appropriate to say something about the scientific names that zoologists use for animals. We have made an effort to keep unnecessary technical words out of the book, but this does not apply to the Latin names of the animals in it, which are really just about the only decent names the animals have. They sound pretty stuffy all right, but take our word for it, they are in most cases the only reliable way of saying what you want to say. Common names are sloppy and ambiguous and have caused a great deal of misunderstanding.

Take the terrible confusion surrounding the names "gopher" and "salamander" in Florida. As used in the Southeast, both names refer to creatures that live in the ground. In Florida a salamander is a rat-shaped animal that throws up mounds of sand all about the landscape, and everywhere else is called a gopher. In Florida it is called a salamander just because early tourists misunderstood the first settlers when they called it "sandy-mounder." John Kilby found an old colored woman who still called it sandy-mounder. Everywhere else a salamander is a spring lizard or a mud puppy or a water dog—a tailed amphibian—except in a few places where it is a fireman, and a few others where it is a hot iron you use to make crême brulee with! But this isn't the end of the mess. In Florida a gopher is not a rodent at all but a turtle (although the English would deny this and insist that it was a tortoise), and people here call it gopher because their great grandfathers used to hear Gold Coast slaves calling it by their own African name for a similar turtle, *gofa*.

This sort of distressing thing is avoided when you use what is called the "binomial" system. The binomial system of naming animals and plants was worked out some two hundred years ago by a Swede named Linnaeus, and is now in use by responsible naturalists the world over. It is a scheme by which each creature gets a name composed of two parts—one the name of its *genus*, written first and capitalized, and the other the name of the *species*, which comes second and it's not capitalized except by botanists and newspaper writers. (The plural of genus is genera and the name is called the generic name; the plural of species is species and the name is the specific name.) Both names are put in italics because they are Latinized. For example, the spring peeper is called *Hyla crucifer*. Hyla is the genus and lots of other frogs belong to it, just as there may be a number of people in the Smith family. The peeper, however, is not just any Hyla, but a particular one with a particular voice and breeding season and habitat, and with a characteristic crosslike mark on its back. Its specific name is taken from that mark, and the peeper is called *Hyla crucifer,* as the name of Mr. Smith's son John may be written Smith, John.

So there is nothing really harmful about Latin names at all. The only further complication comes if students begin to notice slight differences in localized populations of a species and to describe what are known as *subspecies,* adding a third name at the end of the binomial. In the case of the peepers, for instance, the Florida peeper population was found to be slightly different, although not separate and distinct, from its northern relatives and was named *Hyla crucifer bartramiana* after the early Quaker naturalist and explorer of Florida, William Bartram. It is customary to include as part of the name of an animal the name of the person who described it, and since Francis Harper was the one who introduced the Florida peeper to Science, the full formal name is *Hyla crucifer bartramiana* Harper.

Most writers of books on reptiles devote a number of pages to debunking snake stories. What they do is tell a lot of cock-and-bull tales, and then point out that these are all just folk-lies that nobody educated ought to put any stock in. Although we have suspected that some of the writers made up some of their stories just to have the fun of exploding them, the debunking was on the whole a healthful thing. But it seems to us it has been run into the ground, and since our book is pretty long already, we decided to save space and fulfill whatever responsibility we have in that line by simply urging readers not to believe *anything* they hear about snakes.

Besides that, we want to call attention to a few miscellaneous misconceptions that are current and popular in one part of Florida or another, and that people really ought to get rid of at once.

There is a queer notion, for instance, that the shrill peeping you hear along the roads after rains from flooded ditches and flatwoods is the voice of the "scorpion" lizard, the skink, Eumeces. This is not true. The peeping is done by the little oak toad, *Bufo quercicus*. No Florida lizard has a voice. On the other hand, all Florida frogs sing. Each has its own breeding song that can easily be recognized by one who has studied them. You can buy recordings of frog songs. Learning to know them is a great deal of fun. The only other vocal animal treated in this book is the alligator, which rumbles and grunts and bellows about swamps and marshy lakes when it thinks of female alligators on warm nights.

This same lizard, Eumeces, is involved in another quite stubborn myth. Practically everybody thinks it is poisonous. This is no mere regionalism but an idea prevalent almost throughout the broad American range of the genus. All through Central America, for instance, related species are known in Spanish as *escorpiones* and are believed to be deadly. Actually there are no poisonous lizards in Florida at all, and no poisonous amphibians. Toads will make you sick if you bite them but they won't bite you. The only venomous Florida reptiles are the poisonous snakes: three kinds of rattlesnakes, copperhead, cottonmouth, and the small, inoffensive but very venomous corals. The rear-fanged Crown snakes are innocuous to humans.

There is a great deal of irresponsible talk about the sizes attained by some of our cold-blooded animals, particularly snakes and fish. Just as sure as you display the corpse of a six-foot rattlesnake that you have killed some aggressive type will start jawing about the one three times that size that a friend of his killed. Well, Ross Allen of Silver Springs has seen far more Florida rattlesnakes than any man alive, and the longest one that has come into his establishment was 7' 3". Years ago he issued a standing offer of $200 for an 8' one, but nobody has yet collected the prize. There may be a few bigger rattlers about, but not many nowadays, and not much bigger. The longest of all the Florida snakes are the indigo and the coachwhip, both with maximum lengths around nine feet. According to Ross Allen, the biggest Florida crocodile was old Zulu, a 14′ 7″ crocodile that lived in the pen at Silver Springs for years until killed by Big George, the 15′ alligator there. Big George is the largest alligator ever seen by Ross Allen. The largest fresh-water turtle is the alligator snapper of the rivers from the Suwannee drainage westward, with a top weight of certainly more than a hundred pounds and probably of twice that. The whole subject of fish sizes is so delicate and dangerous that talking about it would probably only lose us readers. It is said, for example, that the world's record largemouth bass was not a Florida specimen at all but a Georgia one. Such emotionally charged issues as this seem to us out of place in a book of this sort, and we shall leave them to the fishing-columnists and tackle manufacturers.

In the preface we spoke of our deep satisfaction over the wealth of cold-blooded vertebrates that occur in Florida. The extraordinary list of 333 species may be itemized as follows:

35	turtles	1	alligator
25	lizards	29	salamanders
60	snakes	28	frogs
1	crocodile	154	fresh-water fishes

Some who read this book may wonder at the list of species we have classed as "fresh-water" fishes. Our criterion here has been simply whether a fish is frequently taken in fresh water—in water that would quench your thirst, say, if you drank it. The reason the list looks so unreasonably long is the fact that the fresh waters of Florida are more heavily invaded by marine fishes than those of any other part of the United States. You find flounders and needlefish in the middle of the peninsula. Croakers abound in Lake George, about 125 miles from the mouth of the St. Johns, and the bass and crappie fishermen only cuss and reach for a club when they haul in a stingaree out of a Marion County creek. This invasion by marine species reaches a peak in Homosassa Springs in Citrus County, where for no reason known to science the big sea trout and snook and snappers and a dozen others pile up in the crystal boil in tiers like cordwood. One of the writers has been fishing for sheepshead all his life and the finest string he ever caught came out of the bottom of that spring before it became one of Florida's most worth-while tourist attractions. So we have not padded the list at all, but merely put down the things we know are found in the state and provided a way to identify them.

THE FISHES

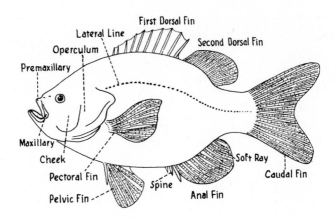

Fig. 1 Diagram showing external structures of a fish.

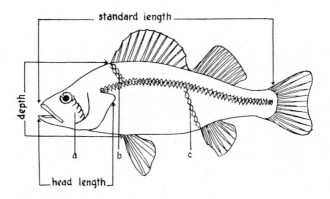

Fig. 2 Diagram showing measurements of a fish and indicating how scale counts are made. (a) Cheek scales. (b) Scales above lateral line. (c) Scales below lateral line.

FISH GLOSSARY

ADIPOSE FIN—A thick fin without rays.

ADNATE—Fused; grown together.

BARBEL—A fleshy filament or projection, usually about the head.

BRANCHIOSTEGALS—Bony rays that support the membranes on the lower side of the head of a fish.

CAUDAL—Pertaining to the tail; the caudal fin.

CAUDAL PEDUNCLE—The region between the caudal fin and the dorsal and anal fins. The fleshy portion in front of the caudal fin.

CLEFT—The slit of the mouth.

CONFLUENT—Not separated; continuous.

DORSAL—Pertaining to the back.

EMARGINATE—Slightly notched.

FIN RAYS—The supporting elements in fins. These are of two types: spines (which see), and soft rays (which see).

FRENUM—A broad band of tissue holding two bones together.

GILL RAKERS—The tooth-like projections along the inner edges of the bony arches that support the gills.

HETEROCERCAL TAIL—An unsymmetrical tail, the upper lobe of which is often longer than the lower. The backbone may extend into the upper lobe, or may merely curve upward before reaching it as in the case of the Mudfish (*Amia*).

HOMOCERCAL TAIL—A symmetrical tail in which the backbone ends at the base of the fin and does not curve upward or enter the fin.

HUMERAL SCALE—A body scale above the base of the pectoral fin and immediately behind the opercle.

INFRAORBITAL CANAL—A sensory canal below the orbit.

ISTHMUS—The ventral part of the throat and breast between the gill openings.

LABIAL GROOVES—Narrow grooves extending anteriorly from each corner of the mouth in some sharks.

LATERAL—Pertaining to the sides.

LATERAL LINE—A series of small pits or tubes forming a line along the sides of most fish.

MAXILLARIES—The outer bones of the upper jaw.

OCELLATED—Having the appearance of an eye; rounded, and surrounded by a ring of another color.

OPERCLE—Posterior part of the bony covering of the gill chamber.

ORBIT—The eye socket.

PERITONEUM—The shiny membrane that lines the body cavity.

PHARYNGEAL TEETH—Teeth which are borne on two bones which are modified gill arches.

PREMAXILLAE—The most anterior bones of the upper jaw.

PREOPERCLE—Anterior part of the bony covering of the gill chamber.

PRINCIPAL RAYS—Branched soft rays reaching the margin of the fin.

RUDIMENTARY RAYS—Unbranched soft rays which may or may not reach the margin of the fin.

SERRATE—Saw-edged.

11

Soft Rays—Fin rays which are segmented, flexible, and often branched. They are designated by Arabic numerals.

Spines—Median (unpaired) fin rays which are not segmented and are not branched at the tip. They are designated by Roman numerals.

Spiracle—A round opening above and behind the eye.

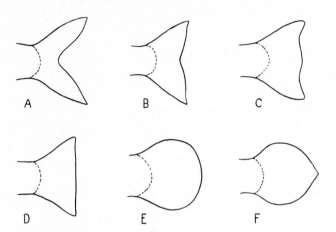

Fig. 3   Variation in caudal fin structure. (a) Forked. (b) Emarginate. (c) Doubly emarginate. (d) Truncate or Square. (e) Rounded. (f) Pointed.

Terminal—At the end.

Truncate—Cut off square; not rounded or forked.

Vent—The posterior opening of the digestive tract.

Ventral—Pertaining to the underside of the body.

Vertical Fins—The unpaired fins on the median line of the body; to wit, the dorsal, caudal, and anal fins.

Methods of Making Fish Measurements and Counts

Spines and Soft Rays—In a fin including both spines and soft rays, spines are indicated by Roman numerals and soft rays by Arabic numerals. The two numbers are separated by a comma if the two parts of the fin are confluent; for example: III,7. If the two parts of the fin are separate, as in the dorsal fins of many fishes, they are separated by a hyphen; for example: X-13.

Principal Rays—Unless otherwise specified, only principal soft rays are counted. In making this count take into consideration each of the soft rays that are branched, plus one unbranched soft ray.

RUDIMENTARY RAYS—In the catfishes, it is difficult to tell principal from rudimentary rays and thus in this group the total ray count is given.

SCALES ALONG LATERAL LINE—This is a count of the scales along the side of the fish in the row occupied by the lateral line. All scales are counted, whether or not they happen to bear lateral line pores. This count terminates at the structural base of the tail. Scales on the caudal fin itself are not counted.

SCALES ALONG SIDE—This is the count used for fishes which lack a lateral line. It is made by counting the scales in a row from the opercle to the structural base of the tail.

SCALES ABOVE LATERAL LINE—This is the count of the scales in the row which extends obliquely downward and backward from the anterior margin of the dorsal fin to the lateral line.

SCALES BELOW LATERAL LINE—The scales in the row extending obliquely dorsally and anteriorly from the margin of the anal fin to the lateral line.

PREDORSAL SCALES—The number of scales in a row along the median line from the back of the head to the anterior margin (origin) of the dorsal fin.

HEIGHT OF FIN—The distance from the body to the tip of the longest fin ray in the fin.

LENGTH OF FIN—The distance from the anterior to the posterior margin of a vertical fin along the median line of the body.

DEPTH—The greatest vertical distance from the mid-line of the back to the mid-line of the belly.

STANDARD LENGTH—The distance from the tip of the snout to the structural base of the tail. In this book, standard length is implied unless otherwise specified.

TOTAL LENGTH—The distance from the tip of the snout to the tip of the longest ray of the tail.

HEAD LENGTH—Distance from the tip of the snout to the posterior margin of the opercle.

SNOUT LENGTH—Distance from the tip of the snout to the anterior margin of the orbit.

PHARYNGEAL TEETH—To count these teeth, it is necessary to remove the bones on which they are borne. The teeth are usually arranged in two rows on each bone with the smaller number of teeth in the outer row. Thus, a count of 2,4-4,2 would indicate that the teeth in the various rows from the left to the right side of the body of the fish are: 2 in the outer row on the left, 4 in the inner row on the left, 4 in the inner row on the right, 2 in the outer row on the right. A count of 4-4 would indicate that that particular fish had only one row of teeth on each bone. The bones on which these teeth are borne are directly behind the last gills.

KEY TO THE FISHES

1	Mouth with true jaws..	3
1'	Mouth without jaws; a circular opening adapted for sucking...	2
2 (1)	Body not mottled; dorsal fin continuous rather than divided into 2 distinct fins..	
	...........Southern Brook Lamprey, *Ichthyomyzon gagei*, p.	33
2'	Body definitely mottled; dorsal fin divided into 2 distinct fins......................Sea Lamprey, *Petromyzon marinus*, p.	33
3 (1)	Body not disklike; tail not like a whip.............................	5
3'	Body disklike; tail whiplike and longer than the body......	4
4 (3)	Tail compressed with a wing like expansion above and a larger one below; anterior margins of body slightly concave anteriorly thus producing a slightly elongated snout ....Southern Sting Ray, *Dasyatis sabina*, p.	34
4'	Tail simply keeled above, but with a winglike expansion below; anterior margins of the body nearly straight, meeting in a broad angle at the tip of the snout...................... ....Whip Sting Ray, *Dasyatis hastata*, p.	34
5 (3)	Tail heterocercal. (Although the tails of the mudfish and the garfishes may not appear to be heterocercal on superficial examination, they belong in this group).................	6
5'	Tail not heterocercal..	12
6 (5)	Mouth ventral in position..	7
6'	Mouth terminal in position..	9
7 (6)	Body without rows of large plates along the back and sides	8
7'	Body with rows of large plates along the back and sides ....Common Sturgeon, *Acipenser oxyrhynchus*, p.	36

8 (7) Labial grooves extending forward from the angles of the mouth; snout pointed..

...................Sharp-nosed Shark, *Scoliodon terraenovae*, p. 35

8′ No pronounced labial grooves at the angles of the mouth; snout short and broadly rounded.....................................

.............................Bull Shark, *Carcharhinus leucas*, p. 36

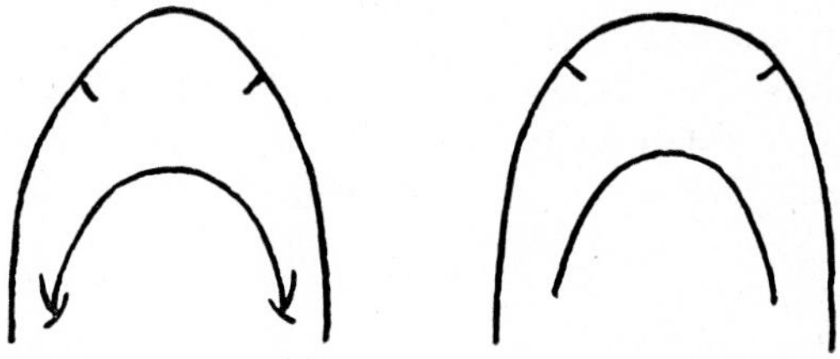

Fig. 4 Ventral view of head and mouth of Sharp-nosed Shark (left); of Bull Shark (right).

9 (6) Mouth extended into a long bill-like structure; dorsal fin short.. 10

9′ Mouth normal, not bill-like; dorsal fin very long............

....Mudfish, *Amia calva*, p. 39

10 (9) Snout not twice as long as rest of head........................ 11

Fig. 5 Top of head of Longnose Gar (left); of Spotted Gar (right).

10′ Snout twice as long as rest of head or longer.....................

.............................Longnose Gar, *Lepisosteus osseus*, p. 38

11 (10) Large teeth of upper jaw in 2 rows on each side..........

............................Alligator Gar, *Lepisosteus spatula*, p. 39

11′ Large teeth of upper jaw in a single row on each side; distance from front of orbit to edge of opercular membrane less than 2/3 length of snout.............................

..........Northern Spotted Gar, *Lepisosteus productus*, p. 37

11″ Large teeth of upper jaw in a single row on each side; distance from front of orbit to edge of opercular membrane more than 2/3 length of snout.............................

........Florida Spotted Gar, *Lepisosteus platyrhincus*, p. 38

12 (5) Both eyes on one side of body, *or* body very elongate and encased in a bony armor.. 152

12'   Eyes normal in position and body not encased in a bony armor..   13
13 (12) Dorsal fin normal in structure....................................   14
13'   Anterior dorsal fin modified into an ovate sucker-like structure............Shark Remora, *Echeneis naucrates,* p. 114
14 (13) Dorsal fin without spines *or* with only 1 spine...............   15
14'   Dorsal fin with spines preceding the soft rays............   89
15 (14) Body covered with scales.....................................   16
15'   Body naked (or with very minute scales buried in skin)   52
16 (15) Head without scales...   17
16'   Head more or less covered with scales, at least on the sides..   62

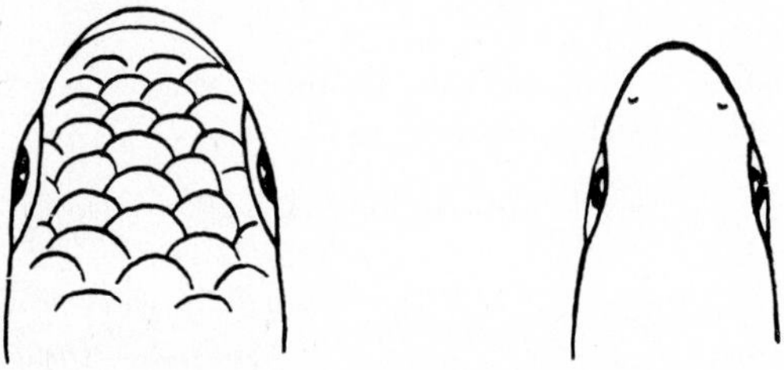

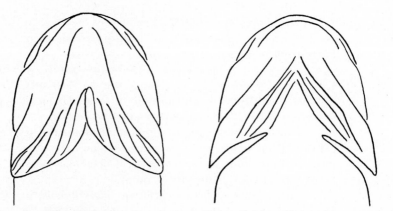

Fig. 6   Dorsal view of head covered with scales (left); of head without scales (right).

17 (16) Gill membranes free from isthmus.........................   18
17'   Gill membranes united with isthmus.......................   30
18 (17) Lateral line wanting..   20

Fig. 7   Gill membranes free from isthmus (left); gill membranes united with isthmus (right).

18'   Lateral line present.. 19

19 (18) Scales large, 42-47 along lateral line; last ray of dorsal
         fin elongate....................Tarpon, *Tarpon atlanticus,* p.   40

19'   Scales smaller, about 120 along lateral line; last ray of
         dorsal fin not elongate..
         ....Ten Pounder, *Elops saurus,* p.   40

20 (18) Mouth more or less terminal in position; maxillary never
         reaching much behind the posterior margin of eye;
         dorsal fin placed well forward of anal fin.................... 21

20'   Mouth a deep, undershot cleft; maxillary extending
         posteriorly well behind posterior margin of the eye;
         dorsal fin placed but slightly forward of anal fin, usual-
         ly the posterior margin at least above the anterior mar-
         gin of the anal.. 29

21 (20) Dorsal fin with last ray extending much beyond rest
         of fin; stomach like a fowl's gizzard........................ 22

21'   Dorsal fin without last ray much elongated; stomach
         not like a gizzard... 23

22 (21) Rays in anal fin 29-33; scales along side 52-56............
         ....Gizzard Shad, *Dorosoma cepedianum,* p.   45

22'   Rays in anal fin 20-23; scales along side 40-44.........
         ....Florida
         Threadfin Shad, *Dorosoma petenense vanhyningi,* p.   44

23 (21) Rays in dorsal fin 12-16..................................... 24

23'   Rays in dorsal fin 19....Bug Fish, *Brevoortia smithi,* p.   44

24 (23) Peritoneum lining body cavity white or clear............... 25

24'   Peritoneum lining body cavity black..........................
         ....Glut Herring, *Alosa aestivalis,* p.   42

25 (24) Scales along side 55 or less................................. 26

25'   Scales along side 60-65......................................
         ....American Shad, *Alosa sapidissima,* p.   41

26 (25) Anal rays 20-21... 27

26'   Anal rays 17-19... 28

27 (26) Anal rays 20; scales along side about 55...................
         ....Alabama Shad, *Alosa alabamae,* p.   41

27'   Anal rays 21; scales along side about 50..................
         ....Hickory Shad, *Alosa mediocris,* p.   43

28 (26) Depth about 3 in standard length; eye about 3½ in
         length of head..........Alewife, *Alosa pseudoharengus,* p.   42

28'   Depth about 3¾ in standard length; eye about 4⅓ in
         length of head...........Skipjack, *Alosa chrysochloris,* p.   43

29 (20) Anal rays 25 or 26..
...................Bay Anchovy, *Anchoa mitchilli diaphana*, p.   46
29′   Anal rays 19 or 20................................
................Striped Anchovy, *Anchoa hepsetus hepsetus*, p.   46

Fig.   8   Ventral view of thin, delicate lips (left); of fleshy, folded lips (right).

30 (17) Lips thin, mouth rather delicate...................................   36
30′   Lips thick, fleshy and folded, mouth sucker-like..........   31
31 (30) Rays in dorsal fin 11-13...   32
31′   Rays in dorsal fin 25-30................................
................................Quillback, *Carpiodes cyprinus*, p.   48
32 (31) Lateral line present, at least anteriorly.........................   33
32′   Lateral line absent...   34
33 (32) Dorsal fin with 13 rays; 42-44 scales along lateral line;
        lower lobe of tail black...
..........Blacktail Redhorse, *Moxostoma poecilurum*, p.   49
33′   Dorsal fin with 12 rays; 44-47 scales along lateral line;
        lower lobe of tail not black..
.......................Spotted Sucker, *Minytrema melanops*, p.   49
34 (32) Forty or more scales along side.....................................   35
34′   Scales along side 35-36...
.....................Eastern Chubsucker, *Erimyzon sucetta*, p.   50
35 (34) Dorsal fin with 11 rays; scales along side 40-42.........
.................Alabama Chubsucker, *Erimyzon tenuis*, p.   50
35′   Dorsal fin with 12 rays; scales along side 44-47..........   33
36 (30) Dorsal fin short (much less than 20 rays) and not pre-
        ceded by a serrate bony spine...   37
36′   Dorsal fin elongated (20 or more rays) and preceded by
        a serrate bony spine.................Carp, *Cyprinus carpio*, p.   51
37 (36) Sides of head smooth...   38
37′   Sides of head pitted with numerous cavernous chambers
.......................Silverjaw Minnow, *Ericymba buccata*, p.   60

47 (46)   Anal rays usually 7; 35-36 scales along lateral line;
          floor and roof of mouth not heavily pigmented........... 48
47′   Anal rays usually 8; 32-33 scales along lateral line;
          floor and roof of mouth heavily pigmented...................
          ....Iron-colored Shiner, *Notropis chalybaeus,* p.   57
48 (47)   Scales on sides immediately below the lateral dark stripe
          margined with dark pigment......................................
          ....Central Weed Shiner, *Notropis roseus roseus,* p.   56
48′   Scales on sides immediately below the lateral dark stripe
          not margined with dark pigment...............................
          ....Peterson's Shiner, *Notropis petersoni,* p.   56
49 (42)   Scales in lateral line 38-44............................... 50
49′   Scales in lateral line 33-38............................... 51
50 (49)   Scales between base of head and origin of dorsal fin
          18-20 ....
          ..Lowland Shiner, *Notropis cummingsae cummingsae,* p.   58
50′   Scales between base of head and origin of dorsal fin
          23-25...............Rosefin Shiner, *Notropis roseipinnis,* p.   54
51 (49)   Membranes of dorsal and anal fins with very little or
          no black pigment...
          ....Flagfin Shiner, *Notropis signipinnis,* p.   55
51′   Membranes of dorsal and anal fins extensively pigment-
          ed with black...
          ....Sailfin Shiner, *Notropis hyselopterus,* p.   55
52 (15)   Body not long and snakelike; dorsal and pectoral fins
          with sharp spines in their anterior portions................. 53
52′   Body long and snakelike; dorsal and pectoral fins with-
          out stout spines......................Eel, *Anguilla rostrata,* p.   65
53 (52)   Tail forked.. 54
53′   Tail rounded or squarish, never pronouncedly forked.... 57
54 (53)   No filamentous barbels extending from the nostrils........ 55
54′   Posterior nostrils each with a definite filamentous barbel   56
55 (54)   Lower jaw with but two filamentous barbels; dorsal and
          pectoral spines terminating in long filaments...............
          ....Gafftopsail Catfish, *Bagre marinus,* p.   61
55′   Lower jaw with four filamentous barbels; dorsal and
          pectoral spines not terminating in long filaments........
          ....Sea Catfish, *Galeichthys felis,* p.   61
56 (54)   Sides with scattered dark spots; an unbroken bony
          ridge from the head to the origin of the dorsal fin;

lobes of tail pointed; head relatively narrow................
........................Channel Cat, *Ictalurus punctatus,* p.   61
56'   Sides plain; bony ridge from head to origin of dorsal
fin not quite complete; lobes of tail somewhat rounded;
head broad................White Catfish, *Ictalurus catus,* p.   62
57 (53)   Adipose fin adnate to caudal fin.................................   60
57'   Adipose fin free from caudal fin.................................   58

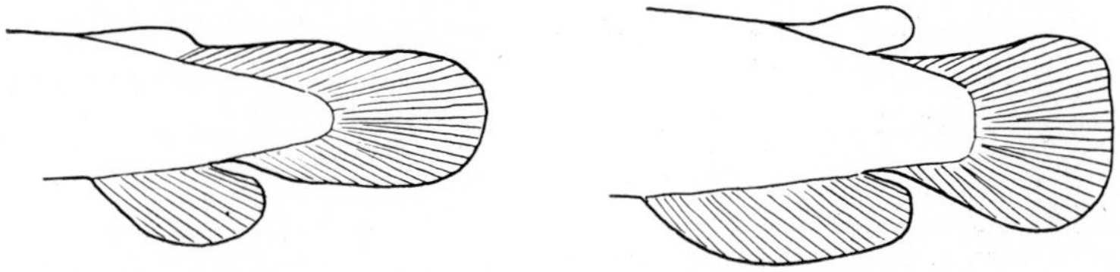

Fig.   9   Adipose fin adnate to caudal fin (left); adipose fin free from caudal
fin (right).

58 (57)   Anal fin with 20 or more rays (including rudiments)   59
58'   Anal fin with 16-18 rays (including rudiments)........
........................Snail Cat, *Ameiurus platycephalus,* p.   63
59 (58)   Sides and belly marbled or spotted; anal fin with 20-22
rays (including rudiments)..............................Southern
Brown Bullhead, *Ameiurus nebulosus marmoratus,* p.   62
59'   Sides and belly plain; anal fin with 25-27 rays (including rudiments)....Yellow Cat, *Ameiurus natalis,* p.   63
60 (57)   Anal fin short, only 13-16 rays (including rudiments)   61
60'   Anal fin long, 22-25 rays (including rudiments)........
........................Longfin Madtom, *Schilbeodes funebris,* p.   64
61 (60)   Color brown to black and nearly plain; spine of dorsal
fin exceeding $\frac{1}{2}$ the height of the dorsal fin.................
........................Tadpole Madtom, *Schilbeodes mollis,* p.   64
61'   Color generally yellowish or tannish, sides usually mottled; spine of dorsal fin less than $\frac{1}{2}$ the height of the
dorsal fin....Gulf Madtom, *Schilbeodes leptacanthus,* p.   65
62 (16)   Tail forked, mouth produced into a beaklike structure....   63
62'   Tail rounded or square; mouth not produced into a beak   65
63 (62)   Beak broad and ducklike; pelvic fins about halfway
between pectoral and anal fins.................................   64
63'   Beak long and needle-like; pelvic fins closer to anal than
to pectoral fins...
................Northern Needlefish, *Strongylura marina,* p.   66

64 (63) Scales along side about 108 or less, branchiostegals
11-13; length 12 inches or less......................................
.......................Redfin Pickerel, *Esox americanus*, p.   47

64' Scales along side about 125; branchiostegals 14-16;
length up to 2 feet.........Chain Pickerel, *Esox niger*, p.   48

65 (62) Posterior angle of jaw not extending posteriorly to below the middle of the eye; lateral margin of the upper
jaw formed by the premaxillae..................................... 66

65' Posterior angle of jaw extending posteriorly to below
the middle of the eye; lateral margin of upper jaw
formed by the maxillaries...
.......................Mud Minnow, *Umbra pygmaea*, p.   47

66 (65) Dorsal fin with 14 or more rays................................... 67

66' Dorsal fin with less than 14 rays............................... 69

67 (66) Anal fin with 10 or more rays................................... 68

67' Anal fin with only 9 or fewer rays (female), or modified into a copulatory organ (male)...............................
.......................Sailfin Molly, *Mollienesia latipinna*, p.   79

68 (67) Scales along side 25-27...
.......................Flagfish, *Jordanella floridae*, p.   77

68' Scales along side 50-55...
.......................Caledonian, *Fundulus seminolis*, p.   70

69 (66) Dorsal fin without a distinct eyelike spot with a light
center... 70

69' A distinct eyelike spot with a light center on the dorsal
fin...
..Spotfin Killifish, *Fundulus confluentus confluentus*, p.   71

70 (69) Scales along side 24-28... 71

70' Scales along side 29 or more..................................... 78

71 (70) Anterior margin of dorsal fin in front of anterior margin
of anal fin.. 73

71' Anterior margin of anal fin in front of anterior margin
of dorsal fin.. 72

72 (71) Anal rays 9-10; scales along side 26-28; depth about 5
in total length..
.......................Ocellated Killifish, *Leptolucania ommata*, p.   67

72' Anal rays 6-9 or anal modified into copulatory organ;
scales along side 24-28; depth 3¾-4 in total length....
.......................Least Killifish, *Heterandria formosa*, p.   78

73 (71) Anal rays usually 10 or more; scales along side 25-26   74

73'   Anal rays 9; scales along side 24.....................Florida
        Gold-spotted Killifish, *Floridichthys carpio carpio,* p.   76
74 (73) Dorsal fin rays 9-10..   75
74'   Dorsal fin rays 11-12...   76
75 (74) Anal fin rays 11-12; scales along side 25; depth 2-2½
        in length; vertical bars on posterior portion of body
        distinct................Diamond Killifish, *Adinia xenica,* p.   68
75'   Anal fin rays 9-10; scales along side 26; depth 3½-3¾
        in length; no distinct vertical bars on posterior portion
        of body...............Rainwater Killifish, *Lucania parva,* p.   66
76 (74) Anal fin rays 9-10; scales along side 26..........................   77
76'   Anal fin rays 11; scales along side 25..........................
        Lake Eustis Sheepshead Killifish, *Cyprinodon hubbsi,* p.   76
77 (76) Humeral scale not pronouncedly enlarged, about size
        of adjacent scales; anal 9-10; depth in length 3 or
        more...   75'
77'   Humeral scale much enlarged, several times as large as
        adjacent scales; anal fin rays 10; depth in length 2⅓-3
        ....Southern Sheeps-
        head Killifish, *Cyprinodon variegatus variegatus,* p.   75
78 (70) Anterior margin of dorsal fin in front of, or about
        above, anterior margin of anal fin; dorsal fin large,
        11-14 rays (except *L. goodei*).................................   79
78'   Anterior margin of dorsal fin behind anterior margin
        of anal fin, dorsal fin small, 7-11 rays..................   83
79 (78) Scales along side more than 32; pattern not a single
        broad dark stripe on each side from eye to base of tail;
        dorsal rays 11-14..   80
79'   Scales along side 29-32; pattern composed of a single
        broad dark stripe on each side from eye to base of tail;
        dorsal rays 9..
        ....Red-finned Killifish, *Lucania goodei,* p.   67
80 (79) Dorsal fin rays 12-14...   81
80'   Dorsal fin rays 11...   82
81 (80) Scales along side about 33; length of snout twice the
        diameter of the eye...
        ....Long-nosed Killifish, *Fundulus similis,* p.   70
81'   Scales along side about 36; length of snout not equal to
        twice the diameter of the eye..............................
        ....Striped Killifish, *Fundulus majalis,* p.   71

82 (80) Scales along side 33-36; freckled pattern; occurring along the Gulf Coast... ....Gulf Killifish, *Fundulus grandis grandis,* p.   69

82′ Scales along side 35-38; freckled pattern; occurring along the Atlantic Coast.................................Southern Common Killifish, *Fundulus heteroclitus heteroclitus,* p.   68

83 (78) Scales along side 32 or more; origin of anal fin just about under origin of dorsal fin......................................   84

83′ Scales along side 28-32; origin of anal fin well in front of origin of dorsal fin...   88

84 (83) A distinct dark spot under the eye.................................   85

84′ No distinct dark spot under the eye.............................   86

85 (84) Pattern of longitudinal rows of disconnected spots ....Southern Star-headed Topminnow, *Fundulus notti notti,* p.   73

85′ Pattern either of about 6 longitudinal dark stripes (female) or about 12 vertical dark stripes (male)......... ....Eastern Star-headed Topminnow, *Fundulus notti lineolatus,* p.   74

86 (84) Pattern not consisting of a single broad dark stripe down each side from the eye to the base of the tail.................   87

86′ Pattern consisting of a single broad dark stripe down each side from the eye to the base of the tail................. ....Streaked Topminnow, *Fundulus olivaceus,* p.   75

87 (86) Anal fin rays usually 10; dark vertical bars on the sides absent or few in number; often with gold spots on sides in life.........Golden Topminnow, *Fundulus chrysotus,* p.   73

87′ Anal fin rays usually 9; dark vertical bars on the sides present; never with gold spots on sides in life............. ....Banded Topminnow, *Fundulus cingulatus,* p.   72

88 (83) Scales along side 30-32; range state-wide...................... ....Eastern Mosquito-fish, *Gambusia affinis holbrooki,* p.   77

88′ Scales along side 28-30; range extreme southern Florida ....Mangrove Mosquito-fish, *Gambusia* species, p.   78

89 (14) Dorsal fin a single fin, or the 2 parts separated only by a shallow notch...   90

89′ Two dorsal fins, with the spiny dorsal being a separate fin from the soft (nonspinous) dorsal, or practically separated by a very deep notch.................................   118

90 (89) Vent normally located...   91

90′   Vent below preopercle...
..........................Pirate Perch, *Aphredoderus sayanus*, p.   80
91 (90) Lateral line present...   93
91′   Lateral line absent...   92
92 (91) Dorsal spines V; scales along side 38-42; a black spot on side just below the origin of the dorsal fin............
................Banded Pigmy Sunfish, *Elassoma zonatum*, p.   96
92′   Dorsal spines III or IV; scales along side 27-30; without a conspicuous round black spot on the side just below the origin of the dorsal fin...................................
........Everglade Pigmy Sunfish, *Elassoma evergladei*, p.   97
93 (91) Teeth in front of mouth conspicuous and flattened, somewhat like the corresponding teeth in man, and also somewhat protuberant..   94
93′   Teeth in front of mouth not conspicuous and flattened like the corresponding teeth in man...........................   96
94 (93) Scales along lateral line less than 60...........................   95
94′   Scales along lateral line 65-70....................................
.................................Pinfish, *Lagodon rhomboides*, p. 103
95 (94) Scales along lateral line 46-50; pattern of pronounced vertical dark bars...
................Sheepshead, *Archosargus probatocephalus*, p. 104
95′   Scales along lateral line 55-57; young sometimes vertically barred but the most conspicuous mark a broad, black saddle on the base of the caudal peduncle........
.........................Spot-tail Pinfish, *Diplodus holbrooki*, p. 104
96 (93) Second dorsal spine 5 or more times the length of the first...   97
96′   Second dorsal spine less than 5 times the length of the first..   98
97 (96) The second anal spine not particularly enlarged; scales along lateral line 40-44...
.........................Mojarra, *Eucinostomus argenteus*, p. 105

Fig. 10   Comparison of the second anal spine of the Mojarra (left) with that of the Irish Pompano (right).

97'   The second anal spine much enlarged; scales along
        lateral line 36-38..
        ....Irish Pompano, *Diapterus olisthostomus*, p. 106

98 (96) One tooth on each side of the front of the upper jaw
        elongated beyond the rest of the teeth, thus forming
        canine-like teeth.. 99

98'   Teeth in front of upper jaw uniform in length............ 100

99 (98) Body depth in length 2¾-3; scales along lateral line
        48-52...................Gray Snapper, *Lutjanus griseus*, p. 102

99'   Body depth in length about 2½; scales along lateral
        line 42-46................Schoolmaster, *Lutjanus apodus*, p. 103

100 (98) Anal fin about as long as the dorsal fin................... 101

100'   Anal fin not nearly so long as the dorsal fin........... 102

101 (100) Dorsal spines VII or VIII..
        ....Speckled Perch, *Pomoxis nigromaculatus*, p. 95

101'   Dorsal spines XI to XIII................................
        ....Flier, *Centrarchus macropterus*, p. 96

102 (100) Anal fin with V to VII spines............................... 103

102'   Anal fin with only III spines............................ 104

103 (102) Caudal fin rounded................................
        ....Mud Perch, *Acantharchus pomotis*, p. 95

103'   Caudal fin emarginate................................South-
        ern Rock Bass, *Ambloplites rupestris ariommus*, p. 94

104 (102) Caudal fin rounded................................ 105

104'   Caudal fin emarginate................................ 107

105 (104) No or very few pale or light blue spots on the spiny
        portion of the dorsal fin................................ 106

105'   Numerous pale or light blue spots on the spiny por-
        tion of the dorsal fin................................
        ....Blue-spotted Sunfish, *Enneacanthus gloriosus*, p. 93

106 (105) Scales along lateral line about 28........Black-banded
        Sunfish, *Enneacanthus chaetodon elizabethae*, p. 94

106'   Scales along lateral line about 32................................
        ....Banded Sunfish, *Enneacanthus obesus*, p. 93

Fig. 11   Spiny and soft dorsals without angulate notch (left); separated by
        an angulate notch (right).

107 (104) Depth 2½ or less in length; no angulate notch be-
          tween spiny and soft portions of dorsal fin............ 108
107'   Depth 3 or more in length; spiny and soft portions
          of the dorsal fin separated by an angulate notch.... 114
108 (107) Mouth moderate, maxillary not reaching the level of
          the middle of the eye; tongue without teeth.......... 109
108'   Mouth relatively large, maxillary reaching the level
          of the middle of the eye; tongue usually with teeth
          ....Warmouth, *Chaenobryttus coronarius*, p. 89
109 (108) Pectoral fin short and rounded................. 110
109'   Pectoral fin long and pointed................... 113

Fig. 12   Pectoral fin short and rounded (left); long and pointed (right).

110 (109) Opercular spot with pale margin............................ 112
110'   Opercular spot dark to the edge........................... 111
111 (110) Scales along lateral line 43-48; breast region from
          bright orange to red; without numerous black spots
          resembling fly specks on side of body......................
          ....Redbreast, *Lepomis auritus*, p.   91
111'   Scales along lateral line 38-45; breast region not
          bright orange or red in color; with numerous black
          spots resembling fly specks on side of body............
          ....Stump-knocker, *Lepomis punctatus punctatus*, p.   89
112 (110) Margin of opercular spot green; pectoral fin with
          12 rays; 4 rows of cheek scales..........................
          ....Dollar Sunfish, *Lepomis marginatus*, p.   92
112'   Margin of opercular spot blue; pectoral fin rays
          13-15; 5 or more rows of cheek scales....................
          ....Long-ear Sunfish, *Lepomis megalotis megalotis*, p.   91
113 (109) Opercular spot dark to edge; a dark spot in the dorsal
          fin near the posterior margin............................
          ....Bluegill, *Lepomis macrochirus purpurescens*, p.   92
113'   Opercular spot with a light red margin; no dark spot
          on posterior portion of dorsal fin......................
          ....Shellcracker, *Lepomis microlophus*, p.   90

114 (107) Dorsal fin X,11 or 12; the 2 portions separated by
           a shallow notch.. 115
114′   Dorsal fin X,13, the 2 portions separated by a rather
           deep notch.. 117

Fig. 13   Two portions of dorsal fin separated by a shallow notch (left); by
a deep notch (right).

115 (114) Dorsal fin X, 12; scales along lateral line less than 75 116
115′   Dorsal fin X,11; scales along lateral line 75-80.........
           ....Chipola Bass, *Micropterus* species, p.   87
116 (115) Scales along lateral line 59-63; cheek scales 12-13
           ....Suwannee Bass, *Micropterus notius*, p.   86
116′   Scales along lateral line 62-70; cheek scales 13-16
           ..Northern Spotted Bass, *Micropterus punctulatus*, p.   86

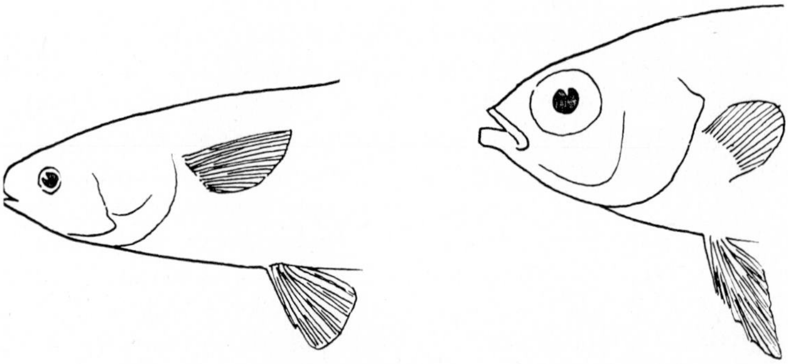

Fig. 14   Pelvic fins abdominal in position (left); thoracic in position (right).

117 (114) Scales along lateral line 59-65; cheek scales 10-11
           ....Northern Large-
           mouth Bass, *Micropterus salmoides salmoides*, p.   88
117′   Scales along lateral line 69-75; cheek scales 11-13
           ....Florida Large-
           mouth Bass, *Micropterus salmoides floridanus*, p.   88
118 (89)   Pelvic fins abdominal in position............................. 119
118′   Pelvic fins thoracic in position.................................. 125
119 (118) Anal spine I; dorsal spines slender; stomach not like
           a fowl's gizzard.. 120

119′   Anal spines II or III; dorsal spines moderately stout; stomach usually like a fowl's gizzard......................... 122

120 (119) Anal with about 16-18 soft rays; 37-47 scales along side... 121

120′   Anal with about 23 soft rays; 72-75 scales along side ....Florida Brook Silversides, *Labidesthes sicculus vanhyningi*, p.   81

121 (120) Scales along side 37-39; about 16 predorsal scales ......Freshwater Glass-minnow, *Menidia beryllina*, p.   80

121′   Scales along side 45-47; about 24 predorsal scales ....Rough Silverside, *Membras martinica*, p.   81

122 (119) Lower lip thin; an adipose eyelid present................. 123

122′   Lower lip thick and fleshy; no adipose eyelid.......... ....Mountain Mullet, *Agonostomus monticola*, p.   83

123 (122) Pattern not of stripes; scales extending up on to the base of the soft dorsal and the anal fins; scales along side 32-39... 124

123′   Pattern of narrow longitudinal stripes or rows of dots; scales not extending onto soft dorsal and anal fins; scales along side 40-42.................................. ....Striped Mullet, *Mugil cephalus*, p.   81

124 (123) Anal fin III,8; scales along side 32-34..................... ....Fan-tail Mullet, *Mugil trichodon*, p.   83

124′   Anal fin III,9; scales along side 37-39..................... ....White Mullet, *Mugil curema*, p.   82

125 (118) Gill membranes free from isthmus........................... 126

125′   Gill membranes united with isthmus...................... 144

126 (125) Anal spines III... 127

126′   Anal spines I or II.. 131

127 (126) Anal fin with 10-12 soft rays................................. 128

127′   Anal fin with 6-7 soft rays..................................... 129

128 (127) Pattern not of 6-7 longitudinal dark stripes; soft dorsal and anal fins rounded..................................... 117

128′   Pattern of 6-7 longitudinal dark stripes on a light background; soft dorsal and anal fins angulate......... ....Striped Bass, *Roccus saxatilis*, p.   85

129 (127) Scales along lateral line more than 67; soft rays in anal fin 6 (the last double)..................................... 130

129′   Scales along lateral line 62-67; soft rays in anal fin 7 (the last double)_____

_____Snook, *Centropomus pectinatus*, p.   84

130 (129)   Scales along lateral line 67-77; second anal spine not reaching to origin of caudal fin_____

_____Snook, *Centropomus undecimalis*, p.   84

130′   Scales along lateral line 80-88; second anal spine reaching to or beyond origin of caudal fin_____

_____Snook, *Centropomus parallelus*, p.   85

131 (126)   Rays in soft dorsal 20 or more_____ 132

131′   Rays in soft dorsal less than 20_____ 136

132 (131)   Barbels present on the chin_____ 133

132′   No barbels present on the chin_____ 134

133 (132)   Rays in soft dorsal 20-23; scales along lateral line 41-45_____Sea Drum, *Pogonias cromis*, p. 107

133′   Rays in soft dorsal 28-29; scales along lateral line about 55_____Croaker, *Micropogon undulatus*, p. 108

134 (132)   Rays in soft dorsal less than 30_____ 135

134′   Rays in soft dorsal 30-34; scales along lateral line 60-70_____Spot, *Leiostomus xanthurus*, p. 107

135 (134)   Scales along lateral line 40-45_____

_____Channel Bass, *Sciaenops ocellatus*, p. 106

135′   Scales along lateral line 90-102_____

_____Speckled Trout, *Cynoscion nebulosus*, p. 108

136 (131)   Anal fin large, about equal to or larger than soft dorsal; interpelvic space and belly either naked or with enlarged and modified median scales_____ 137

136′   Anal fin smaller than soft dorsal; interpelvic space and belly variously naked or covered with normal scales_____ 139

137 (136)   Anal spines II, the first stiff; body well scaled_____ 138

137′   Anal with a single thin, flexible spine; body almost naked except for 1 to 3 series of scales along the lateral line_____

_____Naked Sand Darter, *Ammocrypta beani*, p.   99

138 (137)   Back with 7 oblique dark saddles; gill membranes with a moderate connection; breast scaled_____

_____Crawl-a-bottom, *Hadropterus nigrofasciatus*, p.   97

148'   Spines in dorsal fin VII, soft rays 15..................
            ....Large-mouth Goby, *Microgobius gulosus*, p. 113
149 (148) Scales along side 24-41.............................. 150
149'   Scales along side 60-70..............................
            ....River Goby, *Awaous taiasica*, p. 113
150 (149) Scales along side 25-30.............................. 151
150'   Scales along side 35-40..............................
            ....Mapo, *Bathygobius soporator*, p. 111
151 (150) Body short and deep, depth 3⅗ in standard length;
            mouth very oblique; soft rays in anal fin 9 or 10....
            ....Crested Goby, *Lophogobius cyprinoides*, p. 112
151'   Body slender and fusiform; depth 4½ to 5½ in
            standard length; mouth horizontal; soft rays in anal
            fin 10 to 12..
            ....Darting Goby, *Gobionellus boleosoma*, p. 112
152 (12)   Both eyes on one side; body flattened...................... 153
152'   Body very elongate and encased in a bony armor.........
            ....Scovell's Pipefish, *Syngnathus scovelli*, p. 109
153 (152) Both eyes on left side of body............................ 154
153'   Both eyes on right side of body...................North-
            ern Round Sole, *Trinectes maculatus fasciatus*, p. 116
154 (153) Rays in dorsal fin 70-80............................. 155
154'   Rays in dorsal fin 85-95............................. 156
155 (154) Scales along side 45-58..............................
            ....Whiff, *Citharichthys spilopterus*, p. 115
155'   Scales along side 90-100..............................
            ....Gulf Flounder, *Paralichthys albigutta*, p. 115
156 (154) Depth about 2⅓ in length, anal fin rays 65-73......
            ......Southern Flounder, *Paralichthys lethostigma*, p. 116
156'   Depth about 3 to 3⅓ in length; anal fin rays 75-80
            ....Tonguefish, *Symphurus plagiusa*, p. 117

ACCOUNTS OF SPECIES

Petromyzon marinus Linnaeus
Sea Lamprey (Plate 1)

General Appearance.—An elongate, eel-like animal without paired fins or scales and with a permanently open mouth.

Distinguishing Characters.—A single nasal opening on top of the head; 7 nearly circular gill openings behind the eye; mouth without jaws; no paired fins; dorsal fin distinctly separated into anterior and posterior portions; pattern of regular mottling; 64 or more body segments between last gill opening and anus.

Description.—Head slightly longer than the branchial area; buccal disk large with conical teeth arranged in rows of 4 to 7 teeth each, lateral teeth on each side of mouth bicuspid. Eyes small but developed in the adult. Gill openings a row of 7 rounded openings on each side posterior to the eye. Nostril a single opening on top of head just in front of the eyes. Paired fins lacking. Dorsal fin divided into definite anterior and posterior portions. Number of body segments between last gill opening and anus 64 or more. Color bluish-brown above, whitish below, ground color overlain by dark mottlings. Length of adults 2 to 3 feet.

General Distribution.—Atlantic coasts of Canada, the United States, and Europe.

Florida Range.—Recorded from the St. Johns River.

Habitat.—Large rivers.

Ichthyomyzon gagei Hubbs and Trautman
Southern Brook Lamprey

General Appearance.—An elongate, eel-like animal without paired fins or scales and with a permanently open mouth.

Distinguishing Characters.—A single nasal opening on top of the head; 7 nearly circular gill openings behind the eyes; mouth without jaws; no paired fins; dorsal fin with a slight notch but not divided into 2 separate fins; 61-64 body segments between last gill openings and anus.

Description.—Head slightly shorter than the branchial area; buccal disk large with 7-8 conical teeth in the lateral rows. Eyes small but

33

developed in the adult. Gill openings a row of 7 rounded openings on each side posterior to the eye. Nostril a single opening on top of the head just in front of the eyes. Paired fins lacking. Dorsal fin with a shallow notch but not divided into definite anterior and posterior fins. Number of body segments between last gill opening and anus 61-64. Color rather dark uniform grayish, darker above than below. Length 4 to 5 inches.

General Distribution.—The Lower Mississippi Valley.

Florida Range.—The western panhandle.

Habitat.—Small streams and brooks.

Dasyatis sabina (Le Sueur)
Southern Sting Ray; Stingaree *(Plate 2)*

General Appearance.—A circular, flat fish with a long, whiplike tail and no dorsal fin.

Distinguishing Characters.—Body flattened, with no vertical fins or scales; mouth on ventral surface. Tail more or less compressed with a winglike expansion above, a larger one below. Anterior margins of the body slightly indented anteriorly to produce a slightly elongate snout.

Description.—Body disk subcircular. Anterior margins of body slightly concave. Snout produced. Margins of lateral projections convex posteriorly, making the disk somewhat rounded. Tail less than twice as long as the disk, more or less compressed with winglike expansions above and below, the lower slightly larger. Eyes conspicuous, on top of head. Mouth ventral in position, upper jaw with a deep indentation, receiving a corresponding prominence of the lower. Teeth small, paved, a few papillae usually present inside the mouth behind the lower jaw. A median row of tubercles on the dorsum and 1 or 2 tubercles on each shoulder. Color brown above, paler below.

General Distribution.—Brazil to Chesapeake Bay.

Florida Freshwater Range.—Any fresh water connecting with the Gulf of Mexico or the Atlantic Ocean, at times quite some distance from salt water.

Habitat.—Rivers, springs, and spring-runs.

Dasyatis hastata (De Kay)
Whip Sting Ray; Stingaree *(Plate 2)*

General Appearance.—A flat fish with no scales or dorsal fins and with a long, whiplike tail.

Distinguishing Characters.—Body flattened, without dorsal fins or scales; mouth on ventral surface. Tail simply keeled above but with a winglike expansion below. Anterior margins of the body nearly straight, meeting in a broad angle at the tip of the snout.

Description.—Body disk nearly quadrangular, about ¼ again as wide as long. Anterior margins of the body not indented, snout not produced. Lateral and hind angles of body rounded. Ventral fins barely visible from above, their posterior margins rounded. Tail more than 1½ times the length of the disk, simply keeled above, but with a winglike expansion below. Eyes conspicuous, on top of head. Mouth ventral in position. Teeth small, paved. Mouth with 3 papillae. Dorsum smooth in young; a row of tubercles along the middle of the back and tail in adults with shorter rows on each shoulder. Color brownish above, paler below.

General Distribution.—Atlantic Coast from Brazil to Florida.

Florida Range.—The East Coast.

Habitat.—Recorded from the St. Johns River.

Scoliodon terraenovae (Richardson)
Sharp-nosed Shark *(Plate 3)*

General Appearance.—A small, slender, grayish shark, often with a dark-bordered tail fin.

Distinguishing Characters.—Spiracles lacking; labial grooves at corners of the mouth; origin of anal fin anterior to origin of second dorsal fin.

Description.—Head pointed with an elongate proboscis projecting anteriorly. No spiracles present. Eye large, 2.2-2.3 per cent of total length. Body somewhat spindle-shaped, elongate. Tail strongly heterocercal, upper lobe much the longer. Distance from tip of snout to origin of the first dorsal fin equal to about ⅓ of total length. Second dorsal fin much smaller than first. Origin of anal fin anterior to origin of second dorsal fin. Color brownish to olive-gray above, whitish below. Dorsal and caudal fins more or less dark along their margins, particularly in young specimens. A small shark, rarely attaining 36 inches in total length.

General Distribution.—The tropical and subtropical Atlantic Ocean.

Florida Range.—Canals in southern Florida.

Habitat.—Canals connecting with the sea.

Note.—Although it is well known that sharks enter the fresh waters of Florida, none has been positively identified as to species. Stewart

Springer suggested to us that this and the following species are the ones likely to be found in our waters. Specimens definitely taken in fresh water are much to be desired.

Carcharhinus leucas (Müller and Henle)
Bull Shark (Plate 3)

General Appearance.—A grayish, rather stout shark with a short, broad snout.

Distinguishing Characters.—Spiracles lacking; no pronounced labial grooves at the corners of the mouth; origin of anal fin slightly posterior to the origin of the second dorsal fin.

Description.—Snout short and broadly rounded. No spiracles present. Eye small, 1.5 per cent of total length. Body somewhat spindle-shaped, elongate. Tail strongly heterocercal, upper lobe much the longer. Distance from the tip of the snout to the origin of the first dorsal fin but slightly more than $\frac{1}{4}$ the total length. Second dorsal fin much smaller than the first. Origin of the anal fin slightly posterior to the origin of the second dorsal. Color grayish above, whitish below. Attains a length of about 10 feet.

General Distribution.—New York to Brazil.

Florida Range.—Probably all large rivers entering the sea.

Habitat.—Occasionally invades large streams.

Note.—Although it is well known that sharks enter the fresh waters of Florida none has been positively identified as to species. Stewart Springer suggested to us that this and the preceding species are the ones likely to be found in our waters. Specimens definitely taken in fresh water are much to be desired.

Acipenser oxyrhynchus Mitchill
Common Sturgeon (Plate 4)

General Appearance.—A big, roughly plated fish with a ventral mouth.

Distinguishing Characters.—Tail heterocercal; snout elongated; mouth ventral. Dorsal plates 10-16, lateral plates 24-36; ventral plates 9-11. Anal fin with 23-30 rays.

Description.—Head pointed with an elongated proboscis projecting anteriorly. Eye small, oval, 5-7 times in length of snout. Body somewhat spindle-shaped, elongate. Caudal peduncle much smaller than rest of body. Tail strongly heterocercal, upper lobe much the longer. Dorsal fin with 30-44 rays, posterior in position. Pelvic fins abdominal in position. Anal fin with 23-30 rays. Mouth on ventral side of the head. Five rows of large plates along body as follows: a row of dorsal plates between head and dorsal fin with 10-16 plates; a row of 24-36 plates along each side between head and base of tail; a row of 9-11 plates along each side of belly between opercles and pelvic fins. Color dull tan. Sturgeon attain a length of 9 feet, but Florida specimens average smaller.

General Distribution.—The Atlantic Coast from the St. Lawrence River to the Gulf of Mexico.

Florida Freshwater Range.—Rivers entering the sea.

Habitat.—Big rivers.

Note.—There is an early published record for the short-nosed sturgeon in Florida. Recent specimens from both the St. Johns and Suwannee rivers seem referable to the common sturgeon however, so we use this name. The possibility remains that both species may be found in Florida waters.

Lepisosteus productus Cope
Northern Spotted Gar

General Appearance.—A dull-colored, cylindrical fish with hard scales and long jaws.

Distinguishing Characters.—Mouth extended into a bill-like structure; distance from front of orbit to edge of opercular membrane less than ⅔ the length of snout.

Description.—Snout long, its length 5 or 6 times its least width; distance from front of orbit to edge of opercular membrane less than ⅔ the length of the snout. Body elongate, depth about 8 in standard length. Dorsal fin posterior in position, with 8 soft rays. Tail heterocercal, although not obviously so. Caudal fin rounded. Anal fin with 8 soft rays. Scales ganoid, rhomboid in shape, arranged in oblique rows running downward and backward. Scale rows along sides 54-58, generally 56. Median dorsal row of scales enlarged transversely. Ground color olive-green to muddy with spots on top of the head and diffuse spots on body, particularly near the base of the dorsal, anal, and caudal fins. Young individuals with a dark stripe down the sides. Length up to about 30 inches but averaging smaller.

General Distribution.—The Mississippi Valley and the Gulf Coast.

Florida Range.—The western panhandle.

Habitat.—Probably most large bodies of water and many small ones.

Lepisosteus platyrhincus De Kay
Florida Spotted Gar (Plate 4)

General Appearance.—A dull-colored, cylindrical fish with hard scales and long jaws.

Distinguishing Characters.—Mouth extended into a bill-like structure; distance from front of orbit to edge of opercular membrane more than ⅔ length of snout.

Description.—Snout long but rather broad. Distance from front of orbit to edge of opercular membrane more than ⅔ length of snout. Body elongate, depth about 8 in standard length. Dorsal fin posterior in position, with about 8 soft rays. Tail heterocercal, although not obviously so. Caudal fin rounded. Anal fin with about 8 soft rays. Scales ganoid, rhomboid in shape, arranged in oblique rows running downward and backward. Scale rows along side of body 54-58. Median dorsal row of scales enlarged transversely. Ground color olive-green to muddy. Top of head not normally spotted. Diffuse spots near bases of the dorsal, anal, and caudal fins. Young individuals with a dark stripe down the side. Length up to about 30 inches, but averages less.

General Distribution.—Florida and southern Georgia.

Florida Range.—Northern Florida and the peninsula.

Habitat.—Most large bodies of water and many small ones.

Lepisosteus osseus (Linnaeus)
Longnose Gar

General Appearance.—A dull-colored, cylindrical fish with hard scales and extremely elongated, narrow jaws.

Distinguishing Characters.—Jaws twice or more than twice as long as the rest of the head. Length of snout 15-20 times its own width.

Description.—Snout extremely elongate, its length 15-20 times its width; snout at least twice as long as the rest of the head. Head about 3 times in length. Body elongate, depth 12 in length. Dorsal fin soft, posterior in position, 8 soft rays. Tail heterocercal, although not obviously so. Anal fin with 9 rays. Scales ganoid, rhomboid in shape, arranged in oblique rows running downward and backward. About 62 scales along lateral line. Young with a distinct black lateral line along each side from snout to base of tail; adult more uniformly muddy-colored with a tendency to be spotted, particularly about the fins. Length of large adults up to 5 feet.

General Distribution.—Atlantic Coast lowlands from Maryland to Louisiana and the Mississippi, northward into the Great Lakes.

Florida Range.—State-wide.

Habitat.—Large rivers and lakes connecting with them.

Lepisosteus spatula Lacépède
Alligator Gar

General Appearance.—A dull-colored, cylindrical fish with hard scales and a ferocious-looking mouth.

Distinguishing Characters.—Mouth extended into a bill-like structure, with two rows of large teeth on each side in the upper jaw.

Description.—Snout not quite so long as rest of head; its least width contained $3\frac{1}{2}$ times in its length. Body elongate, cylindrical. Dorsal fin posterior in position, with 9 soft rays. Tail heterocercal, although not obviously so. Caudal fin rounded in adults. Anal fin with 8-9 soft rays. Scales ganoid, rhomboid in shape, arranged in oblique rows running downward and backward. Scale rows along side 61-63. Color of adults uniformly muddy brownish or grayish. Length up to about 10 feet.

General Distribution.—Streams and rivers entering the Gulf of Mexico.

Florida Range.—Eastward in the panhandle to and including the Choctawhatchee River system.

Habitat.—Large streams.

Amia calva Linnaeus
Mudfish; Bowfin *(Plate 4)*

General Appearance.—A dark fish with a very long, soft dorsal fin extending for most of the length of the back, a broad head, and big mouth.

Distinguishing Characters.—Tail heterocercal, though not apparently so; mouth large but not extended into a bill-like structure, dorsal fin very elongate, exceeding $\frac{1}{2}$ the length of the body.

Description.—Head large, mouth large and terminal, but not bill-like. Head length $3\frac{3}{4}$ times in standard length. Dorsal fin low and level, very elongate, with 42-52 soft rays. Caudal fin rounded in superficial appearance but structurally heterocercal. Pelvic fins abdominal in position. Anal fin moderate, rounded, with 10-12 rays. Lateral line nearly straight with 65-70 scale rows along lateral line. Color black to dark olive. Male with a conspicuous ocellus of black and orange at the base of the caudal fin. Attains weights of 10-12 pounds.

General Distribution.—The United States east of the Great Plains.

Florida Range.—State-wide.

Habitat.—Any large body of water and many small ones.

Tarpon atlanticus (Valenciennes)
Tarpon *(Plate 3)*

General Appearance.—A large fish with big, silvery scales, a deeply forked tail, and with the last ray of the dorsal fin very elongate.

Distinguishing Characters.—Scales large, 42-47 along lateral line; tail deeply forked; last ray of dorsal fin elongate; lower jaw projecting.

Description.—Head moderate, 4 times in length. Mouth large, oblique, lower jaw projecting. Head without scales. Eye large, with adipose lid. Dorsal fin short and high, 12 soft rays, last ray very elongate. Caudal deeply forked, both forks about equal in length. Pelvic fins abdominal in position. Anal fin much longer than dorsal fin, with 20-23 rays. Outer margin of anal deeply concave. Lateral line present, 42-47 scales along lateral line. Color bluish-silvery above, silvery on sides and below. Adults average about 60 pounds but may attain a weight of 300 pounds.

General Distribution.—The entire Atlantic and Gulf coasts of the United States.

Florida Range.—Both coasts and widely distributed in fresh water in southern Florida.

Habitat.—Invades fresh water of Florida by rivers and canals that enter the sea.

Elops saurus Linnaeus
Ten Pounder *(Plate 3)*

General Appearance.—A silvery, streamlined fish with a deeply forked tail.

Distinguishing Characters.—Scales small, about 120 along lateral line; tail deeply forked; last ray of dorsal fin not elongate.

Description.—Head moderately short, 4½ in length. Mouth moderate, oblique in position. Head without scales. Eye large, 4-5 in head, with adipose eyelid. Dorsal fin short and rather high, with 20 rays. Dorsal fin depressible into sheath of scales. Caudal fin deeply forked, the points about equal in length. Anal fin shorter than dorsal fin; with 13 rays; depressible into a scaly sheath. Pelvic fins abdominal in position, slightly in front of dorsal. Lateral line present, about 120 scales along lateral line. Color silverish. Adults may attain a length of 3 feet, but they average smaller.

General Distribution.—Throughout the warm seas of the world. In the United States it is common northward to about the region of North Carolina.

Florida Range.—Coastal regions and master streams.

Habitat.—Ranges well up into fresh-water rivers.

Alosa sapidissima (Wilson)
American Shad; Common Shad *(Plate 7)*

General Appearance.—A large, silvery shad with small fins.

Distinguishing Characters.—Body deep, 3 in length; 60-65 scale rows along lateral line; about 60 gill rakers below the angle of the arch.

Description.—Body compressed, depth 3 in length; head deep; free portion of cheeks deeper than long. Jaws without teeth, upper jaw with a deep notch at tip. Gill rakers long and slender, much longer than eye, about 60 rakers below the angle of the arch. Peritoneum white. Fins small, dorsal much nearer snout than base of caudal, 13-15 rays; caudal fin forked, lobes pointed; anal fin low, 19-21 rays. Color above bluish, silvery-white on sides and ventrally. A dark spot behind opercle, sometimes followed by several less conspicuous dots. Maximum size about 2½ feet.

General Distribution.—Atlantic Coast of the United States.

Florida Range.—The East Coast and coastal rivers.

Habitat.—Ascends large rivers for considerable distances.

Alosa alabamae Jordan and Evermann
Alabama Shad *(Plate 7)*

General Appearance.—A large, silvery shad with small fins.

Distinguishing Characters.—Depth of body 1/3 the length; 55 scale rows along lateral line; about 40 gill rakers below the angle of the arch.

Description.—Body deep, compressed, 3 in length; head deep, free portion of cheeks deeper than long. Teeth on maxillary scarcely perceptible. Upper jaw with a small notch at tip. Gill rakers long and slender, the longest about equal to the length of the snout, about 40 gill rakers below the angle of the arch. Peritoneum pale. Fins small. Origin of dorsal fin nearer snout than base of caudal; dorsal fin low, the longest ray shorter than the length of the fin; about 15 rays in dorsal. Caudal fin forked, lobes pointed. Anal fin low with 19-21 rays. Color bluish above, silvery-white on sides and ventrally. A small spot behind opercle. Dorsal, caudal, and pectoral fins darker at tips. Maximum size probably less than two feet.

General Distribution.—Gulf Coast of the United States.

Florida Freshwater Range.—Known from large rivers of western Florida.

Habitat.—Large rivers entering Gulf of Mexico.

Alosa pseudoharengus (Wilson)
Alewife *(Plate 6)*

General Appearance.—A moderate-sized, laterally compressed, silvery fish.

Distinguishing Characters.—Depth of body ⅓ the length; 50-54 scale rows; 17-19 anal rays; eye 3½ in length of head.

Description.—Body rather deep and compressed, heaviest anterior to dorsal fin. Head short, about as deep as long. Lower jaw protruding. Eye large 3½ in length of head. Gill rakers long, 30-40 below the angle of the arch. Peritoneum white. Dorsal fin slightly higher than long, with 16 rays. Caudal fin forked, lower lobe slightly longer than upper. Anal fin low, 17-19 rays. Color bluish above, silvery on sides and ventrally. A dark spot behind the opercle. Faint dark stripes along the scale rows. May exceed 12 inches in maximum length.

General Distribution.—Atlantic Coast of the United States.

Florida Freshwater Range.—Atlantic Coast streams.

Habitat.—Rivers entering the Atlantic.

Alosa aestivalis (Mitchill)
Glut Herring *(Plate 7)*

General Appearance.—A moderate-sized, laterally compressed, silvery fish.

Distinguishing Characters.—Eye small, 4 in length of head; depth 3½ in length; lining of body cavity black.

Description.—Body rather deep and compressed, heavy anteriorly. Head short, about as deep as long. Lower jaw protruding. Eye ¼ the length of head. Gill rakers long, 30-40 below the angle of the arch. Peritoneum black. Dorsal fin slightly longer than high, with about 16 rays. Caudal fin forked, lower lobe but slightly longer than upper.

Anal fin low, 17-19 rays. Color bluish above, silvery on sides and below. A dark spot behind opercle. Faint dark stripes along the scale rows. May attain a length slightly in excess of 12 inches.

General Distribution.—Atlantic Coast of the United States.
Florida Freshwater Range.—Streams entering the Atlantic.
Habitat.—Rivers and large streams.

Alosa mediocris (Mitchill)
Hickory Shad *(Plate 6)*

General Appearance.—A moderate-sized, silvery shad.
Distinguishing Characters.—Dorsal fin rays 15, anal fin rays 21; depth $3\frac{3}{8}$ in length; about 50 scale rows along side of body; lining of body cavity pale.
Description.—Head long, about 4 times in length; profile straight and not very steep. Upper jaw emarginate, lower jaw strongly projecting. Eye with adipose lid. Body profile somewhat elliptical, dorsal fin originating closer to the snout than to the base of the caudal. Depth of body about $3\frac{3}{8}$ in length of body. Fins low, dorsal fin with 15 rays, anal fin with 21 rays. Caudal fin widely forked. About 50 scale rows along sides of body. Color silvery, somewhat bluish above; sides with faint longitudinal stripes. Maximum length up to 2 feet, but averaging smaller.
General Distribution.—Atlantic Coast from Cape Cod to Florida.
Florida Range.—The Atlantic Coast and coastal streams.
Habitat.—Streams and inlets emptying into the Atlantic.

Alosa chrysochloris Rafinesque
Skipjack *(Plate 6)*

General Appearance.—A moderate-sized, silvery shad.
Distinguishing Characters.—Dorsal rays 16, anal rays 18; depth $3\frac{3}{4}$ in the length; eye $4\frac{1}{3}$ in length of head; about 23 gill rakers below the angle of the arch; lining of body cavity pale.
Description.—Head rather slender and pointed, its upper profile straight. Lower jaw strongly projecting, its tip entering the profile. Premaxillary and sometimes tip of lower jaw with persistent teeth. Eye large, $4\frac{1}{3}$ in length of head, with adipose eyelid. Body elliptical, highest near the middle, much compressed. Depth $3\frac{3}{4}$ in length. Dorsal fin with 16 rays. Caudal fin widely forked. Anal fin with 18 rays.

About 52 scale rows along length of body. Gill rakers below angle of arch 23. Color blue above, sides silvery. No dark spots along sides. Length sometimes as much as 15 inches.

General Distribution.—Gulf of Mexico and streams flowing into it; northward to Lake Erie and Lake Michigan.

Florida Range.—The Gulf Coast.

Habitat.—Streams and spring-runs entering the Gulf.

Brevoortia smithi Hildebrand

Bug Fish; Menhaden *(Plate 5)*

General Appearance.—A silvery fish with a forked tail, a dark shoulder spot, and a series of smaller spots behind the shoulder spot.

Distinguishing Characters.—Forked tail; no lateral line; 60-80 scale rows; dorsal fin with 19 soft rays.

Description.—Head large, deep; mouth large, weak, maxillary reaching behind posterior margin of eye. Dorsal fin highest in front, with about 19 rays. Caudal fin deeply forked, lobes of about equal length. Anal fin slightly longer than dorsal but not quite so high, with about 20 rays. Pelvic fins small, abdominal in position; placed but slightly anterior to origin of dorsal. Scales small and arranged in very narrow rows, usually between 60 and 80 along side of body. Color silvery; a round dark shoulder spot followed by about 15 much smaller spots arranged in about 3 rows. Length up to 14 inches, but individuals about 5 inches long much more common.

General Distribution.—The Atlantic Coast of the United States.

Florida Range.—The East Coast.

Habitat.—Migrates up large rivers.

Note.—At about the time of year shad are in the rivers, nearly every specimen of this fish will have a parasitic crustacean (*Cymothoa*) in the roof of its mouth; hence the local name, bug fish.

Dorsoma petenense vanhyningi (Weed)

Florida Threadfin Shad *(Plate 5)*

General Appearance.—A silvery fish with the last ray of the dorsal fin very long.

Distinguishing Characters.—A deep-bodied fish (depth $2\frac{3}{4}$ in length) with 14-15 rays in the dorsal fin, the last ray of which is very elongate; 20-23 rays in the anal fin, and about 40 rows of scales along the side of the body. The stomach is very muscular like the gizzard of a fowl.

Description.—Body compressed and quite deep, the depth about 2¾ in length. Head small, 3½ in length. Jaws about equal, maxillary extending to below the eye. Diameter of eye exceeding length of snout. Eye with adipose lid. Dorsal fin originates slightly closer to tip of snout than to base of caudal fin. Dorsal fin with 14-15 rays, the last of which is markedly elongate and extends to the level of the posterior margin of the anal fin. Caudal fin deeply forked. Anal fin long and low, with 20-23 rays. About 40-44 rows of scales along side of body. Color silvery with a small round spot in the shoulder region. Maximum length about 8 inches, but generally much smaller.

General Distribution.—Florida and the eastern Gulf coastal region.

Florida Range.—State-wide.

Habitat.—Large lakes and streams.

Dorosoma cepedianum (Le Sueur)
Gizzard Shad *(Plate 5)*

General Appearance.—A strongly compressed, silvery fish with the last ray of the dorsal fin very long.

Distinguishing Characters.—A deep-bodied fish (depth 2½ in length) with 12 rays in the dorsal fin, the last ray of which is very elongate; 29-33 rays in the anal fin; and 52-56 rows of scales along the sides. The stomach is very muscular like the gizzard of a fowl.

Description.—Body compressed and quite deep, the depth about 2½ in length. Head small, 4⅓ in length. Mouth quite small, oblique in position, overlapped by the blunt snout. Eye small, 4½ in length of head; with adipose lid. Dorsal fin originating slightly posterior to pelvic fins. Dorsal with 12 rays, the posterior of which is markedly elongate. Caudal fin deeply forked, the lower lobe slightly longer than the upper. Anal fin long and low, with 29-33 rays. About 52-56 rows of scales along the sides of the body. Color silvery, slightly bluish above; a dark round spot present in the shoulder region in the young. Size up to 15 inches, but usually smaller.

General Distribution.—Atlantic coastal regions from Cape Cod to Mexico.

Florida Range.—State-wide.

Habitat.—Rivers and many of the larger lakes.

Anchoa hepsetus hepsetus Bonnaterre
Striped Anchovy

General Appearance.—A little, slender, green fish with a silvery lateral stripe and a deep, undershot mouth.

Distinguishing Characters.—Mouth subterminal and deeply cleft; dorsal fin entirely of soft rays; anal fin with 19-20 rays; a silver stripe along the side.

Description.—Head long, about 3¾ in standard length. Eye large, 3½ in length of head. Mouth large but ventral in position, lower jaw fitting into the cleft of the upper. Snout conical, projecting beyond the tip of the jaw. Dorsal fin quadrangular in shape, with 15 soft rays. Caudal fin forked. Anal fin with 19-20 soft rays. Pelvic fins abdominal in position, anterior to dorsal fin. Scale rows along side of body about 40. Color pale greenish or whitish, very translucent. A silvery lateral band on each side from the head to the base of the tail; this band about as wide as the eye. Size up to 6 inches.

General Distribution.—Cape Cod to Brazil.

Florida Range.—Both coasts.

Habitat.—Coastal regions and fresh water connected with them.

Anchoa mitchilli diaphana Hildebrand
Bay Anchovy

General Appearance.—A little, slender, green fish with a silvery lateral stripe and a deep, undershot mouth.

Distinguishing Characters.—Mouth subterminal and deeply cleft; dorsal entirely of soft rays; anal fin with 25-26 rays; a silver stripe along the side.

Description.—Head long, about 3⅘ in length; eye large, 3 times in head. Mouth large but ventral in position, lower jaw fitting into the cleft of the upper. Snout conical, projecting beyond tip of jaw. Dorsal fin triagonal in shape, with about 14 soft rays. Caudal fin forked. Anal fin long and low, somewhat concave in profile, with 25-26 rays. Pelvic fins abdominal in position, anterior to dorsal fin. Scale rows along side of body 36-38. Color pale greenish or whitish, very translucent; a diffuse silvery stripe about as wide as the eye along each side of the body. Size about 2½ inches.

General Distribution.—Massachusetts to Texas.

Florida Range.—The entire coast.

Habitat.—Sandy shores invading rivers for some distance.

Umbra pygmaea (De Kay)
Mud Minnow (Plate 12)

General Appearance.—A small, big-mouthed, muddy-colored minnow.

Distinguishing Characters.—Posterior angle of jaw extending to below the middle of the eye; tail rounded; mouth not produced into a beak. Lower jaw black.

Description.—Head large, flattened above; head 4 in standard length. Mouth moderate, the posterior angles of the jaws extending to below the eyes. Body broad anteriorly, compressed behind. Dorsal fin with 13 rays. Caudal fin rounded. Anal fin with 7 soft rays. Pelvic fins abdominal in position. Pectoral fins placed low on body. Lateral line absent. About 35 scale rows along side of body. Color dark greenish with about 12 narrow longitudinal pale stripes. A dark bar at the base of the caudal fin. Lower jaw blackish. Length up to 4 inches.

General Distribution.—Long Island to Florida.

Florida Range.—Northeastern Florida.

Habitat.—Muddy streams and swamps.

Esox americanus Gmelin
Redfin Pickerel; Pike (Plate 4)

General Appearance.—An elongate fish with a beak like that of a duck.

Distinguishing Characters.—Mouth extended into a long, flat beak; pectoral fins low on body; less than 110 rows of scales along side of body; branchiostegal rays 11 to 13.

Description.—Head elongate, snout drawn out into a flattened duck-like bill; head $3\frac{3}{5}$ in length; jaws with sharp needle-like teeth. Cheeks and opercles fully scaled. Body elongate, dorsal and anal fins posterior in position. Dorsal fin with 11 or 12 soft rays. Caudal fin forked. Anal fin with 11-12 soft rays. Pelvic fins abdominal in position. Pectoral fins placed low on body. Branchiostegal rays 11-13. Scale rows along sides 105-110. Ground color greenish, sometimes with a series of faint curved bars along the sides, a blackish bar below the eye. Fins usually reddish or pinkish. Size about 12 inches.

General Distribution.—Massachusetts to Florida.

Florida Range.—Southward to the region of Lake Okeechobee.

Habitat.—Small streams and swamps.

Esox niger Le Sueur

Chain Pickerel; Jack Fish

General Appearance.—An elongate fish with a mouth like a duck's beak.

Distinguishing Characters.—Mouth extended into a long, flat beak; pectoral fins low on body; about 125 rows of scales along side of body; branchiostegal rays 14-16.

Description.—Head elongate, snout drawn out into a ducklike bill; head 3½ in length. Jaws with sharp needle-like teeth. Cheeks and opercles fully scaled. Body elongate, dorsal and anal fins posterior in position. Dorsal fin with about 14 soft rays. Caudal fin forked. Anal fin with about 13 soft rays. Pelvic fins abdominal in position. Pectoral fins placed low on body. Branchiostegal rays 14-16. Scale rows along side of body 125. Color greenish-golden with streaks and lines along the sides, giving a reticulated appearance. Fins plain, not pinkish. Length up to 2 feet.

General Distribution.—East and south of the Allegheny Mountains.

Florida Range.—State-wide.

Habitat.—Large rivers and lakes.

Carpiodes cyprinus (Le Sueur)

Quillback *(Plate 8)*

General Appearance.—A heavily built, sucker-like fish with a very long, soft dorsal fin.

Distinguishing Characters.—Elongate, soft dorsal fin with the anterior rays very long; mouth conical and projecting; sucker-like with thick, fleshy lips.

Description.—Head moderate, 3¾-4 in length; muzzle conical, projecting, obtusely pointed. Mouth sucker-like; lips thick and fleshy. Eye small, 4-5 in length of head. Body strongly arched above, depth 2½ - 3 in length. Dorsal fin very long, about ½ length of body. Dorsal fin with 26-27 soft rays, the most anterior elongate, nearly as long as base of fin. Caudal fin deeply forked, the lobes slender, the upper the longer. Anal fin short, 7-8 soft rays. Lateral line developed; 35 scales along lateral line; 7 rows above and 5 rows below lateral line. Color silvery to dusky. Length probably not exceeding 12 inches.

General Distribution.—The Mississippi Valley.

Florida Range.—The western panhandle.

Habitat.—Rivers and streams.

Moxostoma poecilurum Jordan
Blacktail Redhorse

General Appearance.—A fish with a sucker-like mouth and no spiny dorsal fin.

Distinguishing Characters.—No spiny dorsal fin; mouth sucker-like with fleshy lips; jaws toothless; 13 rays in dorsal fin; lateral line usually incomplete; 42-44 scales along lateral line.

Description.—Head moderate, 4⅓ in length. Mouth subinferior, the lips full and fleshy. Body elongate, moderately compressed, somewhat elevated anteriorly. Dorsal fin short and high, with 12 soft rays. Caudal fin forked, lower lobe longer and more slender than the upper. Anal fin short and high, with 7 soft rays. Lateral line partially developed; 42-44 scales along lateral line. Five scale rows above lateral line, 4 below. Ground color muddy brown. All fins except caudal reddish. Caudal fin with upper lobe reddish and lower lobe black, with a distinct white margin along the lower edge. Length about 12 inches.

General Distribution.—The Gulf Coast from Florida to Texas.

Florida Range.—The western panhandle.

Habitat.—Rivers and sandy streams.

Minytrema melanops (Rafinesque)
Spotted Sucker *(Plate 8)*

General Appearance.—A fish with a sucker-like mouth and without a spiny dorsal fin.

Distinguishing Characters.—No spiny dorsal fin; mouth sucker-like with fleshy lips; jaws toothless; 12 rays in dorsal fin; lateral line partially complete; 44-47 scale rows along side of body.

Description.—Head moderate, 4⅓ in length. Eye small, 5-6 in length of head. Mouth inferior, horizontal in position, upper lip well developed, the lower rather small, somewhat infolded; both lips fleshy and plicate. Body oblong, little compressed, depth about 4 in length. Dorsal fin short and high, with 12 soft rays. Caudal fin forked. Anal fin short and high, with 7 soft rays. Lateral line at least partially developed; 44-47 scales along lateral line. Ground color of body pale. Each scale with a dark spot, hence the dark spots are arranged in rows along the side of the body. Maximum length up to 18 inches.

General Distribution.—The Great Lakes region to North Carolina, Florida, and Texas.

Florida Range.—From the Suwannee River drainage westward.
Habitat.—Rivers.

Erimyzon tenuis (Agassiz)
Alabama Chubsucker

General Appearance.—A fish with a sucker-like mouth and without a spiny dorsal fin.

Distinguishing Characters.—No spiny dorsal fin; mouth sucker-like with fleshy lips; jaws toothless; 11 rays in dorsal fin; no lateral line; 40-42 rows of scales along side of body.

Description.—Head stout, short, 4-4⅓ in length. Eye large, 4 times in length of head. Mouth somewhat inferior, upper lip well developed, lower somewhat infolded; both lips fleshy and plicate. Body oblong, somewhat compressed. Depth of body 3 to 3¾ in length. Dorsal fin short and high, with 11 soft rays. Caudal fin forked. Anal fin short and high, with 7 soft rays. Lateral line lacking. Usually 40-42 scale rows along the side of the body. Coloration variable; young individuals pale with a broad black line down the side, adults muddy red in color, darker above than below. Length of adults slightly in excess of 1 foot.

General Distribution.—The Gulf Coast, Alabama, and Florida.
Florida Range.—Northern and western Florida.
Habitat.—Rivers.

Erimyzon sucetta (Lacépède)
Eastern Chubsucker *(Plate 8)*

General Appearance.—A fish with a sucker-like mouth and without a spiny dorsal fin.

Distinguishing Characters.—No spiny dorsal fin; mouth sucker-like with fleshy lips; jaws toothless; 12 rays in dorsal fin; no lateral line; 35-36 rows of scales along side of body.

Description.—Head stout, short, 4½ in length. Eye large, 4½ times in length of head. Mouth somewhat inferior, upper lip well developed, lower somewhat infolded; both lips fleshy and plicate. Body oblong, somewhat compressed. Depth of body about 3 in length. Dorsal fin short and high, usually with 12 soft rays. Caudal fin forked. Anal fin short and high with 7 soft rays. Lateral line lacking. Usually 35-36 rows of scales along side of body. Coloration variable; young individuals pale with a broad black line down the side, adults muddy red in color, darker above than below. Length of adults up to 1 foot.

General Distribution.—The eastern United States from New York to Florida.

Florida Range.—State-wide.

Habitat.—Quite ubiquitous, occurring in most bodies of fresh water of medium to large size.

Cyprinus carpio Linnaeus
Carp

General Appearance.—A robust fish with a tiny mouth and a long dorsal fin.

Distinguishing Characters.—Mouth tiny; lips thin, not thick and fleshy; dorsal fin with 20 or more rays preceded by a stout, bony spine.

Description.—Body robust, somewhat compressed. Head rather pointed with a rounded snout. Mouth rather small, anterior in position, with 4 barbels. Fins moderately high. Dorsal fin long, with 20 or more soft rays preceded by a serrate bony spine; anterior portion of dorsal fin higher than the rest. Caudal forked. Anal fin III,5. Pelvic fins abdominal in position. Lateral line present, nearly straight in profile. Scales along lateral line 37-39. Occasional specimens may have most of the scales missing and the few remaining much enlarged. Color variable, from brownish-tan to yellowish- and olive-green. Size generally less than 5 pounds or so.

General Distribution.—An Asiatic fish widely introduced and established in Europe and the United States.

Florida Range.—The western panhandle.

Habitat.—Ponds, small lakes, and rivers.

Notemigonus crysoleucas bosci (Valenciennes)
Southeastern Golden Shiner (*Plate 9*)

General Appearance.—A deep-bodied, laterally compressed, golden- and silvery-colored fish with a small, delicate mouth.

Distinguishing Characters.—Rays of anal fin 14-17; no barbels at base of maxillary; dorsal fin with about 8 rays.

Description.—Head rather flat between the eyes; tapering to a small terminal mouth; head about 4⅓ in standard length. Mouth small, terminal and oblique; the maxillary scarcely reaching the eye; no barbels at the base of the maxillary. Eye about 3 in length of head. Body strongly compressed in adults; more spindle-shaped in young. Dorsal fin with 8 rays. Caudal fin forked. Anal fin long, with 14-17 rays. Pelvic fins abdominal in position. Lateral line complete, strongly decurved. Scales along lateral line 43-50; 8 scales above lateral line, 2 below. Color of adults golden above, silvery below. Young with a dark lateral stripe. Length up to 12 inches.

General Distribution.—The south Atlantic states.

Florida Range.—State-wide.

Habitat.—Rather ubiquitous, occurring in all sorts of places.

Semotilus atromaculatus (Mitchill)
Southeastern Creek Chub *(Plate 9)*

General Appearance.—A big, forked-tail minnow with a dark stripe down each side.

Distinguishing Characters.—Scales along lateral line 45-55; a small barbel at the base of each maxillary; dorsal fin with 8 rays.

Description.—Head moderate, about 4 in standard length. Eye relatively small, about 5 in length of head. A small barbel at the base of each maxillary. Body stout, arched in front of the dorsal fin. Dorsal fin with 8 soft rays. Caudal fin forked. Anal fin with 7 or 8 soft rays. Pelvic fin abdominal in position. Lateral line present, somewhat de-curved. Scales along lateral line 45-55; 9 scales above lateral line, 5 below. Bluish-dusky above, creamy below with a broad lateral dark stripe which is black in the young but which fades in larger individuals A dark spot at the base of the origin of the dorsal fin. Total length up to 7 inches.

General Distribution.—Virginia and Tennessee southward to Florida.

Florida Range.—Extreme northern Florida and the panhandle.

Habitat.—Clear sandy and rocky streams.

Opsopoeodus emiliae Hay
Pugnose Minnow

General Appearance.—A small, graceful minnow with scarcely any mouth.

Distinguishing Characters.—Mouth very small, scarcely any lateral cleft; rays in anal fin 7-9; no barbels at base of maxillary; dorsal fin with 9 rays.

Description.—Head moderate, about $4\frac{1}{2}$ in standard length. Muzzle blunt and rounded. Mouth very small, with little lateral cleft. Eye about 3 in length of head. Body rather elongate, somewhat compressed, not elevated. Depth about $4\frac{2}{5}$ in standard length. Lateral line present, complete or nearly so. Scales along lateral line about 40; 5 scales above lateral line, 3 below. Origin of dorsal fin closer to tip of snout than to base of tail; dorsal fin with about 9 rays. Caudal fin deeply forked but lobes not strongly pointed. Anal fin with 7-9 soft rays. Pelvic fins abdominal in position. About 16 scales between back of head and origin of dorsal fin. Breast scales largely absent. Color yellowish above, silvery below. Rather narrow, indistinctly defined dark stripe along each side from snout to base of tail. Size 1½ to 2 inches.

General Distribution.—Lake Erie to Florida.

Florida Range.—State-wide.

Habitat.—Sandy streams and lakes.

Hybopsis amblops (Rafinesque)
Southern Bigeye Chub

General Appearance.—A graceful, pale-colored minnow with a narrow, pale stripe down the side.

Distinguishing Characters.—A small barbel at the base of each maxillary; 34-36 scales along lateral line; dorsal fin short (7-8 soft rays).

Description.—Body moderately robust, spindle-shaped; somewhat compressed. Head moderate; mouth with a tiny barbel at the base of each maxillary. Eye large, about equal to its distance from the tip of the snout. Vertical fins rather high. Dorsal fin with 7-8 soft rays. Caudal fin deeply forked. Anal fin with about 7 soft rays. Pelvic fins abdominal in position. Lateral line present, slightly decurved. Scales along lateral line 34-36; 5 scale rows above lateral line, 4 below. Scales from back of head to origin of dorsal fin 17 or fewer. Pharyngeal teeth, 1,4-4,1 or 0. An inconspicuous, narrow lateral stripe along the side from the opercle to the base of the tail. Flesh-colored above and below the lateral stripe, but little darker on the dorsum than on the belly. Length of adults 2-3 inches.

General Distribution.—The Gulf Coast.

Florida Range.—The western panhandle.

Habitat.—Clear streams.

Hybopsis harperi (Fowler)
Spring Redeye Chub *(Plate 10)*

General Appearance.—A small, trim, pinkish minnow.

Distinguishing Characters.—Scales along lateral line 30-35; a small barbel at the base of each maxillary; dorsal fin short (7-8 soft rays).

Description.—Body only moderately robust in side view, spindle-shaped; somewhat compressed. Head moderate; mouth with a tiny barbel at the base of each maxillary. Eye large, about equal to its distance from tip of snout. Vertical fins rather high. Dorsal fin with 7 to 8 soft rays. Caudal fin deeply forked. Anal fin with about 7 soft rays. Pelvic fins abdominal in position. Lateral line present, slightly decurved. Scales along lateral line 30-35; 5 scales above lateral line, 4 below. Scales from back of head to origin of dorsal fin 20 or more. Pharyngeal teeth 4-4. A dark lateral stripe runs along each side from the tip of the snout to the base of the tail; above this is a narrow stripe of white and the rest of the dorsum is pink to pinkish tan. Sides below dark lateral stripe, flesh-colored. Large specimens about 2 inches in total length.

General Distribution.—Florida.

Florida Range.—North and west Florida south to Lake County.

Habitat.—Clear springs and spring-runs.

Notropis roseipinnis Hay
Rosefin Shiner

General Appearance.—A trim, little minnow with a dark lateral stripe down the side and rose-colored fins.

Distinguishing Characters.—Eleven rays in anal fin; 41-44 scale rows along lateral line; 23-25 scales from back of head to origin of dorsal fin.

Description.—Head short, the muzzle pointed. Head about 4½ in standard length. Eye about 3½ in length of head. Mouth large, oblique; the maxillary reaching the level of the front of the eye. No barbels at the base of the maxillary. Body moderately stout, somewhat compressed; depth about 4 in standard length. Fins rather large. Dorsal fin with 8 rays. Caudal fin forked. Anal fin with 11 rays. Pelvic fins abdominal in position. Lateral line present, decurved. Scales along lateral line 41-44; 8 or 9 scales above lateral line, 3 below. Scales from back of head to origin of dorsal fin 23-25. Pharyngeal teeth 2, 4-4,2. Rusty above. A dark lateral stripe from tip of snout to base of tail; this stripe somewhat obsolete in larger individuals. Lateral stripe terminating in a small black spot at base of tail. Tip of chin dark. Vertical fins rosy. Length up to 2¼ inches.

General Distribution.—The Gulf Coast from Mississippi to Florida.

Florida Range.—The panhandle.

Habitat.—Clear streams.

Notropis hypselopterus (Günther)
Sailfin Shiner

General Appearance.—A trim, little minnow with a dark stripe down the side and two rose-colored spots at the base of the tail.

Distinguishing Characters.—Membranes of dorsal and anal fins with dark pigment; scales in lateral line 34-35; anal fin with 11 rays.

Description.—Head short, flattened above, the muzzle pointed. Head about 4¼ in standard length. Eye about 3 in length of head. Mouth large, oblique, the jaws about equal. No barbels at the base of the maxillary. Body short, compressed; depth about 4 in standard length. Fins rather large. Dorsal fin with 8 rays. Caudal fin forked. Anal fin with 11 rays. Pelvic fins abdominal in position. Lateral line present, decurved. About 34-35 scales along lateral line; 6 scales above lateral line, 3 below. Usually 22-24 scales between back of head and origin of dorsal fin. Pharyngeal teeth 2,4-4,2. Rusty above, a light band along the side bordered below by the dark lateral stripe which runs from the tip of the snout to the base of the tail. Tip of chin dark. An oval dark spot on the base of the tail bordered above and below by rosy-colored light spots. Vertical fin membranes with dark pigment. Total length up to 2 inches.

General Distribution.—The southeastern lowlands.

Florida Range.—Northern and western Florida southward to Hillsborough County.

Habitat.—Sand- and rock-bottomed streams.

Notropis signipinnis Bailey and Suttkus
Flagfin Shiner

General Appearance.—A trim, little minnow with a dark stripe down the side and two sulphur-yellow spots at the base of the tail.

Distinguishing Characters.—Membranes of dorsal and anal fins with little or no black pigment; scales in lateral line usually 34 or 35; anal fin with 11 rays.

Description.—Head short, flattened above; the muzzle pointed. Head about 4¼ in standard length. Eye about 3½ in length of head. Mouth large, oblique, the jaws about equal. No barbels at the base of the maxillary. Body short, compressed; depth about 4 in standard length. Fins rather large. Dorsal fin with 8 rays. Caudal fin forked. Anal fin with 11 rays. Pelvic fins abdominal in position. Lateral line present, decurved. About 34 or 35 scales along lateral line; 6 scales above lateral line, 3 below. Usually 16-18 scales from back of head to origin of dorsal fin. Pharyngeal teeth 2,4-4,2. Rusty above, a light band along the side bordered below by a dark lateral stripe which runs from the tip of the snout to the base of the caudal fin. Tip of chin dark. An oval dark spot at the base of the tail bordered above and below by sulphur-yellow light spots. Vertical fins yellow at bases and red-orange at their margins. Total length nearly 2 inches.

General Distribution.—Restricted to the Gulf coastal region.

Florida Range.—The panhandle.

Habitat.—Clear streams.

Notropis roseus roseus (Jordan)
Central Weed Shiner

General Appearance.—A graceful minnow with a dark stripe down the side.

Distinguishing Characters.—Anal rays 7; 35-36 scales along lateral line; no pronounced oval black spot at base of tail; about 15 scales from the back of the head to the origin of the dorsal fin. Scales on side immediately below lateral stripe margined with dark pigment.

Description.—Head rather short, bluntly rounded, about 4⅓ in standard length. Eye large, about 3 in length of head. Mouth moderate, slightly oblique, the jaws about equal. No barbel at the base of the maxillary. Body rather stout, slightly compressed. Depth about 4½ in standard length. Fins moderate. Dorsal fin with 8 rays. Caudal fin forked. Anal fin with 7 rays. Pelvic fins abdominal in position. Lateral line complete, decurved. Scales along lateral line 35-36; 5 scale rows above lateral line, 3 below. About 15 scales between back of head and origin of the dorsal fin. Pharyngeal teeth 2,4-4,2. Olivaceous above, lighter below; a prominent lateral dark stripe along each side from the tip of the snout to the base of the caudal fin. Tip of chin black. Vertical fins rosy in life. Total length up to about 2½ inches.

General Distribution.—Lowland streams of the Gulf Coast.

Florida Range.—The western panhandle.

Habitat.—Streams and spring runs.

Notropis petersoni Fowler
Peterson's Shiner

General Appearance.—A graceful, little minnow with a dark stripe down the side.

Distinguishing Characters.—Anal rays 7; 35-36 scales along lateral line; no pronounced oval black spot on the base of the tail; 13-15 scales from back of head to origin of dorsal fin; scales on side immediately below lateral stripe not margined with dark pigment.

Description.—Head rather short, bluntly rounded, about 4⅓ in standard length. Eye moderate, about 3⅓ in length of head. Mouth moderate, the jaws about equal, slightly oblique. No barbel at the base of the maxillary. Body rather stout, slightly compressed. Depth about 4⅓ in standard length. Dorsal fin with 8 rays. Caudal fin forked. Anal fin with 7 rays. Pelvic fins abdominal in position. Lateral line complete, slightly decurved. Scales along lateral line 35-37; 5 scale rows above lateral line, 3 below. About 14 scales between back of head and origin of dorsal fin. Pharyngeal teeth 1,4-4,1 or 2. Olivaceous above, flesh-colored below; with a dark lateral stripe on each side from the tip of the snout to the base of the tail. Lower lips pale.

General Distribution.—North Carolina to northern Florida.

Florida Range.—Northern Florida and southward in the peninsula to Brevard County.

Habitat.—Streams, springs, and spring-runs.

Notropis chalybaeus (Cope)
Iron-colored Shiner (Plate 10)

General Appearance.—A graceful minnow with a dark stripe down its side.

Distinguishing Characters.—Anal rays 7-8; 32-33 scales along lateral line; dark lateral stripe not terminating in a pronounced oval spot at the base of the tail. Inside of mouth with dark pigment.

Description.—Head flat above, rather narrow, tapering to a somewhat pointed muzzle. Head about 3⅘ in standard length. Eye large, 3 in length of head. Mouth oblique, the lower jaw slightly the longer. No barbel at the base of the maxillary. Body rather elongate, the depth about 5 in standard length. Fins rather high. Dorsal fin with 8 rays. Caudal fin forked. Anal fin with 7-8 rays. Pelvic fins abdominal in position. Lateral line present, decurved. Scales along lateral line 32-33; 6 scales above lateral line, 3 below. Scales between back of head and origin of dorsal fin 15-16. Pharyngeal teeth 2,4-4,2. Rusty-colored above, straw-colored below; a prominent dark lateral stripe on each side from tip of snout to the base of the caudal fin. Tip of chin black. Total length slightly more than 2 inches in large individuals.

General Distribution.—New Jersey to Florida.
Florida Range.—Southward to Brevard County.
Habitat.—Woodland streams.

Notropis cummingsae cummingsae Myers
Lowland Shiner *(Plate 10)*

General Appearance.—A trim, little minnow with a dark stripe down the side.

Distinguishing Characters.—Scales in lateral line 38-40; anal fin rays 11; 18-20 scales from back of head to origin of dorsal fin.

Description.—Head short, flattened above; the muzzle rounded. Head $4\frac{1}{3}$ to $4\frac{2}{3}$ in standard length. Eye 3 to $3\frac{3}{4}$ in length of head. Mouth large, oblique; the jaws about equal in length. No barbel at the base of the maxillary. Body rather stout, compressed; depth 4 to $4\frac{2}{5}$ in standard length. Fins rather large. Dorsal fin with 8 rays. Caudal fin forked. Anal fin with 10-11 rays. Pelvic fins abdominal in position. Lateral line present, decurved. Scales along lateral line 38-40; 6 rows of scales above lateral line, 3 below. Usually 18-20 scales from back of head to origin of dorsal fin. Pharyngeal teeth, 1,4-4,1. Dark olive above, a light band of coppery-brown bordered below by a lateral dark stripe of dull steel-blue. Tip of chin dark. Fins very slightly pigmented. Length about 2 inches.

General Distribution.—The lowlands from North Carolina to western Florida.

Florida Range.—Southward to Marion county and westward to the Ochlocknee River.

Habitat.—Streams.

Notropis venustus (Girard)
Blacktail Shiner

General Appearance.—A minnow with an incomplete dark lateral stripe and a black spot at the base of the tail.

Distinguishing Characters.—A prominent, oval, black spot on the base of the tail; about 15 scales from back of head to origin of dorsal fin; lateral line complete; rays in anal fin 8.

Description.—Head moderate, rather pointed. Head about 4 in standard length. Eye moderately large, about $3\frac{3}{5}$ in head. Mouth oblique, the jaws about equal in length. No barbel at the base of the maxillary. Body moderately stout, depth about $3\frac{3}{5}$ in standard length. Fins moderate. Dorsal fin with 7-8 rays. Caudal fin forked. Anal fin with 7-8 rays. Pelvic fins abdominal in position. Lateral line present, decurved. Scales along lateral line 37-39; five scales above lateral line, 3 below. About 15 scales between back of head and origin of dorsal fin. Pharyngeal teeth 1,4-4,1. Brownish above, lighter below. A dark stripe along each side from tip of snout to base of caudal fin; this stripe becoming obsolete anteriorly in mature specimens. A very prominent dark oval spot on the base of the tail at the end of the lateral stripe. Tip of chin slightly darkened. Length up to 3 or 4 inches.

General Distribution.—Texas to Florida.

Florida Range.—The panhandle.

Habitat.—Sandy and pebbly streams.

Notropis longirostris (Hay)

Eastern Longnose Shiner

General Appearance.—A trim, little minnow with hardly any color.

Distinguishing Characters.—Dark lateral stripe inconspicuous or absent, about 12 scales between back of head and origin of dorsal fin; lateral line complete; about 36 scales along lateral line.

Description.—Head small, about 4¼ in standard length. Eye about 4 in head. Mouth nearly horizontal; upper jaw projecting beyond the lower. No barbel at the base of the maxillary. Body slender, depth about 5 in standard length. Fins moderate. Dorsal fin with 8 rays. Caudal fin forked. Anal fin with 7-8 rays. Pelvic fins abdominal in position. Lateral line present, slightly decurved. About 36 scales along lateral line; 4 scales above lateral line, 3 below. About 12 scales between back of head and origin of dorsal fin. Pharyngeal teeth 1,4-4,1. Entire body straw-colored with a faint, narrow, darker streak along each side from the eye to the base of the tail; vertical fins slightly dusky. A small minnow 2 inches or less in length.

General Distribution.—Mississippi to Florida.

Florida Range.—The panhandle.

Habitat.—Clear streams.

Notropis maculatus (Hay)

Red Minnow

General Appearance.—A graceful, often reddish, little minnow with a spot on the base of the tail.

Distinguishing Characters.—Lateral line incomplete; rays in anal fin 7-8.

Description.—Head flattened above; snout rounded. Head about 4½ in standard length. Eye about 3½ in head. Mouth small, terminal, slightly oblique. No barbel at the base of the maxillary. Body slender, depth about 5 in length. Fins moderate; dorsal fin with 8 rays; caudal fin forked. Anal fin with 7-8 rays. Pelvic fins abdominal in position. Lateral line incomplete. Scales along side of body 36-38. Scales above lateral line 5, 3 below. About 15 scales between back of head and origin of dorsal fin. Pharyngeal teeth 4-4. Pinkish-red above, paler below. A fairly prominent dark lateral stripe from the tip of the snout to the base of the caudal fin where it terminates in a distinct oval dark spot about the size of the eye. Length about 2 inches or a little more.

General Distribution.—Mississippi to Florida.

Florida Range.—State-wide.

Habitat.—Creeks, rivers, and large lakes. This is the only species of *Notropis* commonly found in Florida lakes.

Ericymba buccata Cope
Silverjaw Minnow *(Plate 9)*

General Appearance.—A small, silvery minnow with a pocked face.

Distinguishing Characters.—Sides of head pitted with numerous cavernous chambers; dorsal fin with 8 rays; lips thin, no barbel at the base of the maxillary.

Description.—Head rather long, somewhat depressed above; muzzle broad and prominent but mouth small, sub-inferior in position. No barbel at the base of the maxillary. Extensive cavernous chambers on sides of head. Head about 4 in standard length. Eye large, about 4 in head. Body fusiform, rather elongate, but little compressed. Fins small. Dorsal fin with 8 rays. Caudal fin forked. Anal fin with 8 rays. Lateral line present; nearly straight. About 33 scales along lateral line, 5 scales above lateral line, 3 below. About 15 scales from back of head to origin of dorsal fin. Much of breast without scales. Color a pale olive above, silvery on sides and below. Length up to 5 inches.

General Distribution.—Pennsylvania and Michigan southward to Florida.

Florida Range.—The panhandle.

Habitat.—Sandy and rocky streams.

Bagre marinus (Mitchill)
Gafftopsail Catfish *(Plate 11)*

General Appearance.—A broad-headed, silvery-blue catfish with a forked tail.

Distinguishing Characters.—Tail deeply forked. Long filaments extending from dorsal and pectoral spines. Only 4 barbels on head.

Description.—Head broad and depressed. Mouth large, upper jaw slightly longer than lower. Teeth on vomer and palatine forming a band. Barbels 4, those on maxillary very elongate. Adipose fins not adnate. Caudal fin deeply forked, upper lobe longer than lower. Anal fin with 23 rays. Color above bluish, with a definite silvery sheen. Ventrally the color is silvery. Attains a weight of several pounds.

General Distribution.—Cape Cod to Texas.

Florida Range.—Coastal streams of entire state.

Habitat.—A marine catfish that invades fresh-water streams.

Galeichthys felis (Linnaeus)
Sea Catfish *(Plate 11)*

General Appearance.—A slender, steel-blue to silvery catfish with a forked tail.

Distinguishing Characters.—Tail deeply forked. No long filaments on spines. Six barbels on head.

Description.—Head and body somewhat elongate. Mouth not greatly enlarged, upper jaw slightly longer than lower. Teeth on vomer and palatine generally in patches, sometimes confluent into bands. Six barbels on head. Dorsal and pectoral fins without long filaments. Adipose fin not adnate. Tail deeply forked, the upper lobe the longer. Anal with 16 rays. Color steel-blue to silvery with silvery sides and belly. Attains a length of 2 feet, but averages smaller.

General Distribution.—Cape Cod to Texas.

Florida Range.—Coastal streams of entire state.

Habitat.—A marine catfish that invades fresh-water streams.

Ictalurus punctatus (Rafinesque)
Channel Cat *(Plate 11)*

General Appearance.—A slim catfish with a forked tail and distinct spots on the side.

Distinguishing Characters.—Tail deeply forked. Eight barbels on head. An unbroken bony ridge from head to origin of dorsal fin. Dark spots along the sides.

Description.—Body long and slender. Head not broad. Mouth comparatively small, upper jaw slightly longer than lower. No teeth on roof of mouth. Dorsal and pectoral fins without elongate filaments. Adipose fin not adnate. Caudal deeply forked; upper lobe slightly longer than lower; tips of lobes pointed. Anal with 25-30 rays. Color above light gray merging to nearly white below with scattered small, rounded dark spots along the sides. Attains a weight of 20-25 pounds but averages much smaller.

General Distribution.—The Mississippi Valley, the Gulf Coast of the United States and Florida.

Florida Range.—Southward to Lake Okeechobee.

Habitat.—The larger rivers and streams of the state.

Ictalurus catus (Linnaeus)
White Catfish

General Appearance.—A dark, robust catfish with a forked tail.

Distinguishing Characters.—Forked tail. Eight barbels on head. An incomplete bony ridge from head to origin of the dorsal fin. Pattern uniform, generally bluish-black, without distinct small spots.

Description.—Head very broad, body robust. Body depth $3\frac{1}{2}$ to $3\frac{3}{4}$ in total length. No teeth on roof of mouth. Dorsal fin inserted about halfway between tip of snout and adipose fin. Dorsal and pectoral fins without long filaments. Adipose fin not adnate. Caudal forked; upper lobe longer than lower; tips of lobes slightly rounded rather than sharply pointed. Anal fin with 19-22 rays. Color black, blue, or sometimes pale, although in general Florida specimens tend to be dark. Attains a length of several feet.

General Distribution.—New Jersey to Texas.

Florida Range.—Southward to Lake Okeechobee.

Habitat.—Large bodies of water, particularly streams.

Ameiurus nebulosus marmoratus (Holbrook)
Southern Brown Bullhead; Speckled Cat

General Appearance.—A moderate-sized, mottled catfish with a square tail.

Distinguishing Characters.—Square-cut tail; adipose fin free at posterior end; anal rays 20-24; mottled pattern.

Description.—Head and body moderately elongate, the head 3⅕ 3⅗ in body length. Upper jaw longer than lower, the mouth sub-terminal. Eye small. Profile nearly straight. Eight barbels on head. Dorsal spine 1⅘-2½ in length of head. Adipose fin not adnate. Caudal fin square or slightly emarginate. Anal fin with 20-24 rays. Color brownish with splotches or mottlings of black along the sides. Belly generally mottled. A moderate-sized catfish, the large adults exceeding a foot in length.

General Distribution.—Indiana southward and eastward to Florida.

Florida Range.—State-wide.

Habitat.—All sorts of fresh waters, including many very muddy or weed-choked places.

Ameiurus platycephalus (Girard)
Snail Cat; Flat Bullhead *(Plate 12)*

General Appearance.—A medium-sized (10 inches or less), slender catfish with pattern of rounded gray or golden spots.

Distinguishing Characters.—Caudal fin more or less square-cut or slightly emarginate; 16-20 rays in anal fin.

Description.—Body elongate. Head flat and broad, upper jaw some-what projecting. Barbels on head 8. No teeth on roof of mouth. Dorsal fin ⅔ length of head. Adipose fin not adnate. None of the fins termi-nating in a long filament. Anal with 16-20 rays. Tail rounded or slightly emarginate. Ground color dark bluish-brown, sides with nu-merous small rounded, light spots. Length to about 10 inches.

General Distribution.—North Carolina to the Chattahoochee River, Florida.

Florida Range.—Southward to Central Florida and westward to the Chattahoochee basin.

Habitat.—Partial to deep holes in rapidly flowing rivers like the Oklawaha and Santa Fe.

Ameiurus natalis (Le Sueur)
Yellow Cat; Butter Cat

General Appearance.—A catfish usually slightly less than a foot in length, with the adipose fin free posteriorly and a square or slightly rounded tail; and yellowish in color.

Distinguishing Characters.—Tail square or slightly rounded; adi-pose fin free posteriorly; anal fin with 25-27 rays.

Description.—Head and body stout, at times obese. Depth 3½ to 4 in length. Profile low, head broad, $3\frac{1}{2}$ to 4 in body length. Mouth wide, upper jaw but slightly longer than lower. Eye small. Eight barbels on head. Dorsal spine $2\frac{1}{5}$-$2\frac{3}{5}$ in head. Adipose fin not adnate. Caudal fin with truncate, or rounded, hind margin. Anal fin with 25-27 rays. Ground color brownish-yellow, darker above, fading to yellow on the belly. Maximum weight less than 2 pounds.

General Distribution.—The eastern United States.

Florida Range.—State-wide.

Habitat.—All sorts of lakes, ponds, and streams.

Schilbeodes funebris (Gilbert and Swain)
Longfin Madtom

General Appearance.—A trim, little, brown catfish with dusky-margined fins.

Distinguishing Characters.—Adipose fin fused to caudal fin; anal fin with 22-25 rays.

Description.—Head and body slender. Head not particularly depressed. Head about 4 in standard length. Body elongate, not pronouncedly arched in region of dorsal fin. Eight barbels on head. Spines slender. Pectoral spines serrate; the length of the pectoral spine about 3 in length of head. Adipose fin broadly adnate to body and to caudal fin, but with a definite notch between adipose and caudal. Caudal fin but slightly rounded. Anal fin long, with 22-25 rays. Color uniformly brownish or blackish except the margins of the vertical fins, which may be dusky. Length up to about 4 inches.

General Distribution.—The lower Gulf Coast.

Florida Range.—The panhandle.

Habitat.—Streams.

Schilbeodes mollis (Hermann)
Tadpole Madtom (Plate 12)

General Appearance.—A tiny, muddy brown catfish with a large, broadly rounded tail fin.

Distinguishing Characters.—Adipose fin fused to caudal fin; caudal fin rounded; form robust; pattern uniform; spine of dorsal fin exceeding $\frac{1}{2}$ the height of dorsal fin.

Description.—Head and body robust; depth 4-$5\frac{1}{2}$ in length; body somewhat arched in region of dorsal fin. Head broad, jaws nearly equal in length. Eye small. Eight barbels on head. Spine of dorsal fin exceeding ½ the height of the dorsal fin. Adipose fin broadly fused with body and caudal fin. Caudal fin broadly attached to body, its posterior margin rounded. Anal fin with 14-16 rays. Spine of pectoral fin not serrate on posterior margin. Coloration a muddy brown, lighter ventrally, with no definite pattern. Size small, never more than a few inches in length; Florida specimens usually less than 2 inches.

General Distribution.—The eastern United States.

Florida Range.—Southward to Lake Okeechobee.

Habitat.—Muddy and weed-choked bodies of water.

Schilbeodes leptacanthus (Jordan)
Gulf Madtom

General Appearance.—A tiny, slender catfish with rounded tail and pale brown or yellow ground color, usually with mottling of dark gray along the sides.

Distinguishing Characters.—Adipose fin fused to caudal fin; caudal fin rounded; form slender; mottled pattern. Spine of dorsal fin less than ½ the height of dorsal fin.

Description.—Head and body slender; depth of body 5½ in length. Body elongate, not pronouncedly arched in region of dorsal fin. Head narrow. Upper jaw longer than lower, protruding. Eye small. Eight barbels on head. Spine of dorsal fin less than ½ as high as dorsal fin. Adipose fin broadly adnate to body and caudal fin. Caudal fin rounded posteriorly. Anal fin with about 14 rays. Pectoral spine retrorsely serrate on outer edge. Ground color brownish or yellowish with mottlings of a darker hue on sides and dorsal and anal fins. A small fish only a few inches in length.

General Distribution.—Streams of the southeast.

Florida Range.—Southward to Lake County.

Habitat.—Sandy and rocky streams.

Anguilla rostrata De Kay
Eel *(Plate 1)*

General Appearance.—A slimy, long snaky-looking fish.

Distinguishing Characters.—A long snakelike fish with tiny scales so buried in the skin that it appears naked. No pelvic fins.

Description.—Head long and conical, moderately pointed; the lower jaw slightly projecting. Eye small, placed well forward over the angle of the jaw. Jaws with bands of small sharp teeth. Body very elongate. Dorsal fin placed well back on body and continuous with caudal and the anal fins. Caudal fin rounded. Pectoral fins well developed, situated above gill openings. Pelvic fins absent. Lateral line well developed. Color greenish to brownish. Length up to about 4 feet.

General Distribution.—The Atlantic Coast of North America and the lower streams of the Atlantic drainage.

Florida Range.—State-wide.

Habitat.—Rivers and streams; lakes and ponds connecting with rivers.

Strongylura marina (Walbaum)
Northern Needlefish

General Appearance.—A skinny, green fish with a long, pointed beak.

Distinguishing Characters.—Beak long and needle-like; pelvic fins closer to anal fin than to pectorals; caudal fin shallowly forked.

Description.—Body slender, depth about $5\frac{1}{2}$ in length of head. Head about 2 9/10 in standard length. Eye large. Jaws about twice as long as rest of head, with numerous tiny sharp teeth. Dorsal fin above anal fin in position. Dorsal fin I,14 or 15. Caudal fin shallowly forked. Anal fin I,17 or 18. Pelvic fins small, closer to anal fin than to pectorals. Pectoral fins high on body, just behind the head. Lateral line present, scales along lateral line about 300. A slight keel on each side of the caudal peduncle. Color green above, lighter on sides, and pale below. Average length less than 2 feet, but may attain a length of nearly 4 feet.

General Distribution.—The Atlantic Coast from Massachusetts to Texas.

Florida Range.—Streams entering the Atlantic Ocean and Gulf.

Habitat.—Rivers entering the sea; streams and lakes of the St. Johns drainage.

Lucania parva (Baird and Girard)
Rainwater Killifish *(Plate 14)*

General Appearance.—A small, insipid-looking fish one or two inches long.

Distinguishing Characters.—Anal fin rays 9-10; dorsal fin rays 10-12, scales along side 25 or 26; depth 3 or more in standard length.

Description.—Body compressed, back somewhat arched; depth $3\frac{1}{4}$-$3\frac{3}{4}$ in standard length. Head narrow, compressed, tapering to a vertically rounded snout; head $3\frac{1}{2}$ in standard length. Mouth small; teeth pointed. Eye large, about 3 in length of head. Origin of dorsal fin in advance of origin of anal; with 10-12 soft rays. Caudal fin broadly rounded. Anal fin with 9-10 soft rays. Pelvic fins abdominal in position. Lateral line absent. Scales along side 25-26. About 8 rows of scales from origin of dorsal fin to mid-line of venter. Color grayish with each scale margined with darker pigment. Length up to about 2 inches.

General Distribution.—The Atlantic Coast from Connecticut to Mexico.

Florida Range.—Both coasts.

Habitat.—Brackish water, invading fresh water for some distance.

Lucania goodei Jordan
Red-finned Killifish *(Plate 14)*

General Appearance.—A tiny fish with a dark stripe along the side from the eye to the tail.

Distinguishing Characters.—Scale rows along side 29-32; a dark stripe on each side from the eye to the base of the tail; dorsal rays 9; origin of dorsal fin well in advance of origin of anal fin.

Description.—Body tiny, rather elongate, not strongly compressed; depth about 4¼ in standard length. Head short and bluntly pointed; about 4 in standard length. Mouth small, terminal, with pointed teeth in a single series. Eye large, about 2⅔ in length of head. Origin of dorsal fin well in advance of origin of anal; with 9 soft rays. Caudal fin rounded. Anal fin with 9 soft rays. Pelvic fins abdominal in position. Lateral line absent. Scales along side 29-32; 7 rows of scales from origin of dorsal fin to mid-line of venter. A conspicuous dark stripe along each side from the eye to the base of the tail; base of caudal fin red in life in males. Length up to 1½ inches.

General Distribution.—Peninsular Florida.

Florida Range.—Same.

Habitat.—Small ponds, streams, and ditches.

Leptolucania ommata (Jordan)
Ocellated Killifish

General Appearance.—A tiny, greenish fish with a dark, eyelike spot on the base of the tail.

Distinguishing Characters.—Anal rays 9-10; scale rows 26-28; depth about 5 in standard length; teeth pointed.

Description.—Body fusiform, slender, slightly compressed; depth about 5 in standard length. Head moderate, about $3\frac{1}{3}$ in standard length. Mouth very small, its cleft almost vertical; teeth tiny, pointed, and arranged in a single row. Eye rather large, about $2\frac{1}{2}$ in head. Origin of dorsal fin posterior to origin of anal. Dorsal fin with 6-7 soft rays. Caudal fin rounded. Anal fin with 9-10 soft rays. Pelvic fins abdominal in position. Lateral line absent. Scales along side 26-28; 9 rows from origin of dorsal fin to mid-line of venter. A greenish to straw-colored fish with a dark ocellus on the base of the tail. Maximum length about 1 inch.

General Distribution.—Largely restricted to Florida.

Florida Range.—Florida southward to Osceola County.

Habitat.—Weedy places in streams and ditches.

Adinia xenica (Jordan and Gilbert)

Diamond Killifish

General Appearance.—A small, compressed fish, somewhat diamond-shaped in profile.

Distinguishing Characters.—Anal fin rays 11-12; scale rows about 25; depth $2-2\frac{1}{2}$ in standard length; teeth pointed.

Description.—Body compressed, rather deep and somewhat diamond-shaped in profile; depth $2-2\frac{1}{2}$ in standard length. Head pointed, about 3 in standard length. Mouth small, teeth all pointed, small and arranged in bands. Eye large, about 3 in length of head. Origin of dorsal fin anterior to origin of anal; dorsal fin with 9-10 soft rays. Caudal fin rounded. Anal fin with 11-12 soft rays. Pelvic fins abdominal in position. Lateral line absent. About 25 scales along side of body. About 10 rows of scales from origin of dorsal fin to mid-line of venter. A silvery-green, little minnow with numerous pearly vertical bars on the sides. Length up to about 2 inches.

General Distribution.—The Gulf Coast of the United States.

Florida Range.—The Gulf Coast.

Habitat.—Salt water and streams entering salt water.

Fundulus heteroclitus heteroclitus (Linnaeus)

Southern Common Killifish *(Plate 17)*

General Appearance.—A heavy-set, speckled little fish with a small mouth.

Distinguishing Characters.—No lateral line; scale rows along side 35-38; a freckled pattern; dorsal fin rays 11.

Description.—Body thick-set, short, and deep; depth 3½-4 in standard length. Head short and blunt, broad and flat on top; head length 3-3⅔ in standard length. Lower jaw projecting beyond upper. Teeth pointed, in several series. Eye moderate, about 5 in length of head. Anterior margin of dorsal fin in front of anterior margin of anal fin; dorsal fin with 11 soft rays. Caudal fin rounded. Anal fin with 10-11 soft rays. Pelvic fins abdominal in position. Lateral line absent. Scales along side 35-38; about 13-14 scale rows from origin of dorsal fin to mid-line of belly. Dorsal color olivaceous to dull dark green, pale to yellowish-orange below. Most of the scales have light spots or light centers, which gives the fish a freckled appearance. Length up to 6 inches.

General Distribution.—Virginia to southern Florida.

Florida Range.—The Atlantic Coast.

Habitat.—Salt marshes and fresh-water streams and inlets of the lowland drainage.

Fundulus grandis grandis Baird and Girard
Gulf Killifish

General Appearance.—A heavy-set, freckled little fish with a small mouth.

Distinguishing Characters.—No lateral line; scale rows along side 33-36; a freckled pattern; dorsal rays 11.

Description.—Body thick-set, short and deep; depth 3¼-4 in standard length. Head short and blunt, broad and flat on top; head length 3-3⅔ in standard length. Lower jaw projecting beyond upper. Teeth pointed, in several series. Eye moderate, about 5 in length of head. Anterior margin of dorsal fin in front of anterior margin of anal fin; dorsal fin with 11 soft rays. Caudal fin rounded. Anal fin with 10-11 soft rays. Pelvic fins abdominal in position. Lateral line absent. Scales along side 33-36; about 13-14 scale rows from origin of dorsal fin to mid-line of belly. Dorsal color olivaceous to dull dark green, pale to yellowish-orange below. Most of the scales have light spots or light centers, which gives the fish a freckled appearance. Length up to 6 inches.

General Distribution.—The coastal regions of the Gulf of Mexico.

Florida Range.—Southern Florida and the Gulf Coast.

Habitat.—Salt marshes and lowland fresh-water streams and inlets.

Fundulus seminolis Girard
Caledonian (Plate 16)

General Appearance.—A slender, olive-green little fish that makes good bass bait.

Distinguishing Characters.—No lateral line. Scales along side 50-55; anal fin with 13 rays.

Description.—Body slender, not compressed; depth about 6 in standard length. Head long and pointed; 3½-4⅓ in standard length. Mouth small, terminal; teeth pointed and arranged in 2 rows. Eye moderate, about 4 in length of head. Origin of dorsal fin in advance of origin of anal; with about 17 soft rays. Caudal fin slightly rounded. Anal fin with 13 soft rays. Pelvic fins abdominal in position. Lateral line absent. Scales along side 50-55; 17-18 scale rows from origin of dorsal fin to mid-line of belly. Ground color olive-green but with many of the scales having narrow dark edges, which gives the fish a somewhat speckled appearance. Length up to 6 or 7 inches.

General Distribution.—Peninsular Florida.

Florida Range.—The same.

Habitat.—Rivers, swamps, and certain types of lakes.

Fundulus similis (Baird and Girard)
Long-nosed Killifish

General Appearance.—A greenish, rather heavy-bodied little fish with indistinct vertical bars on the side and a long nose.

Distinguishing Characters.—No lateral line; about 33 scales along the side. Dorsal rays 11-13; head 3¼ in standard length.

Description.—Body oblong, little arched and little compressed; depth about 4 in standard length. Head somewhat elongate and narrow; about 3¼ in standard length. Snout rather elongate; longer than twice the diameter of the eye. Mouth small, terminal. Teeth tiny, pointed; arranged in several series. Eye small, its diameter about 7 in length of head. Anterior margin of dorsal fin in advance of anterior margin of anal fin. Dorsal fin with 11-13 soft rays. Caudal fin rounded. Anal fin with 10 soft rays. Pelvic fins abdominal in position. Lateral line absent. About 33 scales along side; about 11 rows of scales from origin of dorsal fin to mid-line of belly. Olive-green above; pale to bronze-colored below; about 10-15 indistinct, narrow vertical bars on the sides. Length up to 6 inches.

General Distribution.—The Gulf Coast of the United States.

Florida Range.—The Gulf Coast.

Habitat.—Salt-water marshes and fresh waters connected with them.

Fundulus majalis (Walbaum)
Striped Killifish *(Plate 17)*

General Appearance.—A rather heavy-bodied little fish with narrow bars on the sides.

Distinguishing Characters.—No lateral line; about 36 scales along the side; dorsal fin rays 12; head 3¾ in standard length.

Description.—Body oblong, little arched and little compressed; depth about 4 in standard length. Head somewhat elongate and narrow; about 3¾ in standard length. Snout twice or slightly less than twice as long as diameter of eye. Mouth small, terminal, and oblique. Teeth tiny, pointed, and arranged in bands. Eye small, its diameter about ½ the length of the snout. Anterior margin of dorsal fin anterior to anterior margin of anal fin. Dorsal fin with 12 soft rays. Caudal fin rounded. Anal fin with 10 soft rays. Pelvic fins abdominal in position. Lateral line absent. Scales along side about 36; about 13 rows of scales from the origin of the dorsal fin to the mid-line of the belly. Color olivaceous above, pale to yellowish-orange below; either with about 12 narrow vertical bars on the sides or with 1 or 2 narrow horizontal stripes along the sides. Length up to about 6 inches.

General Distribution.—The Atlantic Coast from Cape Cod to Florida.

Florida Range.—The East Coast.

Habitat.—Salt marshes and fresh waters connected with them.

Fundulus confluentus confluentus Goode and Bean
Spotfin Killifish *(Plate 17)*

General Appearance.—A fish 3 or 4 inches long, usually with an eyelike spot on the dorsal fin.

Distinguishing Characters.—No lateral line; scales along side about 35-37; dorsal fin with 10-11 rays; often an eyelike spot on the posterior margin of the dorsal fin.

Description.—Body moderately slender, not compressed; depth about 4 in standard length. Head short and relatively narrow; head 3-3½ in standard length. Mouth terminal, lower jaw not projecting. Teeth pointed, in narrow bands on each jaw. Eye moderate, about 4 in length of head. Anterior margin of dorsal fin but little if any in advance of anterior margin of anal fin; dorsal fin with 10-11 soft rays. Caudal fin slightly rounded. Anal fin with 10 soft rays. Pelvic fins abdominal in position. No lateral line. Scales along side 35-37. About 15 rows of scales between origin of dorsal fin and mid-line of belly. Olive-brownish above, pale yellowish to golden below. Usually with about 15 dark, narrow vertical bars on each side. Often with an eyelike spot on the posterior margin of the fin. Length up to about 4 inches.

General Distribution.—From eastern Florida to Louisiana.

Florida Range.—State-wide.

Habitat.—Salt marshes and fresh waters connected with them.

Fundulus cingulatus Cuvier and Valenciennes
Banded Topminnow

General Appearance.—A small fish with reddish fins and vertical bars on the sides.

Distinguishing Characters.—Lateral line absent; anal rays usually 9; narrow vertical bars on the sides; no distinct dark spot under the eye; anterior margin of dorsal fin above or slightly behind anterior margin of anal fin.

Description.—Body short and robust, slightly arched above, body compressed in the region of the caudal peduncle. Head short, about 3½ in standard length. Mouth small and terminal; lower jaw not projecting beyond upper. Teeth small and pointed, in several series. Eye moderate, its diameter about equal to the length of the snout; eye about 4 in length of head. Anterior margin of dorsal fin above or slightly behind origin of anal fin. Dorsal fin with 8-9 soft rays. Caudal fin rounded. Anal fin usually with 9 soft rays. Pelvic fins abdominal in position. Lateral line absent. About 33-34 scales along the side; with about 10 rows of scales from the origin of the dorsal fin to the mid-line of the belly. Color pale greenish or bronze, with narrow vertical bars on the sides but without gold flecks. Fins reddish. Length up to about 2 inches.

General Distribution.—The Gulf Coast.

Florida Range.—The western panhandle and southward in the peninsula to Lake County.

Habitat.—Rivers and streams.

Fundulus chrysotus Holbrook
Golden Topminnow *(Plate 16)*

General Appearance.—A small fish with robust body and gold flecks on the sides.

Distinguishing Characters.—Lateral line absent; anal rays usually 10; gold flecks on the sides in life; no distinct dark spot under the eye; anterior margin of dorsal fin above or slightly behind anterior margin of anal fin.

Description.—Body short and robust; slightly arched above; body compressed in the region of the caudal peduncle. Head short, length about 3½ in standard length. Mouth small and terminal; lower jaw not projecting beyond upper. Teeth small and pointed, in several series. Eye moderate, its diameter about equal the length of the snout; eye about 4 in length of head. Anterior margin of dorsal fin above or even slightly behind anterior margin of anal fin. Dorsal fin with about 9 soft rays. Caudal fin rounded. Anal fin with usually 10 soft rays. Pelvic fins abdominal in position. Lateral line absent. About 32-33 scales along side; with about 12 rows of scales from the origin of the dorsal fin to the mid-line of the belly. Color pale to olive-brown, with gold flecks on the sides in life and without any or with very few vertical dark bars on the sides. Length up to 2 inches.

General Distribution.—South Carolina to Louisiana.

Florida Range.—State-wide.

Habitat.—Ditches, sloughs, swamps, showing little preference for any particular type of habitat.

Fundulus notti notti (Agassiz)
Southern Star-headed Topminnow *(Plate 15)*

General Appearance.—A little bait fish with a dark patch under the eye and a light patch on the head.

Distinguishing Characters.—No lateral line; a dark patch under the eye; pattern of longitudinal rows of disconnected spots; anterior margin of anal fin just about under anterior margin of dorsal fin. Scales along side 34-36.

Description.—Body fusiform, compressed; back not much arched; depth about 4⅓ in standard length. Head rather elongate; flattened above; about 3⅔ in standard length. Snout obtuse; slightly less in length than the greatest diameter of the eye. Mouth terminal, slightly oblique; teeth small and pointed. Eye large, about 2⅔ in length of head. Origin of dorsal fin just about above origin of anal fin. Dorsal fin with 7-8 soft rays. Caudal fin elongate, rounded. Anal fin with 8-9 soft rays. Pelvic fins abdominal in position. Lateral line absent. About 34-36 scales along side; about 10 rows of scales from origin of dorsal fin to mid-line of belly. Color pale silvery with a conspicuous dark spot under each eye and 6-8 longitudinal rows of spots along the sides. Orange-red about the mouth and cheeks. Length about 2½ inches.

General Distribution.—The Gulf Coast from Mississippi to Florida.
Florida Range.—The western panhandle.
Habitat.—Ponds, streams, and ditches.

Fundulus notti lineolatus (Agassiz)
Eastern Star-headed Topminnow *(Plate 15)*

General Appearance.—A little bait fish with a dark patch under the eye and a light patch on the head.

Distinguishing Characters.—No lateral line; a dark patch under the eye; pattern of about 6 longitudinal stripes along the side (female) or of about 12 vertical dark bars (male); anterior margin of anal fin just about under anterior margin of dorsal fin. Scale rows 36-38.

Description.—Body fusiform, compressed; back not much arched; depth about 4½ in standard length. Head rather elongate; flattened above; about 3⅔ in standard length. Snout obtuse; slightly less in length than the greatest diameter of the eye. Mouth terminal, slightly oblique; teeth small and pointed. Eye large, about 2⅔ in length of head. Origin of dorsal fin just about above origin of anal fin. Dorsal fin with 7-8 soft rays. Caudal fin elongate, rounded. Anal fin with 8-9 soft rays. Pelvic fins abdominal in position. Lateral line absent. About 36-38 scales along the side; about 10 rows of scales from the origin of the dorsal fin to the mid-line of the belly. Color pale silvery with a conspicuous dark spot under each eye. Pattern either of about 6 longitudinal stripes on the side (female) or about 12 dark vertical bars on the sides (male). Often orange-red around the mouth and cheeks. Length about 2½ inches.

General Distribution.—Florida to the Carolinas.
Florida Range.—Southward to Highlands County.
Habitat.—Ponds, streams, and ditches; certain types of lakes.

Fundulus olivaceus (Storer)
Streaked Topminnow (Plate 16)

General Appearance.—A slender little fish with a broad, dark band down each side from the tip of the snout to the tail.

Distinguishing Characters.—No lateral line; a broad, dark stripe down each side from the tip of the snout to the base of the tail; scale rows along side about 34; anterior margin of dorsal fin just above anterior margin of anal fin.

Description.—Body fusiform, compressed posteriorly; back not much arched; depth about 4½ in standard length. Head rather elongate, flattened above; about 4 in standard length. Snout somewhat produced, the lower jaw scarcely projecting. Teeth small and pointed. Eye moderate, its diameter about 3 in length of head. Origin of dorsal fin almost above origin of anal fin. Dorsal fin with about 9 soft rays. Caudal fin elongate, rounded. Anal fin with about 11 soft rays. Lateral line absent. About 34 scales along side. About 11 rows of scales between origin of dorsal fin and mid-line of the belly. Color tannish-olive with a broad, dark lateral stripe along each side from the tip of the snout to the base of the caudal fin. Length up to 3½ inches.

General Distribution.—The Mississippi Valley and the Gulf states.

Florida Range.—The western panhandle.

Habitat.—Streams.

Cyprinodon variegatus variegatus (Lacépède)
Southern Sheepshead Killifish (Plate 13)

General Appearance.—A small, chunky, strongly compressed fish with a mottled pattern.

Distinguishing Characters.—Dorsal fin with 11 rays; anal fin with 10 rays; depth in length 3 or less.

Description.—Body strongly compressed; depth 2⅓-3 in standard length. Back strongly arched in profile. Head rather small, 3¼-3⅗ in standard length; tapering rapidly to a small terminal mouth. Teeth in a single series, wedge-shaped, with two notches in each, which makes them three-pronged. Eye large, about 3½ in length of head. Origin of dorsal fin well in advance of origin of anal fin. Dorsal fin with 11 rays. Caudal fin broadly rounded. Anal fin with 10 rays. Pelvic fins abdominal in position. Scales along side 25-26. Scale rows between origin of dorsal fin and mid-line of belly about 11. Greenish or bluish-gray, often with vertical blotches on the sides. Brassy orange about the head and often with an orange shading on the sides. Length up to 3 inches in large individuals.

General Distribution.—Atlantic Coast of the United States from Cape Cod southward.

Florida Range.—Coastal regions generally.

Habitat.—Salt marshes and fresh water connecting with them; ascending rivers for some distance.

Cyprinodon hubbsi Carr
Lake Eustis Sheepshead Killifish

General Appearance.—A laterally compressed little fish about an inch long.

Distinguishing Characters.—Anal fin rays 11; scale rows about 25; depth in length, $3\frac{1}{2}$-$4\frac{1}{2}$.

Description.—Body slightly compressed, not deep, the depth $3\frac{1}{2}$-$4\frac{1}{2}$ in standard length. Back not strongly arched. Head 3-$3\frac{4}{5}$ in standard length, tapering rapidly to a small terminal mouth. Teeth in a single series, wedge-shaped, with two notches in each, making them trifid. Eye $2\frac{3}{5}$-$3\frac{1}{5}$ in length of head. Origin of dorsal fin well in advance of origin of anal fin. Dorsal fin with 11 rays. Caudal fin squarish. Anal fin with 11 rays. Pelvic fins abdominal in position. Scales along side 25-26. Color pale with about 8 vertical bars of dark olivaceous on the sides. Length up to $1\frac{1}{4}$ inches.

General Distribution.—Restricted to Florida.

Florida Range.—Lake Eustis and environs.

Habitat.—The sandy and sometimes grassy lake shores.

Floridichthys carpio carpio (Günther)
Florida Gold-spotted Killifish *(Plate 13)*

General Appearance.—A chubby little fish with yellowish or orange spots on the sides.

Distinguishing Characters.—No lateral line; anterior margin of dorsal fin in front of anterior margin of anal fin; scales along side about 24.

Description.—Body compressed, depth about $2\frac{2}{5}$ in standard length; back rather arched. Head large, about 3 in standard length. Mouth small, terminal, slightly oblique. Teeth incisor-like, tricuspid. Eye moderate, about $3\frac{1}{3}$ in head. Origin of dorsal fin well in advance of origin of anal fin. Dorsal with about 11 soft rays. Caudal fin squarish; anal fin with about 9 soft rays. Pelvic fins abdominal in position. Lateral line absent. Scales along side about 24. Scale rows from origin of dorsal fin to mid-line of belly 9. Color silvery to olive with golden or orange spots or blotches on the sides except in young individuals. Length 2 or 3 inches.

General Distribution.—The Gulf Coast from Key West to Texas.

Florida Range.—The Gulf Coast.

Habitat.—Salt marshes and fresh water connected with them.

Jordanella floridae Goode and Bean
Flagfish *(Plate 13)*

General Appearance.—A little, gray fish an inch or two long, with a dark blotch on the side.

Distinguishing Characters.—Scales along side 25-27; anal fin with 11-13 soft rays; dorsal fin with a single spine and 14-16 soft rays.

Description.—Body strongly compressed, depth 2-2¼ in standard length. Back strongly arched in profile. Head 3½ in standard length, tapering rapidly to a small terminal mouth. Teeth flattened, chisel-like; one or two notches in each tooth so that some are bifid and some trifid. Eye large, 3½-4 in length of head. Origin of dorsal fin well in advance of origin of anal fin. Dorsal fin I,14-16. Caudal fin rounded. Anal fin 11-13. Pelvic fins abdominal in position. Scales along side 25-27. About 12 rows of scales from origin of dorsal fin to mid-line of belly. Color grayish with a large dark spot on each side. Maximum length in excess of 2 inches.

General Distribution.—Florida and the lower Gulf Coast.

Florida Range.—State-wide.

Habitat.—Swamps, swamp streams, and ditches.

Gambusia affinis holbrooki Girard
Eastern Mosquito-fish *(Plate 15)*

General Appearance.—A little, white-bellied, pregnant-looking fish.

Distinguishing Characters.—Scale rows 30-32; dorsal rays 8; head 3½-4 in standard length.

Description.—Body not strongly compressed, more fusiform; depth 3⅔-4 in standard length. Back not strongly arched in profile. Head 3½-4 in standard length. Mouth small and terminal. Teeth in broad villiform bands. Eye moderate, 3½ in length of head. Origin of dorsal fin behind origin of anal fin. Dorsal fin with 8 rays. Caudal fin rounded. Anal fin with 8-10 rays (females), or modified into a copulatory structure (males). Pelvic fins abdominal in position. Scales along sides 30-32. Scale rows from origin of dorsal fin to mid-line of belly about 8. Color grayish above, whitish below, female with a black pregnancy spot. The vertical fins speckled. Melanistic individuals common. Length up to 2 inches.

General Distribution.—New Jersey to Florida.

Florida Range.—State-wide.

Habitat.—All sorts of fresh waters.

Note.—This form integrades with *G. a. affinis* in extreme western Florida.

Gambusia species

Mangrove Mosquito-fish

General Appearance.—A little, white-bellied, pregnant-looking minnow.

Distinguishing Characters.—Scale rows 28-31; dorsal rays 7-9; head $3\frac{1}{3}$-$3\frac{2}{3}$ in standard length.

Description.—Body compressed, depth 3-$3\frac{1}{3}$ in standard length. Back not strongly arched in profile. Head $3\frac{1}{3}$-$3\frac{2}{3}$ in standard length. Mouth small and terminal. Teeth in broad villiform bands. Eye moderate, $2\frac{4}{5}$-$3\frac{1}{5}$ in length of head. Origin of dorsal fin behind origin of anal fin. Dorsal fin usually with 8 rays, rarely 7 or 9. Caudal fin rounded. Anal fin with 10 rays, the last double (females), or modified into a copulatory structure (males). Pelvic fins abdominal in position. Scales along sides usually 29 or 30, very rarely 28 or 31. Scale rows from origin of dorsal fin to mid-line of belly about 9. Color grayish above, whitish below, with longitudinal rows of black spots on sides of body. The vertical fins (except anal) speckled. Length up to 2 inches.

General Distribution.—Extreme south Florida.

Florida Range.—Biscayne Bay southward to Key West.

Habitat.—Brackish and salt water, associated with the red mangrove, very rarely in fresh water.

Heterandria formosa Agassiz

Least Killifish *(Plate 14)*

General Appearance.—Tiniest of fishes, with a spot on the dorsal fin.

Distinguishing Characters.—Scales along side 24-28; anal rays 6-9;

depth about 3¾-4 in standard length; anterior margin of anal fin below or slightly in advance of origin of dorsal fin.

Description.—Body short, slightly compressed; depth about 3¾-4 in standard length. Back but slightly arched. Head moderate, 3½-3⅔ in standard length; tapering to a small terminal mouth. Teeth small and pointed, in a single series. Eye large, about 3 in length of head. Origin of dorsal fin slightly behind origin of anal fin. Dorsal fin with 7 rays. Caudal fin rounded. Anal fin with 6-9 rays (female), or modified into a copulatory organ (male). Pelvic fins abdominal in position. Lateral line absent. Scales along side 24-28; about 9-10 rows of scales between origin of dorsal fin and mid-line of belly. Ground color olive-brown with a darker stripe down each side and traces of vertical bars superimposed on the dark lateral stripe. A dark spot on the dorsal fin of males and on the dorsal and anal fins of females. Maximum size about 1 inch—the smallest North American fish.

General Distribution.—South Carolina to Florida.

Florida Range.—State-wide.

Habitat.—Quiet water with trash or vegetation, swamps, ditches, and the margins of nearly any body of water.

Mollienesia latipinna Le Sueur
Sailfin Molly

General Appearance.—A pretty little fish with a big dorsal fin.

Distinguishing Characters.—Anal fin with 8 rays; dorsal fin usually with 14-16 rays.

Description.—Body oblong, compressed; depth 2¾-3 in standard length. Back but slightly arched. Head very small, depressed; head length about 4 in standard length. Mouth tiny, vertical, without lateral cleft. Teeth small, pointed, in several bands. Eye moderate, about 3 in length of head. Dorsal fin long, 14-16 rays; very high in adult males. Caudal fin rounded. Anal fin with 8 rays (female), or modified into a copulatory organ (male). Origin of anal behind origin of dorsal fin. Pelvic fin abdominal in position. Scales along side about 26. Scale rows between origin of dorsal fin and mid-line of belly 9-10. Ground color of males olive-greenish, of females olivaceous. Each scale on back and sides with dark spots, thus forming indistinct rows or stripes. Breeding males beautifully tinged with bright greenish-blue or blue. Melanistic individuals common. Length up to about 3 inches.

General Distribution.—The coasts and lowland streams and swamps from the Carolinas to Mexico.

Florida Range.—State-wide.
Habitat.—Salt water and fresh-water streams and swamps.

Aphredoderus sayanus (Gilliams)
Pirate Perch *(Plate 18)*

General Appearance.—A humpbacked little fish with the anus under the throat.

Distinguishing Characters.—Vent jugular in position.

Description.—Body oblong; back arched at the origin of the dorsal fin; body compressed posteriorly. Head moderate; about 3 in standard length; depressed above. Mouth large, terminal, the lower jaw slightly projecting. Sides of head scaly. Eye moderate, above 5 in length of head. Dorsal fin III,11 or IV,10. Caudal fin square or slightly concave. Anal fin II,6. Pelvic fins thoracic in position. Vent jugular in position. Lateral line absent or imperfect. Scales along side 45-60. Color dark olive with occasionally a lavender tinge. A narrow, dark vertical bar at the base of the tail. Total length up to 5 inches.

General Distribution.—New York to Texas.

Florida Range.—State-wide.

Habitat.—Lowland swamps and streams.

Menidia beryllina (Cope)
Freshwater Glass-minnow *(Plate 29)*

General Appearance.—A silvery-greenish, streamlined little fish.

Distinguishing Characters.—Scales along side 37-39; anal with 16-18 soft rays; 2 dorsal fins.

Description.—Body very slender, fusiform; depth 5-5½ in standard length. Head about 4⅓ in standard length. Mouth terminal, oblique, the lower jaw short and weak. Sides of head scaly. Eye very large, 3 in length of head. Dorsal fin V-I,9, occasionally with 8 or 10 soft rays. Caudal fin forked. Anal fin I,16 to 18. Pelvic fins abdominal in position. No lateral line. Scales along side 37-39. About 8 rows of scales from origin of dorsal fin to mid-line of belly. Color greenish, a narrow lateral stripe of silver. Length up to about 4 inches.

General Distribution.—Coastal regions, Massachusetts to Mississippi.

Florida Range.—Coastal waters, and streams and lakes connecting with salt water.

Habitat.—Streams and lakes.

Membras martinica (Cuvier and Valenciennes)
Rough Silverside *(Plate 29)*

General Appearance.—A silvery-greenish, streamlined little fish.

Distinguishing Characters.—Scales along side 45-47; anal with 16-17 soft rays; 2 dorsal fins.

Description.—Body very slender, fusiform; depth 5-5½ in standard length. Head about 4⅖ in standard length. Mouth terminal, oblique; the lower jaw short and weak. Sides of head scaly. Eye very large, about 3⅓ in head. Dorsal fin V-I,7. Caudal fin forked. Anal fin I,16 to I,18. Pelvic fins abdominal in position. No lateral line. Scales along side 45-47. About 8 rows of scales from origin of dorsal fin to mid-line of belly. Color greenish, with a narrow silver stripe down each side. Length about 4 inches.

General Distribution.—The Atlantic Coast from New York to Mexico.

Florida Range.—Recorded in fresh water from the St. Johns River.

Habitat.—Coastal regions and large rivers.

Labidesthes sicculus vanhyningi (Bean and Reid)
Florida Brook Silversides

General Appearance.—A silvery-greenish, long-bodied little fish.

Distinguishing Characters.—Scales along side 72-75; anal with about 23 soft rays; 2 dorsal fins.

Description.—Body very slender, fusiform; depth about 6 in standard length. Head flat above, about 4½ in standard length. Mouth terminal, jaws produced into a short, depressed beak. Sides of head scaly. Eye large, about 3½ in length of head. Dorsal fin IV-I,11. Caudal fin forked. Anal fin I,23. Lateral line absent. Scales along side 72-75. Color green with a narrow pale stripe down each side. Total length up to 4 inches but averaging smaller.

General Distribution.—The lower southeastern states.

Florida Range.—State-wide.

Habitat.—Streams and clear-water lakes.

Mugil cephalus Linnaeus
Striped Mullet *(Plate 28)*

General Appearance.—A fish with 2 dorsal fins and a sucker-like mouth.

Distinguishing Characters.—Scales not extending onto the soft dorsal and anal fins; scale rows 40-42; adipose eyelid.

Description.—Body moderately elongate, not much compressed, depth $3\frac{5}{6}$-4 in standard length. Head 4-$4\frac{1}{3}$ in standard length, tapering to a rather small mouth. Sides of head scaly. Eye with an adipose eyelid; rather small, 5-7 in length of head. Dorsal fin IV-I,8. Caudal fin forked. Anal fin III,8. Pelvic fins abdominal in position. Lateral line absent. Scales along side 40-42. About 13 rows of scales between origin of dorsal fin and mid-line of belly. Color bluish-gray above, whitish below. Many scales along the back and sides have dusky centers, thus forming dark streaks along the sides. Length up to 2 feet.

General Distribution.—Widely distributed in the seas of the world.

Florida Range.—Both coasts; frequent in coastal fresh waters.

Habitat.—Ascends fresh-water streams for great distances.

Mugil curema Cuvier and Valenciennes
White Mullet *(Plate 28)*

General Appearance.—A fish with 2 dorsal fins and a sucker-like mouth.

Distinguishing Characters.—Scales extending onto the base of the soft dorsal and anal fins; anal fin III,9; scale rows 37-39; adipose eyelid.

Description.—Body moderately elongate; not much compressed. Depth $3\frac{5}{6}$-4 in standard length. Head $4\frac{1}{3}$ in standard length; tapering to a rather small mouth with a thick, fleshy upper lip. Sides of head scaly. Eye with an adipose eyelid; $3\frac{3}{4}$ in length of head. Dorsal fin IV-I,8. Caudal fin forked. Anal fin III,9. Pelvic fins abdominal in position. Scales extending onto the base of the soft dorsal fin and the anal fin. Lateral line absent. Scales along side 37-39. About 12 rows of scales from origin of first dorsal to mid-line of belly. Color bluish-olive above, whiter below. No conspicuous dusky streaks along the sides. Attains a weight of only a pound or two.

General Distribution.—Cape Cod to Brazil.

Florida Range.—Known from fresh water in Florida from the St. Johns River and its tributaries.

Habitat.—The sea and master streams.

Mugil trichodon Poey
Fan-tail Mullet

General Appearance.—A fish with 2 dorsal fins and a sucker-like mouth.

Distinguishing Characters.—Scales extending onto the base of the soft dorsal and anal fins; anal fin III,8; scale rows 32-34; adipose eyelid.

Description.—Body rather robust; not much compressed; depth 3⅔ in standard length. Head 4⅕ in standard length, tapering to a small mouth with a thick upper lip. Sides of head scaly. Eye with an adipose eyelid. Dorsal fin IV-I,8. Caudal fin forked. Anal fin III,8. Pelvic fins abdominal in position. Scales extending onto the base of the soft dorsal and anal fins. Lateral line absent. Scales along side 32-34. About 11 rows of scales between origin of dorsal fin and midline of belly. Bluish-olive above, silver below. No dusky streaks along the sides. A dark blotch at the base of the pectoral fins. Maximum length about 1 foot.

General Distribution.—Florida to Brazil.

Florida Range.—Southern Florida.

Habitat.—Coastal and brackish waters, straying into fresh water.

Agonostomus monticola (Bancroft)
Mountain Mullet *(Plate 28)*

General Appearance.—A fish with 2 dorsal fins and a sucker-like mouth.

Distinguishing Characters.—Lower lip thick and fleshy, upper lip thin, no adipose eyelid.

Description.—Body moderately stout, not much compressed; depth 3¾ in standard length. Head 3⅔ in standard length, tapering to the small mouth, which has a lateral cleft extending posteriorly to the level of the margin of the eye. Eye without an adipose eyelid. Sides of head scaly. Dorsal fin IV-I,8. Caudal fin forked. Anal fin III,9. Pelvic fins abdominal in position. Scales not extending onto the base of the soft dorsal and anal fins. Lateral line absent. Scales along side 40-42. About 12 rows of scales between origin of dorsal fin and midline of belly. Color pale brownish above, whitish below. Yellow around the base of the caudal fin. Length of Florida specimens 8 inches or less.

General Distribution.—The Caribbean area.

Florida Range.—Streams of the Atlantic drainage and Pinellas County on the West Coast.

Habitat.—Small, swift streams.

Centropomus undecimalis (Bloch)
Snook (*Plate 27*)

General Appearance.—A large fish with a big mouth, 2 dorsal fins, and a narrow dark stripe down the side.

Distinguishing Characters.—Scales along lateral line 67-77; second anal spine not reaching to base of caudal fin; soft rays in anal fin 6.

Description.—Body robust, little compressed; depth 4-4¼ in standard length. Head depressed, 2⅔-3 in standard length. Mouth large, lower jaw projecting beyond upper. Maxillary reaching to or extending beyond a vertical from center of the eye. Eye moderate, more than 5½ in length of head. Gill rakers 7-9 on lower limb of first arch, not counting rudiments. Cheeks scaly. Dorsal fin VIII-I,11. Caudal fin forked. Anal fin III,6. Second anal spine not reaching origin of caudal fin. Scales along lateral line 67-77. Nine rows of scales above lateral line, 15-17 below. Dark olive to bluish above, whitish below; a conspicuous narrow black stripe along the lateral line. Size large, attaining weights of 50 pounds or more.

General Distribution.—Florida and the West Indies.

Florida Range.—Invading fresh waters of the peninsula.

Habitat.—The sea and fresh-water streams and canals.

Centropomus pectinatus Poey
Snook

General Appearance.—A fish with a big mouth, 2 dorsal fins, and a narrow dark stripe down the side.

Distinguishing Characters.—Scales along lateral line 62-67; second anal spine reaching to or extending somewhat beyond base of caudal fin; soft rays in anal fin 7.

Description.—Body robust, little compressed; depth 3¾ in standard length. Mouth large, lower jaw projecting beyond upper. Maxillary not reaching to a vertical from center of eye. Eye 6 in length of head. Gill rakers 13-16 on lower limb of first arch, not counting rudiments. Cheeks scaly. Dorsal fin VIII-I,10. Caudal fin forked. Anal fin III,7. Second anal spine reaching to or beyond origin of caudal fin. Scales along lateral line 62-67. Dark olive to bluish above, whitish below.

A conspicuous narrow black stripe along the lateral line. Size small, not attaining more than 3 pounds in weight.

General Distribution.—Southern Florida and the West Indies.

Florida Range.—Southern Florida.

Habitat.—Salt water and the fresh-water canals leading to Lake Okeechobee.

Centropomus parallelus Poey
Snook

General Appearance.—A fish with a big mouth, 2 dorsal fins, and a narrow dark stripe down the side.

Distinguishing Characters.—Scales along lateral line 80-88; second anal spine reaching to or beyond base of caudal fin; soft rays in anal fin 6.

Description.—Body robust, little compressed; depth 3¾ in standard length. Head depressed, 2½ in standard length. Mouth large, lower jaw projecting beyond upper. Maxillary reaching to or extending beyond a vertical from center of eye. Eye less than 5½ in length of head. Gill rakers 10-12 on lower limb of first arch, not counting rudiments. Cheeks scaly. Dorsal fin VIII-I,10. Caudal fin forked. Anal fin III,6. Second anal spine reaching to or beyond origin of caudal fin. Scales along lateral line 80-88. Dark olive to bluish above, whitish below. A conspicuous narrow black stripe along lateral line. Not exceeding 5 pounds in weight.

General Distribution.—Southern Florida and the West Indies.

Florida Range.—Southern Florida.

Habitat.—Salt water and the fresh-water canals leading to Lake Okeechobee.

Roccus saxatilis (Walbaum)
Striped Bass *(Plate 27)*

General Appearance.—A pale-colored fish with narrow dark stripes down the sides and a big mouth.

Distinguishing Characters.—First ray of second dorsal fin spiny; pattern of 6-8 narrow longitudinal stripes on each side over a light ground color.

Description.—Body rather elongate, little compressed; depth 3½-4 in standard length. Mouth large, oblique, the maxillary extending to above the level of the middle of the eye. Lower jaw projecting. Cheeks scaly. Eye small, 8 in length of head. Fins moderate in height. Dorsal fins separate, IX-I,12. Caudal fin forked. Anal fin III,11. Pelvic fins thoracic in position. Scales along lateral line 66-68. Scale rows above lateral line 8, below 11. Color quite pale, with 6-8 narrow longitudinal dark stripes along each side. Maximum size in excess of 100 pounds but averaging much smaller.

General Distribution.—The Atlantic Coast, Canada to Florida.

Florida Range.—The northern portion of the East Coast, invading the St. Marys and St. Johns rivers as far as their headwaters.

Habitat.—Salt water and rivers.

Micropterus notius Bailey and Hubbs
Suwannee Bass

General Appearance.—A small, relatively slender bass with dark blotches along the sides.

Distinguishing Characters.—Notch between spiny and soft portions of dorsal fin shallow; pyloric caecae mostly unforked; maxillary extending to about the level of the posterior margin of the eye; 12-13 rows of cheek scales; dorsal fin X,12; 59-63 rows of scales along lateral line; scales around caudal peduncle 27-29.

Description.—Body somewhat elongate, not strongly compressed; depth 3⅕ in length. Twelve or 13 rows of cheek scales. Mouth large, sturdy, but slightly oblique; maxillary extending about to the level of the posterior margin of the eye. Fins moderately high. Notch between spiny and soft portions of the dorsal fin shallow. Dorsal fin X,12. Anal fin III,10. Caudal fin emarginate. Pectoral fins with 15-16 rays. Scales along lateral line 59-63; 8-9 rows of scales above lateral line; 16-19 below. Scales around caudal peduncle 27-29. Pyloric caecae mostly simple, unbranched. Pattern of about 12 vertical dark brown blotches along the sides on a background of light brown or tan. Size small, probably seldom, if ever, exceeding 12 inches in total length.

General Distribution.—Restricted to Florida.

Florida Range.—Restricted to the Suwannee River system.

Habitat.—Swift-flowing rivers and spring runs.

Micropterus punctulatus (Rafinesque)
Northern Spotted Bass

General Appearance.—A clean-cut, slender bass with spots on the back.

Distinguishing Characters.—Notch between spiny and soft portions of dorsal fin shallow; pyloric caecae mostly unforked; maxillary extending to about the posterior margin of the eye; 13-16 rows of cheek scales; dorsal fin X,12; 62-70 rows of scales along lateral line; scales around caudal peduncle 23-25.

Description.—Body somewhat elongate, not strongly compressed. Depth 3½-4 in standard length. Rows of scales on cheek 13-16. Mouth large, sturdy, and but little oblique; maxillary extending to about the level of the posterior margin of the eye. Fins moderately high. Notch between spiny and soft portions of the dorsal fin shallow. Dorsal fin X,12; anal fin III,10. Caudal fin emarginate. Pectoral fins generally with 15 rays. Scales along lateral line 62-70; 8 rows of scales above lateral line, 15-17 below. Scales around caudal peduncle 23-25. Pyloric caecae simple, mostly unbranched. Pattern a row of confluent spots forming a stripe along the side, with generally a row of more or less discrete spots above this line. Size moderate for a bass; it attains a top weight of about 4 pounds.

General Distribution.—A large portion of the Mississippi Valley.

Florida Range.—The Apalachicola River westward.

Habitat.—Rivers.

Micropterus species

Chipola Bass; Shoal Bass

General Appearance.—A moderate to large-sized bass with small scales.

Distinguishing Characters.—Notch between spiny and soft portions of dorsal fin shallow; pyloric caecae mostly simple, unbranched; maxillary not extending beyond level of posterior margin of the eye; 14 rows of cheek scales; dorsal fin X,11; more than 75 rows of scales along the lateral line; scales around the caudal peduncle more than 30.

Description.—Body stout, not strongly compressed. Fourteen rows of scales on cheek. Mouth large, sturdy, and but slightly oblique; maxillary not extending beyond the level of the posterior margin of the eye. Fins moderately high. Notch between the spiny and soft portions of the dorsal fin shallow. Dorsal fin X,11. Anal fin III,10. Caudal fin emarginate. Pectoral fin with 16 rays. Scales along lateral line 77; 10 rows of scales above lateral line, 20 below. Scales around caudal peduncle 31. Pyloric caecae mostly simple and unbranched. Color pattern of the adult rather uniform. The pattern of the young has not been described. Length of adults up to at least 16 inches.

General Distribution.—Not known outside of Florida.

Florida Range.—The Chipola River system.

Habitat.—Probably fairly fast-flowing streams and spring runs.

Micropterus salmoides salmoides Lacépède
Northern Largemouth Bass

General Appearance.—A heavy-bodied bass with a large mouth.

Distinguishing Characters.—Notch between spiny and soft portions of dorsal fin deep; pyloric caecae forked; maxillary extending beyond the level of the eye when the mouth is closed; 59-65 scales along lateral line; 7-8 rows of scales above lateral line, 14-15 below.

Description.—Body somewhat elongate, not strongly compressed. Ten to 11 rows of scales on cheeks. Mouth large, sturdy, and but slightly oblique; maxillary extending beyond level of eye. Fins moderately high. Spiny and soft dorsal separated by a very deep notch. Dorsal fin X,13. Anal fin III,11. Caudal fin emarginate. Pectoral fins with 15 rays. Scales along lateral line 59-65; 7-8 rows of scales above lateral line, 14-15 below. Scales around caudal peduncle 26-27. Pyloric caecae bifid. Young with a broad, dark lateral stripe which becomes broken into a series of blotches anteriorly. The pattern becomes obsolete with size (and age) and large adults are more uniformly dark brown in color. This bass does not reach quite so large a size as the Florida Largemouth.

General Distribution.—The Great Lakes southward to the Gulf of Mexico. Northward along the Atlantic Coast to Virginia.

Florida Range.—Extreme northern Florida and the panhandle.

Habitat.—Rivers and lakes.

Micropterus salmoides floridanus (Le Sueur)
Florida Largemouth Bass

General Appearance.—A heavy-bodied bass with a large mouth.

Distinguishing Characters.—Notch between spiny and soft portions of dorsal fin deep; pyloric caecae forked; maxillary extending beyond level of eye when mouth is closed; 69-73 scale rows along lateral line; 8-9 scale rows above lateral line, 17-18 below.

Description.—Body somewhat elongated; not strongly compressed. Eleven to 13 rows of scales on cheeks. Mouth large, sturdy and but slightly oblique; maxillary extending beyond level of eye. Fins moderately high. Spiny and soft portions of dorsal fin separated by a very deep notch. Dorsal fin X,13. Anal fin III,11. Caudal fin emarginate. Pectoral fins with 14-15 rays. Scales along lateral line 69-73; 8-9 rows of scales above lateral line, 17-18 below. Scales around caudal peduncle 28-31. Pyloric caecae bifid. Young with a broad, dark lateral stripe which becomes broken into a series of blotches anteriorly. The pattern becomes obsolete with size (and age) and large adults are more nearly uniform dark brown in color. Reaches weight well in excess of ten pounds, fourteen-pound individuals being not rare.

General Distribution.—Restricted to Florida.

Florida Range.—The peninsula.

Habitat.—Lakes, ponds, streams, and marshes.

Chaenobryttus coronarius (Bartram)
Warmouth *(Plate 22)*

General Appearance.—A rather thick-bodied, big-mouthed pan fish with a high, spiny dorsal fin.

Distinguishing Characters.—Tail emarginate; anal fin not so long as dorsal; anal with III spines; mouth relatively large; teeth present on tongue.

Description.—Body an elongate oval; not strongly compressed; depth 2-2½ in standard length. Six to 8 rows of scales on cheeks. Mouth sturdy and strongly oblique, maxillary extending well beyond the level of the anterior margin of the eye. Teeth present on tongue. No conspicuous opercular spot. Fins moderately high. Dorsal fin X,9-10. Anal fin III,8-9. Caudal fin emarginate. Scale rows along lateral line 40-46. Six rows of scales above lateral line, 11-12 below. Color dark olive to brassy or muddy brown, clouded with darker shades. Vertical fins mottled with dusky. Size up to 8 inches.

General Distribution.—The eastern United States.

Florida Range.—State-wide.

Habitat.—All sorts of aquatic situations, although perhaps most abundant in smaller swamp shore lakes.

Lepomis punctatus punctatus (Valenciennes)
Stump-knocker

General Appearance.—A strongly compressed, brownish pan fish with lots of black dots on the sides.

Distinguishing Characters.—Tail emarginate; pectoral fin broad and rounded; scales on breast not much smaller than those on sides; opercular spot without a bright-colored margin.

Description.—Body ovate, strongly compressed, depth about 2 in length. Mouth moderate, maxillary extending past anterior margin of eye. Seven rows of cheek scales. Fins moderate. Anal fin not nearly so large as dorsal. Dorsal fin X,11. Anal fin III,10. Caudal fin emarginate. Pectoral fin broad and somewhat rounded. Scale rows along lateral line 38-45. Seven to 9 rows of scales above lateral line, 14-16 below. Palatine teeth present. Color a dirty brown with numerous dark spots somewhat resembling fly-specks on the sides of the body and head. Size up to 6 inches.

General Distribution.—South Carolina to Florida.

Florida Range.—Southward to Highlands County.

Habitat.—Lowland streams and lakes connecting with such streams.

Note.—This form integrades with the red-spotted sunfish (*Lepomis punctatus minatus*) in extreme western Florida.

Lepomis microlophus (Günther)
Shellcracker

General Appearance.—A bright silvery pan fish with red margins on the opercular spots.

Distinguishing Characters.—Tail emarginate; pectoral fin long and pointed; a bright red posterior margin on the opercular spot; no definite dark spot at the base of the posterior end of the dorsal fin.

Description.—Body compressed; ovate in profile, depth 2-2¼ in length. Snout rather produced; maxillary reaching level of anterior margin of eye. Five rows of scales on cheeks. Fins moderately high. Dorsal fin X,10-12. Anal fin III,9-11. Caudal fin emarginate. Pectoral fins long and pointed. Scales along lateral line 44-45. Six rows of scales above lateral line, 15 below. Palatine teeth absent. Color silvery-olive or silvery-bluish above, silvery below. Opercular spot with a bright red posterior margin. Length up to 10 inches.

General Distribution.—Georgia to Texas.

Florida Range.—State-wide.

Habitat.—Large lakes and rivers.

Lepomis auritus (Linnaeus)
Redbreast *(Plate 23)*

General Appearance.—A pan fish with a red or orange breast and no bright-colored margin on the opercular spot.

Distinguishing Characters.—Tail emarginate; pectoral fin short and rounded; opercular spot uniformly dark; scales on breast much smaller than those on sides.

Description.—Body ovate, moderately compressed; depth 2-2½ in length. Mouth oblique, maxillary reaching past front of eye. Cheek scales in about 6 rows. Fins moderately high. Dorsal fin X,11 or 12. Anal fin III,8-10. Caudal fin emarginate. Scales along lateral line 43-48; 6 rows of scales above lateral line, 15 rows below lateral line. Scales on breast much smaller than those on sides of body. Palatine teeth present. Color olive to brownish-gray above, paler below. Breast region from bright orange to red. Adult size up to 8 inches, but Florida specimens average smaller.

General Distribution.—Maine to Texas.

Florida Range.—Southward to central Florida.

Habitat.—Streams.

Lepomis megalotis megalotis (Rafinesque)
Long-ear Sunfish *(Plate 22)*

General Appearance.—A compressed, ovate sunfish with a bright blue margin to the opercular flap.

Distinguishing Characters.—Tail emarginate; pectoral fin broad and rounded; opercular spot with a bright blue margin; 13-15 rays in the pectoral fin.

Description.—Body compressed; short and deep, depth 1¾-2½ in length. Mouth small, oblique, the maxillary extending to a point opposite middle of eye. Five or more rows of scales on cheeks. Fins moderately high. Dorsal fin X,10-12. Anal fin III,8-10. Caudal fin emarginate. Scales along lateral line 39-44. Scales above lateral line 5; scale rows below lateral line 14. Scales on breast not much smaller than scales on sides. Pectoral fins broad and rounded, with 13-15 rays. Palatine teeth absent. Color bluish above, orange below; cheeks orange with bright blue streaks. Soft portions of vertical fins with the rays bluish and the membrane orange. Opercular flap with the posterior margin brilliant blue. Size of largest adults in excess of 6 inches, average smaller.

General Distribution.—Gulf Coast drainage.
Florida Range.—The panhandle.
Habitat.—Streams.

Lepomis marginatus (Holbrook)
Dollar Sunfish

General Appearance.—A small, strongly ovate sunfish with a green margin on the opercular flap.

Distinguishing Characters.—Tail emarginate; pectoral fin broad and rounded; opercular spot with a bright green margin; 12 rays in pectoral fin.

Description.—Body short and rounded; depth 2 in length. Mouth oblique, maxillary reaching anterior margin of eye. Four rows of scales on cheeks. Fins moderately high. Dorsal fin IX or X,12. Anal III,10. Caudal fin emarginate. Scales along lateral line 35-45. Scales on breast not much smaller than scales on sides. Pectoral fin broad and rounded. Rays in pectoral fin 12. Palatine teeth absent. Color dark olive with darker vertical bars. Head and body with numerous bluish-green stripes and spots. Opercular flap margined with bright green. Size small, perhaps up to 6 inches.

General Distribution.—South Carolina to Alabama.
Florida Range— Southward to central Florida.
Habitat.—Small ponds and streams.

Lepomis macrochirus purpurescens Cope
Bluegill; Bream; Copperbelly *(Plate 23)*

General Appearance.—A pan fish with a dark opercular spot and a dark round spot at the posterior end of the dorsal fin.

Distinguishing Characters.—Tail emarginate; pectoral fin long and pointed; opercular spot without a red margin.

Description.—Body ovate, compressed; depth 2-2¼ in length. Mouth small, oblique, maxillary barely reaching front of eye. About 5 rows of scales on cheeks. Fins moderately high. Dorsal fin X,11 or 12. Anal fin III,10 to 12. Caudal fin emarginate. Scales along lateral line 44-50; 7 rows of scales above lateral line, 16 rows below lateral line. Color variable depending on age and sex. Young with distinct broad dark bars on the sides; adults with bars obsolete. Adults often with a copper-colored head and breast. A dark spot usually discernible at the base of the last rays in the dorsal fin. Adults up to 12 inches in length but average smaller.

General Distribution.—Southeastern United States.

Florida Range.—State-wide.

Habitat.—Commonest in larger bodies of water.

Enneacanthus obesus (Girard)
Banded Sunfish *(Plate 19)*

General Appearance.—A small (3 inches or less), chubby sunfish with about 6 or 7 indistinct bars on the sides and with a rounded tail margin.

Distinguishing Characters.—Tail rounded behind in lateral outline; median spines in dorsal fin not pronouncedly longer than the other spines; usually 9 spines in dorsal fin; sides and vertical fins without bright blue spots.

Description.—Body compressed; but not strongly so. Depth 1⅘-2 in length. Four rows of scales on cheeks. Opercular spot dark, more than ½ the size of the eye. Fins moderately high. Spiny dorsal fin not strongly arched in profile. Dorsal fin usually IX,10. Anal fin usually III,10. Caudal fin rounded or truncate rather than emarginate. Scales along lateral line 32. Four rows of scales above lateral line, 10 below. Scale rows around caudal peduncle 19-22. Color dark with 5-8 rather indistinct vertical dark bars along the sides. Size up to 3 inches.

General Distribution.—Southern New Hampshire to Florida.

Florida Range.—Southward to central Florida.

Habitat.—Sluggish to moderately swift-flowing streams.

Enneacanthus gloriosus (Holbrook)
Blue-spotted Sunfish *(Plate 19)*

General Appearance.—A small (3 inches or less), strongly compressed sunfish with scattered, bright blue spots along the sides.

Distinguishing Characters.—Tail rounded; median spines of dorsal fin not pronouncedly longer than the other spines; usually 9 spines in the dorsal fin; sides and vertical fins with bright blue spots.

Description.—Body ovate, strongly compressed. Depth 2¼ in length. Four rows of scales on cheeks. Mouth moderate, very oblique; maxillary reaching just past the level of the anterior margin of the eye. Opercular spot less than ½ the size of the eye and with a blue border.

Fins moderately high. Spiny dorsal fin not strongly arched in profile. Dorsal fin usually IX,10. Anal fin usually III,9. Caudal fin rounded rather than emarginate behind. Scales along lateral line 30. Three rows of scales above lateral line, 9 below. Scale rows around caudal peduncle 16-18. Color dark, the sides of the body and the vertical fins with numerous scattered, rounded, bright blue spots. Size up to 3 inches.

General Distribution.—New York to Florida.

Florida Range.—The entire state except for the western panhandle.

Habitat.—Sluggish streams and lakes.

Enneacanthus chaetodon elizabethae (Bailey)
Black-banded Sunfish *(Plate 18)*

General Appearance.—A very small, strongly compressed sunfish with distinct vertical black bars on the sides.

Distinguishing Characters.—Tail rounded, or truncate, not emarginate; median spines of spiny dorsal fin markedly longer than anterior and posterior spines; usually 9 spines in the dorsal fin; 17-18 rows of scales around the caudal peduncle; pattern without bright blue spots.

Description.—Body ovate; strongly compressed. Depth 1⅘-2 in length. Three or four rows of scales on cheeks. Mouth small, slightly oblique, the maxillary extending to the level of the anterior margin of the eye. Opercular spot small and inconspicuous. Fins moderately high. Spiny dorsal arched in profile. Dorsal fin usually IX,12. Anal fin usually III,12. Caudal fin slightly rounded or truncate, not emarginate. Scale rows along lateral line 28. Five rows of scales above lateral line, usually 11 below. Scale rows around caudal peduncle 17-18. Color grayish or brownish with 4-6 strongly marked vertical black bars on the sides of the head and body. Length about 2 inches.

General Distribution.—Southern Georgia and northern Florida.

Florida Range.—Southward to Marion County.

Habitat.—Shallow sand-hill lakes with abundant vegetation.

Ambloplites rupestris ariommus Viosca
Southern Rock Bass *(Plate 20)*

General Appearance.—A fairly thick-bodied, big-mouthed pan fish with a high spiny dorsal fin.

Distinguishing Characters.—Tail emarginate; anal not so long as dorsal; anal fin with VI-VII spines.

Description.—Body an elongate oval, not strongly compressed; depth 2-2½ in standard length. Six to 8 rows of scales on cheek. Mouth sturdy and strongly oblique, maxillary extending well beyond the level of the anterior margin of the eye. No conspicuous opercular spot. Fins moderately high. Dorsal fin XI,10. Anal fin VI-VII,10. Caudal fin emarginate. Scale rows along lateral line 38-40. Five rows of scales above lateral line, 12 below. Color brownish or greenish with indistinct mottlings or marblings of a darker shade on the sides of the head, body, and vertical fins. Size of adults up to 8 inches.

General Distribution.—The Lower Mississippi Valley and the Gulf Coast.

Florida Range.—The panhandle.

Habitat.—Deep streams, particularly in weedy and loggy places.

Acantharchus pomotis (Baird)
Mud Perch *(Plate 20)*

General Appearance.—A small, heavy-set pan fish with stripes along the sides.

Distinguishing Characters.—Anal fin shorter than dorsal; 5 or 6 spines in anal fin; tail rounded.

Description.—Body oblong, not strongly compressed. Head and jaws moderately stout. Mouth oblique, maxillary reaching pupil of eye. Depth about 2¼ in length. Six rows of scales on cheek. Fins moderately high. Dorsal fin XII,10 or 11. Anal fin V or VI,10. Caudal fin rounded. Scale rows along lateral line 32-37; 5-7 rows of scales above lateral line, 12 below. Color tan or olive-brown with 5 to 8 dark longitudinal stripes along side of body and about 4 dark longitudinal stripes along side of head. Length up to 5 inches.

General Distribution.—New York to northern Florida.

Florida Range.—North Florida southward to Alachua County.

Habitat.—Dark-water creeks and streams.

Pomoxis nigromaculatus (Le Sueur)
Speckled Perch; Crappie *(Plate 21)*

General Appearance.—A greenish, black speckled, big-mouthed, compressed pan fish with a long anal fin.

Distinguishing Characters.—Anal fin nearly as long as dorsal; about 7 spines in the dorsal fin.

Description.—Body compressed, oblong. Depth about 2 in length.

Head long, mouth large, the maxillary reaching to the posterior edge of the pupil of the eye. Six rows of scales on cheeks. Fins high. Anal fin nearly as long as dorsal. Dorsal fin VII or VIII,15. Anal fin VI,17 or 18. Scale rows along lateral line 40-45. Ground color of female silvery-olive, of the male more olive-green. Ground color of both sexes overlaid with speckles or spots of black. Adults rarely attain weights of 3-4 pounds but average much smaller.

General Distribution.—Eastern United States westward to the Great Lakes and Texas.

Florida Range.—State-wide.

Habitat.—Large lakes and streams confluent with them; rivers.

Centrarchus macropterus (Lacépède)
Flier *(Plate 21)*

General Appearance.—A brightly marked, circular looking pan fish of medium size.

Distinguishing Characters.—Anal fin nearly as long as dorsal; about 12 spines in dorsal fin.

Description.—Body ovate, strongly compressed. Head small, mouth moderate in size. Mouth oblique, the maxillary reaching the middle of the eye. Five to 6 rows of cheek scales. Fins high. Anal fin nearly as long as dorsal. Dorsal fin XI to XIII,12. Anal fin VII or VIII,15. About 45 scales along lateral line; 5 rows above lateral line, 14 below. Color greenish or silvery-green; belly yellowish, often with a series of dark marks on sides below lateral line. Usually a black spot or ocellus on the posterior portion of the dorsal fin, which is very conspicuous in the young but fades with age. Length about 6 inches.

General Distribution.—The lowlands from Virginia to Louisiana and northward in the Mississippi Valley to Illinois.

Florida Range.—The northern portion of the state, southward to central Florida.

Habitat.—Streams and lakes connecting with streams.

Elassoma zonatum Jordan
Banded Pigmy Sunfish

General Appearance.—A tiny perchlike fish with a round tail margin.

Distinguishing Characters.—Dorsal spines V; scale rows along side 38-42.

Description.—Body moderately elongate and compressed; depth $3\frac{1}{2}$ in standard length. Mouth small, oblique, the maxillary scarcely reaching the pupil. Teeth stout and conical; in two or three rows. Cheeks scaly. Eye large, 3 in length of head. Fins moderately high. Dorsal fin usually V,9. Caudal fin rounded. Anal fin III,5. Pelvic fins thoracic in position. Lateral line obsolete. Scales along side 38-42. About 19 scale rows from the origin of the dorsal fin to the mid-line of the belly. Ground color olive-greenish with about 10 vertical dark bars on each side. A dark spot on each side below the origin of the dorsal fin. Length up to $1\frac{1}{2}$ inches.

General Distribution.—Southern Illinois to the Gulf Coast.

Florida Range.—Western Florida, eastward and southward to Marion County.

Habitat.—A swamp-water fish.

Elassoma evergladei Jordan
Everglade Pigmy Sunfish *(Plate 18)*

General Appearance.—A tiny perchlike fish with a rounded tail margin; often blotched with brilliant blue.

Distinguishing Characters.—Dorsal spines III or IV; scale rows along side 27-30.

Description.—Body moderately elongate and compressed; depth $3\frac{1}{2}$ in standard length. Mouth small, oblique, the maxillary scarcely reaching the level of the front margin of the pupil. Teeth stout and conical; in two or three rows. Cheeks scaly. Eye large, 3 in length of head. Fins moderately high. Dorsal fin III,8 to IV,9. Caudal fin rounded. Anal fin III,5 to III,7. Pelvic fins thoracic in position. Lateral line obsolete. Scales along side of body 27-30. About 14 rows of scales from origin of dorsal fin to mid-line of belly. Color gray to black often blotched with brilliant blue. Length up to $1\frac{1}{2}$ inches.

General Distribution.—Southern Georgia and Florida.

Florida Range.—State-wide, except the western panhandle.

Habitat.—A swamp-water fish.

Hadropterus nigrofasciatus Agassiz
Crawl-a-bottom

General Appearance.—A slender, trim little fish with two dorsal fins.

Distinguishing Characters.—Breast scaled; back with 7 oblique dark saddles; anal spines II, the first stiff; anal fin equal to or larger than the soft dorsal in size.

Description.—Head about 4 in standard length. Eye moderate, about 4 in length of head and about equal to length of snout. Mouth rather wide, terminal in position; the maxillary reaching the level of front of eye. Body rather elongate, depth about 5 in standard length. Dorsal fins two, XII-11 or 12. Caudal fin emarginate. Anal fin II,9 or 10; equal to or larger than the soft dorsal fin. Pelvic fins thoracic in position. Breast somewhat scaly. Scales along lateral line 55-60. Seven scale rows above lateral line, 15 below. Gill membranes with a moderate connection. Olivaceous above, lighter below. Seven oblique dark saddles along mid-line of back. Dark vertical stripes on the sides. Large Florida specimens may be several inches in length.

General Distribution.—South Carolina to Louisiana.

Florida Range.—South in the peninsula to Orange County.

Habitat.—Swift streams and rivers.

Hadropterus uranidea (Jordan and Gilbert)
Stargazing Darter

General Appearance.—A slender, trim little fish with two dorsal fins.

Distinguishing Characters.—Breast naked or with only one large scale; back with 4 oblique dark saddles; anal spines II; anal fin equal to or larger in size than the soft dorsal.

Description.—Head $3\frac{1}{2}$-$3\frac{3}{4}$ in standard length. Eye moderate, about $3\frac{3}{4}$ in length of head and about equal to length of snout. Mouth rather wide, terminal in position; the maxillary reaching the level of the front of eye. Body rather elongate, terete; depth about $5\frac{2}{3}$ in standard length. Dorsal fins two, X or XI-13. Caudal fins emarginate. Anal fin II,10 or 11; equal to or larger than the soft dorsal. Pelvic fins thoracic in position. Breast naked or with only one large scale. Scales along lateral line 48-56. Six scale rows above lateral line. Gill membranes separate. Olivaceous above, lighter below. Four oblique dark saddles along the mid-line of the back. Dark vertical stripes along the sides. Reaches several inches in length.

General Distribution.—The Lower Mississippi Valley and adjacent Gulf Coast.

Florida Range.—Known in Florida only from the Escambia River.

Habitat.—Large rivers.

Ammocrypta beani Jordan
Naked Sand Darter (Plate 29)

General Appearance.—A slender, trim little fish with two dorsal fins.

Distinguishing Characters.—Body almost naked except for 1 to 3 series of scales along the lateral line; anal fin with a single flexible spine. Anal fin equal in size to or larger than the soft dorsal fin.

Description.—Head slender, 3¾-4 in standard length. Eye moderate. Mouth rather wide, terminal in position, the upper jaw slightly protruding. Body rather elongate, terete; depth 7-8 in standard length. Dorsal fins two, VIII to X-10 or 11. Caudal fin emarginate. Anal fin I,9 or 10; equal to or larger in size than the soft dorsal. Pelvic fins thoracic in position. Head and body naked except for 1 to 3 rows in the region of the lateral line and for scales on the caudal peduncle. Scales along lateral line 63-68. Somewhat translucent without distinct spots or bars. Length 2-3 inches.

General Distribution.—The Gulf Coast.

Florida Range.—The western panhandle.

Habitat.—Clear, sandy streams.

Etheostoma nigrum olmstedi Storer
Eastern Johnny Darter (Plate 29)

General Appearance.—A slender, trim little fish with two dorsal fins.

Distinguishing Characters.—A single anal spine; lateral line straight; anal fin smaller than the soft dorsal.

Description.—Head slender, rather pointed, 4-5½ in standard length. Eye moderately small, 3¾-4 in length of head. Mouth rather small for a darter, terminal in position. Body slender, but little compressed; caudal peduncle elongate; depth 5-6 in standard length. Dorsal fins two, IX-14 or 15. Caudal fin emarginate. Anal fin I,9; smaller than the soft dorsal in size. Pelvic fins thoracic in position. Cheeks and opercles scaly. Lateral line straight. Scales along lateral line 45-55; 5 scale rows above lateral line, 9 below. Olivaceous in color with blotches and zig-zag markings along the sides; usually with a black stripe running downward from the eye. Length about 3 inches.

General Distribution.—Massachusetts to Virginia; central Florida.

Florida Range.—The Oklawaha River. Perhaps introduced.

Habitat.—Sandy streams.

Etheostoma saxatile (Hay)
Speckled Darter

General Appearance.—A slender, trim little fish with two dorsal fins.

Distinguishing Characters.—Anal spines II, the first thin and flexible; lateral line straight; anal fin smaller than soft dorsal.

Description.—Head moderate, tapering to a rather slender snout; head 3¾-4 in standard length. Mouth rather small, terminal in position. Body slender, but little compressed. Depth about 6 in standard length. Dorsal fins two, XI to XIII-11 or 12. Caudal fin rounded. Pelvic fins thoracic in position. Anal fin II,9; anal fin smaller than the soft dorsal in size. Body scaled except for a region on the breast. Lateral line straight but incomplete. Scales along lateral line region 50-55. Scale rows above lateral line 5. Color olivaceous, with about 6 dark bars across the mid-line of the back, and with a generally speckled appearance. Length about 2½ inches.

General Distribution.—The eastern Gulf Coast.

Florida Range.—The western panhandle.

Habitat.—Streams.

Etheostoma okaloosae (Fowler)
Okaloosa Darter *(Plate 30)*

General Appearance.—A slender, trim little fish with two dorsal fins.

Distinguishing Characters.—Gill membranes largely separate; anal spines two, the first heavy and stiff; lateral line straight; anal fin smaller than the soft dorsal fin in size.

Description.—Head rather long, 3-3½ in standard length. Eye 4½-5 in length of head. Mouth moderately small, terminal in position. Body slender, but slightly compressed; depth about 5 in standard length. Gill membranes largely separate. Dorsal fins two, IX-11. Caudal fin rounded. Anal fin II,6; smaller than the soft dorsal in size. Pelvic fins thoracic in position. Cheeks and opercles scaly. Lateral line straight. Scales along lateral line 30-33; 4 scale rows above lateral line, 5 below. Olivaceous above, lighter below, with a few indistinct blotches along the sides. Length about 2 inches.

General Distribution.—The western panhandle.

Florida Range.—The western panhandle.

Habitat.—Sandy streams.

Etheostoma stigmaeum (Jordan)
Snubnose Darter

General Appearance.—A slender, trim little fish with two dorsal fins.

Distinguishing Characters.—Gill membranes broadly united; anal spines II, the first heavy and stiff; lateral line straight; anal fin smaller than soft dorsal.

Description.—Head moderate, tapering to a rather pointed snout. Head about $4\frac{1}{4}$ in standard length. Mouth rather small, terminal in position. Gill membranes strongly united. Body slender, not strongly compressed. Depth about 5 in standard length. Dorsal fins two, X to XIII-12. Caudal fin rounded. Anal fin II,7; smaller than the soft dorsal in size. Pelvic fins thoracic in position. Cheeks and opercles scaly. Lateral line incomplete. Scales along lateral line region 45-55. Scale rows above lateral line 5; 10 below. Olivaceous, with a generally speckled appearance. Length about 2 inches.

General Distribution.—The eastern Gulf Coast.

Florida Range.—The western panhandle.

Habitat.—Streams.

Etheostoma edwini (Hubbs and Cannon)
Brown Darter (*Plate 30*)

General Appearance.—A slender, trim little brown fish with two dorsal fins.

Distinguishing Characters.—Scales along lateral line 36-41; lateral line somewhat arched above pectorals; infraorbital canal complete; anal fin smaller than the soft dorsal.

Description.—Head and snout somewhat blunt. Head $3\frac{3}{4}$-4 in standard length. Infraorbital canal complete. Mouth subterminal in position. Body slender, somewhat compressed. Depth about 5 in standard length. Dorsal fins two, IX or X-9 to 12. Caudal fin rounded. Anal fin II,7; smaller than the soft dorsal in size. Pelvic fins thoracic in position. Breast, cheeks, and opercles scaled. Lateral line incomplete; somewhat arched above the pectoral fins. Scales along lateral line region 36-41. Scale rows above lateral line 4; 6-8 below. Color brownish, with 8-9 dark saddles across the back. In life somewhat speckled. Length less than 2 inches.

General Distribution.—Southern Georgia and northern Florida.

Florida Range.—Southward in the peninsula to the Suwannee River drainage.

Habitat.—Swift streams.

Etheostoma barratti (Holbrook)
Florida Swamp Darter *(Plate 30)*

General Appearance.—A slender, trim little fish with two dorsal fins.

Distinguishing Characters.—Scales along the lateral line 47-60; lateral line arched above the pectorals; infraorbital canal incomplete; anal fin smaller than the soft dorsal.

Description.—Head moderately narrow; tapering to a rather sharp snout. Head about 4 in standard length. Infraorbital canal incomplete. Mouth subterminal in position. Gill membranes broadly united. Body slender, somewhat compressed. Depth about 5 or 6 in standard length. Dorsal fins two, IX to XII-9 to 12. Caudal fin rounded. Anal fin II,6 or 7; smaller than the soft dorsal in size. Pelvic fins thoracic in position. Breast, cheeks, and opercles scaled. Lateral line incomplete, arched above the pectoral fins. Scales along lateral line region 47-60; scale rows above lateral line 2-3; 9-10 below. Brownish above, lighter brown below, with 9-12 dark blotches along the sides. Length up to about 2 inches.

General Distribution.—South Carolina to Florida.

Florida Range.—The peninsula, southward to about the region of Lake Okeechobee.

Habitat.—Streams, swamps, and the swampy edges of large lakes.

Lutjanus griseus (Linnaeus)
Gray Snapper; Mangrove Snapper

General Appearance.—A grayish or coppery, laterally compressed fish with a long dorsal fin and a tough mouth.

Distinguishing Characters.—Scales along lateral line 48-52; depth in length 2¾-3 with distinct, though not too conspicuous, canine-like teeth on each side in the front of the upper jaw.

Description.—Body comparatively elongate, compressed; the back arched. Depth in length 2¾-3. Head somewhat pointed; 2¾ in standard length; mouth strong, conspicuous. Jaws with bands of villiform teeth and 2, or sometimes 4, enlarged canine-like teeth in the front of the upper jaw. Eye rather small, 4⅔ in length of head. Cheeks scaly. Dorsal fin long, X,14. Second dorsal spine not 3 or 4 times the length of the first. Caudal fin forked. Anal fin III,8. Pelvic fins thoracic in position. Lateral line well developed. Scales along lateral line about 50. Scale rows above lateral line 7; 12 below. Color grayish-green above, coppery below; with indistinct and diffuse rows of spots corresponding to the scale rows. Reaches a pound or more in weight.

General Distribution.—Massachusetts to the West Indies.

Florida Range.—Both coasts.

Habitat.—The coastal regions, invading fresh water.

Lutjanus apodus (Walbaum)
Schoolmaster

General Appearance.—A greenish-gray, faintly streaked, laterally compressed fish with a long dorsal fin and a tough mouth.

Distinguishing Characters.—Scales along lateral line 42-46; depth in length about $2\frac{1}{2}$; with distinct, though not too conspicuous, canine-like teeth on each side in the front of the upper jaw.

Description.—Body comparatively elongate, compressed; the back arched. Depth in length about $2\frac{1}{2}$. Head somewhat pointed; $2\frac{1}{2}$ in standard length; mouth strong, conspicuous. Jaws with bands of villi-form teeth and 2, sometimes 4, enlarged canine-like teeth in the front of the upper jaw. Eye rather small, $4\frac{1}{3}$ in length of head. Cheeks scaly. Dorsal fin long, X,14. Second dorsal spine not 3 or 4 times as long as the first. Caudal fin forked. Anal fin III,8. Pelvic fins thoracic in position. Lateral line well developed. Scales along lateral line 42-46. Scale rows above lateral line 6; 13 below. Color greenish-gray, with indistinct, narrow dark streaks along the side corresponding to the scale rows. Attains a pound or more in weight.

General Distribution.—Massachusetts to the West Indies.

Florida Range.—Both coasts.

Habitat.—Salt water and rivers and spring-runs entering the sea.

Lagodon rhomboides (Linnaeus)
Pinfish (Plate 24)

General Appearance.—A strongly compressed fish with protuberant teeth, a spot on the shoulder, and 3 or 4 vertical dark stripes on the sides.

Distinguishing Characters.—Scales along lateral line 65-70; teeth incisor-like and protuberant.

Description.—Body elongate, elliptical, laterally compressed and markedly arched above; depth 2-2⅔ in standard length. Mouth small, terminal, both upper and lower jaws with protruding incisor-like teeth. Head triangular in profile; about 3½ in standard length. Cheeks scaly. Eye 4 in length of head. Dorsal fin XII,11. Caudal fin forked. Anal fin III,11. Pelvic fins thoracic in position. Lateral line well developed. Scales along lateral line 65-70. Scale rows above lateral line 10; below, 7. Color olivaceous to yellowish with a distinct round dark spot on each shoulder and about 4 vertical dark bands on each side. Length about 6 inches.

General Distribution.—Cape Cod to Texas and Cuba.

Florida Range.—Both coasts.

Habitat.—Salt water and rivers and spring-runs entering the sea.

Archosargus probatocephalus (Walbaum)
Sheepshead *(Plate 25)*

General Appearance.—A laterally compressed fish with a pattern like a convict's uniform.

Distinguishing Characters.—Scales along lateral line 46-50; teeth incisor-like and protuberant.

Description.—Body elongate, strongly compressed, strongly arched above. Depth 2-2½ in standard length. Mouth sturdy but not large; both jaws with a row of sharp, incisor-like teeth, which are somewhat protuberant. Head with a steep profile; 3-3½ in standard length. Cheeks scaly. Eye placed high on head, about 4-6 in length of head. Dorsal fin XII,10 to 12. Caudal fin shallowly forked. Anal fin III,10 or 11. Pelvic fins thoracic in position. Lateral line well developed. Scales along lateral line 46-50. Scale rows above lateral line 8; 15 below. Color grayish with about 7 prominent dark vertical bars on each side, which are about as wide as the interspaces. Attains a weight of several pounds, with the average adult about a pound.

General Distribution.—Atlantic and Gulf coasts of the United States.

Florida Range.—Both coasts.

Habitat.—Salt water and fresh-water rivers and spring-runs entering salt water.

Diplodus holbrooki (Bean)
Spot-tail Pinfish *(Plate 25)*

General Appearance.—A strongly compressed fish with protuberant teeth and a black saddle across the base of the tail.

Distinguishing Characters.—Scales along lateral line 55-57; teeth protuberant; a conspicuous black saddle on the caudal peduncle.

Description.—Body elliptical; laterally compressed and markedly arched above. Depth 2½ in standard length in adults. Mouth small, terminal, both upper and lower jaws with protruding, incisor-like teeth. Head triangular in profile, about 3⅔ in standard length. Cheeks scaly. Eye small, 4½ in length of head. Dorsal fin long and low, XII,14 or 15. Caudal fin forked. Anal fin III,13. Pelvic fins thoracic in position. Lateral line well developed. Scales along lateral line 55-57. Scale rows above lateral line 7; 14 below. Color darkish above fading to silvery below. A very noticeable black saddle on the caudal peduncle. Total length up to about 10 inches.

General Distribution.—Cape Hatteras southward to Florida.

Florida Range.—Both coasts except for that of the western panhandle.

Habitat.—Salt water and fresh-water streams entering salt water.

Eucinostomus argenteus Baird and Girard
Mojarra

General Appearance.—A vertically flattened, silvery fish with a long dorsal fin.

Distinguishing Characters.—Anal spines III, the second not particularly enlarged; second dorsal spine 3 or 4 times the length of the first. Last dorsal spine contained in first ray of soft dorsal about twice.

Description.—Body elliptical, strongly compressed, back moderately arched. Depth in standard length in adults 2⅗-3. Mouth small, terminal, extremely protractile. Both jaws with slender villiform teeth. Head 3-3⅓ in standard length. Cheeks scaly. Eye moderate, 2½-3¼ in length of head. Dorsal fin IX,10, the last spine being about ½ the length of the first soft ray. Caudal fin forked. Anal fin III,8, the second spine not particularly enlarged. Pelvic fins thoracic in position. Lateral line continuous. Scales along lateral line 40-44. Scale rows above lateral line 5; 9 below. Buffy above, silvery on the sides and below. Total length up to about 7 inches.

General Distribution.—Atlantic Coast of tropical America, straying as far north as New Jersey.

Florida Range.—Both coasts.

Habitat.—Shallow salt waters and fresh-water streams, especially spring-runs, entering salt water.

Diapterus olisthostomus (Goode and Bean)
Irish Pompano

General Appearance.—A flattened, silvery fish with a big spine in the anal fin.

Distinguishing Characters.—Anal spines III, the second much enlarged; second dorsal spine 3 or 4 times the length of the first. Last dorsal spine entering first ray of soft dorsal about $1\frac{1}{3}$ times.

Description.—Body elliptical, strongly compressed laterally; the back strongly arched. Depth in standard length about 2. Mouth small, terminal, extremely protractile. Both jaws with slender villiform teeth. Head about 3 in standard length. Cheeks scaly. Eye $3\frac{1}{2}$ in length of head. Dorsal fin IX,10; the last dorsal spine entering the first soft dorsal ray about $1\frac{1}{3}$ times. Caudal fin forked. Anal fin III,8, the second spine greatly enlarged. Pelvic fins thoracic in position. Lateral line continuous. Scales along lateral line 36-38. Scale rows above lateral line 5; 9 below. A silvery fish attaining about 12 inches in total length.

General Distribution.—Brazil to Florida and the West Indies.

Florida Range.—The East Coast.

Habitat.—The coastal regions. Recorded in fresh water from Florida only in the St. Johns River.

Sciaenops ocellatus (Linnaeus)
Channel Bass; Redfish *(Plate 26)*

General Appearance.—A reddish fish with a round, black spot toward the upper margin of the base of the tail.

Distinguishing Characters.—Scales along lateral line 40-45; rays in soft dorsal fin 23-25; no barbels present on chin.

Description.—Body elongate, only slightly compressed laterally, back slightly arched. Depth about $3\frac{1}{2}$ in standard length. Mouth moderate, subterminal in position; teeth in both jaws in villiform bands, the outer series in the upper jaw enlarged. No barbels present on the chin. Head about $3\frac{1}{2}$ in standard length. Cheeks scaly. Eye about 7 in length of head. Dorsal fin X-I,23 to 25. Caudal fin truncate. Anal fin II,8. Pelvic fins thoracic in position. Lateral line well developed. Scales along lateral line 40-45; 4 rows of scales above lateral line; 12 below. Color reddish to reddish-brown above, somewhat paler below. A distinct round black spot on the upper portion of the base of the caudal fin; this spot sometimes duplicated on the caudal fin or caudal peduncle. Attains a weight of about 75 pounds but averages much smaller. Specimens from the West Coast of Florida average smaller than those from the East Coast.

General Distribution.—The coastal regions from New York to Texas.

Florida Range.—Both coasts.

Habitat.—Salt water, invading fresh-water rivers and streams, particularly in cold weather.

Leiostomus xanthurus Lacépède
Spot *(Plate 24)*

General Appearance.—A laterally compressed fish with oblique yellow stripes on the sides and back.

Distinguishing Characters.—Rays in soft dorsal 30-34; scales along lateral line 60-70; no barbels present on chin.

Description.—Body moderately elongate, arched above, depth about 3 in standard length. Mouth moderate, terminal to subterminal in position. Upper jaw with numerous minute teeth, lower jaw toothless in adults. No barbels present on the chin. Head about 3½ in standard length. Cheeks scaly. Eye moderate, 4-5 in length of head. Dorsal fin X-I,31 or 32. Caudal fin slightly concave to shallowly forked. Anal fin II,12. Pelvic fins thoracic in position. Lateral line present. Scales along lateral line 60-70; 9 scale rows above lateral line, 12 below. Color bluish above, fading to off-white below. With about 15 narrow, oblique yellowish bars on the back and side and a yellowish spot on each side in the shoulder region. Total length up to about 10 inches.

General Distribution.—Massachusetts to Texas.

Florida Range.—Both coasts.

Habitat.—Salt water, invading fresh water for some distance.

Pogonias cromis (Linnaeus)
Sea Drum *(Plate 26)*

General Appearance.—A humpbacked fish with chin whiskers.

Distinguishing Characters.—Barbels present under chin; rays in soft dorsal 20-23; scales along lateral line 41-45.

Description.—Body rather elongate, strongly arched above, not strongly compressed laterally. Depth about 2⅓ in standard length. Mouth moderate, inferior in position. Teeth on jaws small and arranged in villiform bands. Barbels present under chin. Head 3⅓ in standard length. Cheeks scaly. Eye small, 6-7 in length of head.

Dorsal fin X-I,20 to 23. Caudal fin subtruncate. Anal fin II,5 or 6. Pelvic fins thoracic in position. Lateral line present. Scales along lateral line 41-45; 5 scale rows above lateral line; 9 below. Color silvery-gray to dark brown. Fins dark. Young with 4 or 5 broad, dark vertical bands. Maximum size 146 pounds but only the smaller ones enter fresh water. Larger on the East Coast than along the Gulf shore.

General Distribution.—The Atlantic Coast from Long Island to the Rio Grande.

Florida Range.—Both coasts.

Habitat.—Salt water, invading fresh water in large rivers. Recorded from fresh water in Florida from the St. Johns River.

Micropogon undulatus (Linnaeus)
Croaker (Plate 26)

General Appearance.—A spotted fish with chin whiskers.

Distinguishing Characters.—Barbels present under chin; rays in soft dorsal 28-29; scales along lateral line about 55.

Description.—Body rather elongate, slightly compressed laterally, not strongly arched above. Depth about 3⅓ in standard length. Mouth moderate, subinferior in position; outer teeth in upper jaw somewhat enlarged. Barbels present under chin. Head about 3 in standard length. Cheeks scaly. Eye somewhat small, about 5 in length of head. Dorsal fin X-I,28 or 29. Caudal fin doubly concave. Anal fin II,7. Pelvic fins thoracic in position. Lateral line present. Scales along lateral line about 55; 9 scale rows above lateral line; 16 below. Color tannish above, paler below. About 16 indistinct, short, narrow, oblique dark stripes on each side; the back and dorsal fins with scattered dark spots. Usually 8-12 inches in total length, although may attain a length of 18 inches.

General Distribution.—Cape Cod to Texas.

Florida Range.—Both coasts.

Habitat.—Salt water, ascending fresh-water streams for some distance.

Cynoscion nebulosus (Cuvier and Valenciennes)
Speckled Trout (Plate 27)

General Appearance.—A pale, handsome, yellow washed, silver fish with conspicuous small black spots on the sides and back.

Distinguishing Characters.—Scales along lateral line 90-102; rays in soft dorsal fin 25-27; no barbels present on chin.

Description.—Body elongate, only slightly compressed laterally; back but slightly arched. Depth about 4½ in standard length. Mouth rather large, slightly oblique, terminal in position; teeth strong and pointed. No barbels present on the chin. Head about 3½ in standard length. Cheeks scaly. Eye 6 or 7 in length of head. Dorsal fin X-I,25 to 27. Caudal fin subtruncate. Anal fin II,10. Pelvic fins thoracic in position. Lateral line present. Scales along lateral line 90-102. Scale rows above lateral line 10; 11 below. Color yellowish above, paler below, with numerous distinct black spots on the sides, back, and the dorsal and caudal fins. Maximum weight in excess of 15 pounds but averages much smaller. Much larger individuals occur on the East Coast than in Gulf waters.

General Distribution.—New York to Texas, along the coasts.

Florida Range.—Both coasts.

Habitat.—Salt water; invading fresh-water streams, particularly in cold weather.

Syngnathus scovelli (Evermann and Kendall)
Scovell's Pipefish

General Appearance.—An odd little creature that looks more like a slender piece of dead weed stem than a fish.

Distinguishing Characters.—Body very elongate and encased in a bony armor.

Description.—Snout long and tubular; body exceedingly long and slender, all encased in a bony armor of rings. Bony rings on trunk 21 or less; on caudal part of body 30-34. Dorsal fin present, with 27-35 soft rays. Dorsal fin covering 2-4 body rings and 4-5 tail rings. Brood pouch covering 11-13 tail rings. Brownish or brownish-green in color. Several inches in length.

General Distribution.—Duval County, Florida, to Corpus Christi, Texas.

Florida Range.—Both coasts.

Habitat.—Salt water and streams entering salt water. Invades the St. Johns River as far south as DeLand, and occurs far inland in springs of northern Florida.

Eleotris abacurus Jordan and Gilbert
Slender Sleeper *(Plate 31)*

General Appearance.—A slender, big-mouthed, big-finned fish.

Distinguishing Characters.—Two dorsal fins, pelvic fins not united at base to form a disk; gill openings not extending below angles of jaws.

Description.—Head long and depressed, 3 in standard length; mouth large, maxillary extending to level of posterior margin of eye. Eye small, 8 in length of head. Body slender, depth about $4\frac{1}{3}$ in length. Dorsal fin high, divided into two portions, VI-9. Caudal fins broadly pointed. Anal fin I,8. Pelvic fins thoracic in position, not fused at base to form a sucking disk. Scales small, 50-65 along side of body. Body brownish with faint dots of darker on the scales. Length up to 6 or 8 inches.

General Distribution.—South Carolina to Brazil and the West Indies.

Florida Range.—Both coasts.

Habitat.—Brackish water and fresh-water streams connected with brackish water; storm pools and ditches.

Dormitator maculatus (Bloch)
Fat Sleeper *(Plate 31)*

General Appearance.—A small, heavy-bodied, small-mouthed fish with high vertical fins.

Distinguishing Characters.—Two dorsal fins; pelvic fins not united at base to form a disk; 30-35 scale rows along the sides.

Description.—Head moderate, $3\frac{1}{5}$ in length; mouth small, maxillary not reaching the level of the posterior margin of the eye. Eye small, 4-5 times in length of head. Body stout, depth 3-$3\frac{3}{4}$ in length. Dorsal fin high, divided into two portions, VII-8 or 9. Pelvic fins not united at base to form a ventral disk. Scales rather large, 30-35 rows along side of body. Color dark brown, often with lighter bluish spots. May attain a length of a foot, but most Florida specimens are only a few inches in length.

General Distribution.—South Carolina to Panama.

Florida Range.—Coastal streams of the peninsula.

Habitat.—Streams and fresh-water ditches and canals near salt water.

Gobiomorus dormitor Lacépède
Sleeper (Plate 31)

General Appearance.—A slender, high-finned, big-mouthed fish.

Distinguishing Characters.—Two dorsal fins, pelvic fins not united to form a disk; gill openings extending forward to below the angles of the jaws; 55-57 scale rows along the sides.

Description.—Head large, elongate, 2⅗ in standard length. Mouth large, maxillary reaching to level of posterior margin of eye and above gill openings. Body slender, depth 5-6 in standard length. Dorsal fin high, divided into two portions, VI-9 or 10. Caudal fin rounded. Anal fin I,9. Pelvic fins thoracic in position, not united at base to form a ventral sucker-like disk. Scales in 55-57 rows along side of body. Color brownish or olive, lighter below; spiny dorsal margined with blackish. Head often with dark spots. Attains a length of 2 feet.

General Distribution.—Streams in West Indies, Mexico, and Central America.

Florida Range.—Canals of southern Florida.

Habitat.—Streams and canals entering the sea.

Bathygobius soporator (Cuvier and Valenciennes)
Mapo

General Appearance.—A small, slender fish hardly ever the same color.

Distinguishing Characters.—Pelvic fins fused at base to form a sucking disk; head naked but body scaled; 9-10 soft rays in the dorsal fin. Upper rays in pectoral fin soft and silky.

Description.—Head broad, low, rounded in profile, 3-3½ in standard length. Mouth large, oblique; lips thick. Eye moderate, 4-5 in length of head. Body slender, depth 4½-5½ in length. Dorsal fins separate, VI,9 or 10. Caudal fin short. Anal fin I,7 to 9. Pelvic fins thoracic in position, united at base to form a sucking disk. Upper rays of pectoral fin short, separate, slender, and silky. Head naked but body scaled. Scale rows along side 35-40. Color extremely variable but dorsal and caudal fins usually dusky while the anal is usually clear. Size from 3 to 6 inches.

General Distribution.—Tropical seas.

Florida Range.—Southern Florida.

Habitat.—Salt and brackish waters, entering fresh-water streams and canals.

Lophogobius cyprinoides (Pallas)
Crested Goby

General Appearance.—A two-inch long fish with a big head and high fins.

Distinguishing Characters.—Soft rays in anal fin 9 or 10; depth in standard length about 3⅗; scales along side 25-30; spines in dorsal fin VI.

Description.—Head long, about 3⅗ in standard length; snout short, blunt, about as long as eye. Mouth very oblique, the gape slightly curved; front of upper lip on level of lower border of eye. Profile convex. Eye 3½-4 in length of head. Body short and deep, little compressed; depth about 3⅗ in standard length. Dorsal fins separate, VI-10 or 11. Caudal fin rounded. Anal fin 9 or 10. Pelvic fins thoracic in position and united at base to form a sucking disk. Head naked but body scaled. Scales along side 25-30. Color greenish-black. Length up to about 2 inches.

General Distribution.—West Indies and southern Florida.

Florida Range.—Southern Florida; recorded from fresh water in Lee County.

Habitat.—The sea coasts and fresh-water streams entering the sea.

Gobionellus boleosoma (Jordan and Gilbert)
Darting Goby

General Appearance.—A tiny (about 2 inches), slender, extremely active fish with two dorsal fins and a ventral sucking disk.

Distinguishing Characters.—Pelvic fins fused at base to form a sucking disk; head naked but body scaled; 12 soft rays in the dorsal fin; upper rays of pectoral fin not silky.

Description.—Head moderate, not very blunt; snout as short as or shorter than the eye; mouth not large, horizontal in profile. Head 4 times in standard length. Eye large, placed high, about 4 in length of head. Body slender, fusiform; depth 4½ to 5½ in standard length. Dorsal fins separate, VI-12. Caudal fin long and pointed, slightly longer than head. Anal fin I,10 to 12. Pelvic fins thoracic in position, united at base to form a sucking disk. Upper rays of pectoral fins not silky. Head naked but body scaled. Scale rows along side 25-30. Color light to dark olive-green, mottled with darker. Fins usually tinged with orange. Total length up to 2 inches.

General Distribution.—North Carolina to Panama.

Florida Range.—Recorded from the St. Johns River.

Habitat.—Invades fresh-water streams entering the sea. Lives in shallow water around debris.

Awaous taiasica (Lichtenstein)
River Goby

General Appearance.—A large goby with tiny scales and a white belly.

Distinguishing Characters.—Pelvic fins fused at base to form a sucking disk; head naked but body scaled; 60-70 scales along side of body.

Description.—Head broader than deep, 3¼ in standard length. Mouth large, horizontal; maxillary extending to below posterior margin of eye. Eye small, about 7 in length of head. Body slender, depressed anteriorly, compressed posteriorly. Depth about 5¼ in standard length. Dorsal fins separate, VI-11. Caudal fin rounded, shorter than the head. Anal fin with 11 soft rays. Pelvic fins thoracic in position, fused at base to form a sucking disk. Upper rays of pectoral fins not separate and not silky. Head naked; body scaled. Scales small, 60-70 rows along side. Color olivaceous with dark blotches along the sides and dark streaks radiating from around the eyes; belly white. Length up to about a foot.

General Distribution.—Florida to Panama and the West Indies.

Florida Range.—Recorded from the St. Johns River drainage.

Habitat.—Fresh-water rivers.

Microgobius gulosus (Girard)
Large-mouth Goby

General Appearance.—A small goby with a large mouth.

Distinguishing Characters.—Pelvic fins fused at base to form a sucking disk; head largely naked; body scaled.

Description.—Head large and long, 3-3½ in standard length. Mouth big, oblique, the lower jaw strongly projecting; maxillary extending to level of the eye. Eye 4 in head. Body rather slender, depth 4-5 in standard length. Dorsal fins separate, VII-15; dorsal spines more or less filamentous, the third to fifth at times with rather long filaments. Caudal fin about as long as head, pointed. Anal spineless, 16-17 soft rays. Pelvic fins thoracic in position, fused at base to form a sucking disk. Upper rays of pectoral fins not separate and not silky.

Scales moderate in size, about 42 rows along side of body. Coloration grayish-olive with mottlings of darker on the body. A pale blue stripe on each side of head above the jaw. A small goby, only a few inches in length.

General Distribution.—Duval County, Florida, to Texas.

Florida Range.—Both coasts.

Habitat.—Invades fresh-water streams and canals.

Gobiosoma bosci (Lacépède)
Naked Goby

General Appearance.—A small fish with a big mouth and no scales.

Distinguishing Characters.—Pelvic fins fused at base to form a sucking disk; no scales.

Description.—Head broad, mouth terminal. Body rather short and stocky, depth about 4 in standard length. Dorsal fins separate, VII,12 to 14. Caudal fin rounded. Anal fin usually with 11 soft rays, rarely 10 or 12. Pelvic fins thoracic in position, united at base to form a sucking disk. Upper rays of pectoral fin not silky. Color brownish or blackish, usually with about 9 whitish cross bars on body. Size small, 2½ inches or less.

General Distribution.—Along the coast from New Jersey to Tampico, Mexico.

Florida Range.—Along the entire coast line.

Habitat.—Invades fresh waters and lives in rocky or trashy places.

Echeneis naucrates Linnaeus
Shark Remora *(Plate 32)*

General Appearance.—A skinny, dark-striped fish with sucking grid on the back.

Distinguishing Characters.—Anterior dorsal fin modified into a sucker.

Description.—Body slender and elongate, rounded in cross section. Depth 11 to 12 in standard length. Mouth moderate, terminal in position; lower jaw strongly protruding, its tip flexible. Teeth small, pointed, and uniform in size in adults. Eye 5 in length of the head. Head 5¼ in standard length. First dorsal fin modified into an ovate, flat, transversly laminated sucking grid placed on top of head and neck. Second dorsal fin long, with 32-41 soft rays. Caudal fin lunate to truncate, depending on age. Anal fin elongate, 31-38 soft rays. Pelvic fins thoracic in position. Lateral line present, nearly straight, but very faint. Scales minute. Color grayish with a dark stripe down each side, which is bordered above and below with a lighter stripe. Occasionally attains a length of nearly 3 feet but averaging smaller.

General Distribution.—Tropical seas.

Florida Range.—The Gulf Coast.

Habitat.—Salt water; known from spring-runs.

Citharichthys spilopterus Günther
Whiff

General Appearance.—A very flat fish with both eyes and all its color on the left side.

Distinguishing Characters.—Scales along lateral line 45-48; rays in dorsal fin 72-80; with both eyes on the left side of the body; depth in standard length 2-2¼.

Description.—Snout short, forming an angle with the profile; jaws strongly curved, the upper somewhat hooked over the lower. Both eyes on left side of head. Eye about 6 in length of head. Body moderately elongate, much compressed. Depth slightly more than 2 in standard length. Dorsal fin with 72-80 rays. Caudal fin doubly truncate. Anal fin with 58-61 rays. Pelvic fins thoracic in position. Lateral line nearly straight. Scales along lateral line 45-58. Color on the left side olive-brownish with scattered darker spots and blotches. Total length rarely exceeding 6 inches.

General Distribution.—New Jersey to Brazil.

Florida Range.—Recorded from the fresh waters of Florida only in the St. Johns River.

Habitat.—Sea coasts and rivers entering the sea.

Paralichthys albigutta Jordan and Gilbert
Gulf Flounder

General Appearance.—A very flat fish with both eyes and its color on the left side.

Distinguishing Characters.—Scales along lateral line 90-100; rays in dorsal fin 72-80; eyes and color on left side of body.

Description.—Mouth large, the maxillary extending past the eye. Both eyes on left side of head. Eye 6-7 in length of head. Body elongate-elliptical, strongly compressed. Depth 2¼-2½ in standard length. Dorsal fin with 72-80 rays. Caudal fin doubly truncate. Anal fin with 59-61 rays. Pelvic fins thoracic in position. Lateral line arched over pectoral fins, straight behind. Scales along lateral line 90-100. Color on the left side brownish to olive-brown, with a number of more or less pale spots, which are sometimes obsolete. Attains a total length of about 18 inches.

General Distribution.—South Atlantic and Gulf coasts.

Florida Range.—Recorded from fresh water in Florida only in the St. Johns River.

Habitat.—Both coasts, and large rivers entering the sea.

Paralichthys lethostigma Jordan and Gilbert
Southern Flounder

General Appearance.—A very flat fish with both eyes and its color on the left side of the body.

Distinguishing Characters.—Anal fin rays 65-73; dorsal fin rays 85-95; depth in standard length $2\frac{1}{4}$-$2\frac{1}{2}$; eyes on left side of body.

Description.—Mouth large and oblique; the mandible heavy and projecting. Both eyes on the left side of the head. Eye about 6 in length of head. Body ovate, strongly compressed. Depth $2\frac{1}{4}$-$2\frac{1}{2}$ in standard length. Dorsal fin with 85-95 rays. Caudal fin doubly truncate. Anal fin with 65-73 rays. Pelvic fins thoracic in position. Lateral line arched above pectorals. Scales along lateral line 90-100. Color brownish or olive-brown on the left side with but a few darker mottlings. Attains a weight of about 15 pounds but averages smaller.

General Distribution.—New York to the Gulf of Mexico.

Florida Range.—Recorded from fresh water in Florida only in the St. Johns River.

Habitat.—Both coasts, and large rivers entering the sea.

Trinectes maculatus fasciatus (Lacépède)
Northern Round Sole *(Plate 32)*

General Appearance.—A rounded, very compressed fish with both eyes and all its color on the right side.

Distinguishing Characters.—Eyes and color on the right side of the body; pectoral fins absent; lateral line straight.

Description.—Head small, about 5 in standard length. Mouth small, right lower lip fringed. Eyes on right side. Eye small, 7 in length of head. Body rounded, very compressed; depth nearly twice in standard length. Dorsal fin with 50-55 rays. Caudal fin rounded. Anal fin with 37-46 soft rays. Pectoral fins absent. Pelvic fin of right side connected with the anal by a membrane. Lateral line straight. Scales along lateral line 65-75. Color grayish with indefinite narrow darker vertical bars. Length up to about 6 inches.

General Distribution.—Atlantic and Gulf coasts of the United States.

Florida Range.—Both coasts.

Habitat.—Along the coast, ascending rivers well above tidewater.

Symphurus plagiusa (Linnaeus)
Tonguefish *(Plate 32)*

General Appearance.—A lanceolate, very flattened fish with both eyes on the left side.

Distinguishing Characters.—Depth 3⅓ in standard length; anal fin rays 75-80, dorsal fin rays 85-95; dorsal and anal fins more or less confluent with caudal fin; pelvic fin of right side absent; eyes on left side of body. No pectoral fins.

Description.—Mouth small, twisted toward the blind side. Head 5 in standard length. Both eyes on left side. Body moderately elongate, very compressed; depth 3-3⅓ in standard length. Dorsal fin with 85-95 soft rays. Caudal fin rather pointed. Anal fin with 75-80 soft rays. Vertical fins more or less confluent. Left pelvic fin thoracic in position, that on the blind side absent. No pectoral fins. No lateral line. About 85-95 scales from head to structural base of tail. Color grayish with indistinct cross bars. A small fish, less than a foot in length.

General Distribution.—The coastal region of the South Atlantic and Gulf states.

Florida Range.—Recorded from fresh water in Florida only in the St. Johns River.

Habitat.—Both coasts, and large rivers entering the sea.

PLATE 1

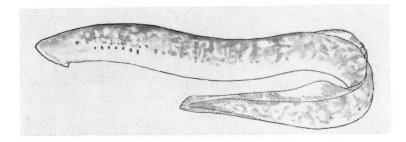

Sea Lamprey, *Petromyzon marinus.*

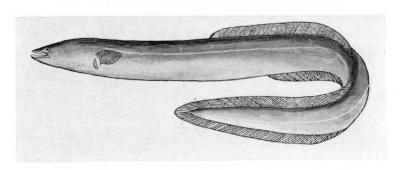

Eel, *Anguilla rostrata.*

PLATE 2

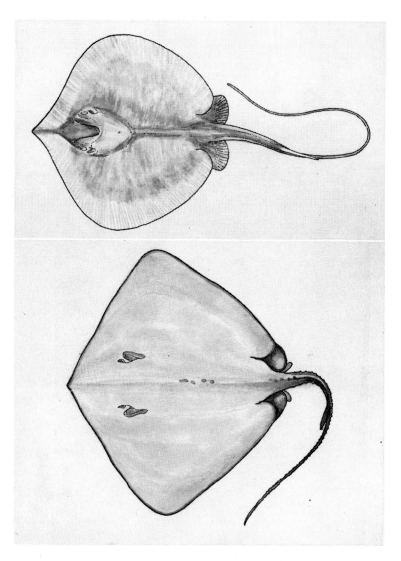

Upper, Southern Sting Ray, *Dasyatis sabina*. Lower, Whip Sting Ray, *Dasyatis hastata*.

PLATE 3

Upper, Shark-nosed Shark, *Scoliodon terraenovae*. Lower, Bull Shark, *Carcharinus leucas*.

Upper, Ten Pounder, *Elops saurus*. Lower, Tarpon, *Tarpon atlanticus*.

PLATE 4

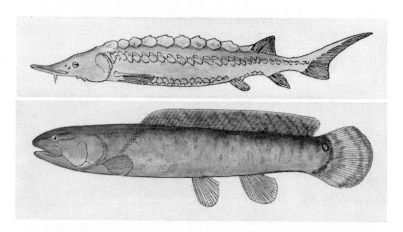

Upper, Common Sturgeon, *Acipenser oxyrhynchus.* Lower, Mudfish, *Amia calva*

Upper, Redfin Pickerel, *Esox americanus.* Lower, Florida Spotted Gar, *Lepisosteus platyrhincus.*

PLATE 5

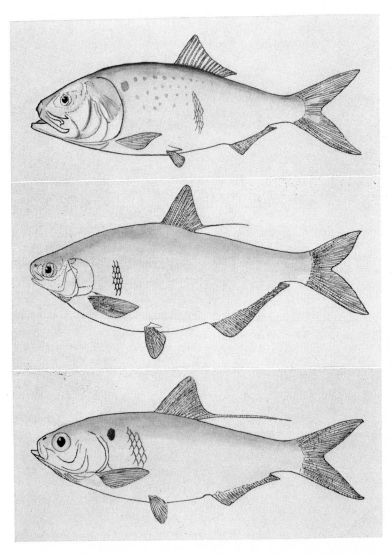

Upper, Bug Fish, *Brevoortia smithi.* Middle, Gizzard Shad, *Dorosoma cepedianum.* Lower, Florida Threadfin Shad, *Dorosoma petenense vanhyningi.*

PLATE 6

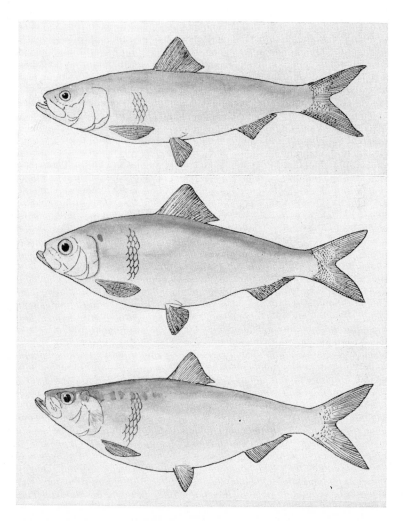

Upper, Skipjack, *Alosa chrysochloris.* Middle, Alewife, *Alosa pseudoharengus.* Lower, Hickory Shad, *Alosa mediocris.*

PLATE 7

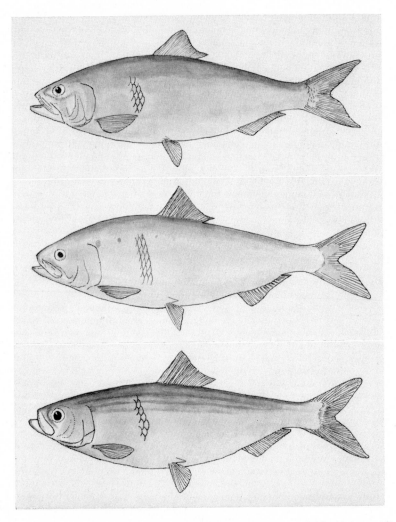

Upper, Alabama Shad, *Alosa alabamae*. Middle, American Shad, *Alosa sapidis-sima*. Lower, Glut Herring, *Alosa aestivalis*.

PLATE 8

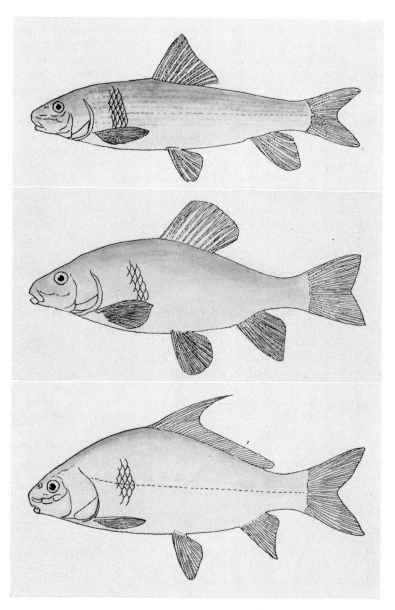

Upper, Spotted Sucker, *Minytrema melanops.* Middle, Eastern Chubsucker, *Erimyzon sucetta.* Lower, Quillback, *Carpiodes cyprinus.*

PLATE 9

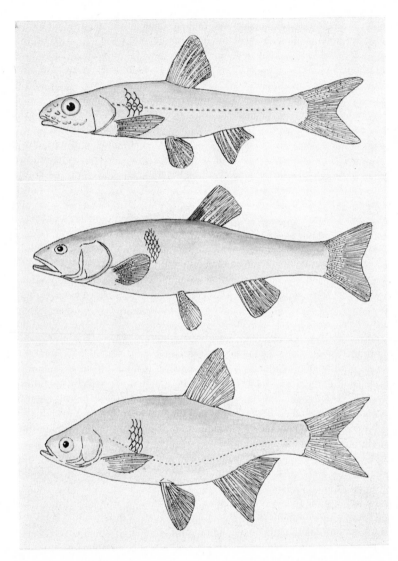

Upper, Silverjaw Minnow, *Ericymba buccata*. Middle, Southeastern Creek Chub, *Semotilus atromaculatus*. Lower, Southeastern Golden Shiner, *Notemigonus crysoleucas bosci*.

PLATE 10

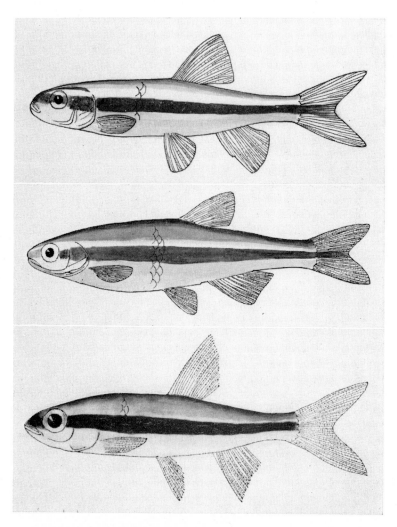

Upper, Spring Redeye Chub, *Hybopsis harperi*. Middle, Lowland Shiner, *Notropis cummingsae cummingsae*. Lower, Iron-colored Shiner, *Notropis chalybaeus*.

Plate 11

Upper, Channel Cat, *Ictalurus punctatus*. Middle, Sea Catfish, *Galeichthys felis*. Lower, Gafftopsail Catfish, *Bagre marinus*.

PLATE 12

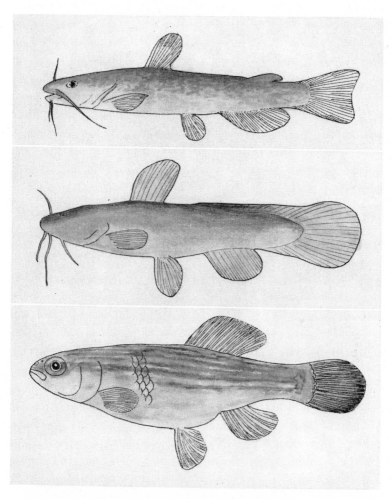

Upper, Snail Cat, *Ameiurus platycephalus*. Middle, Tadpole Madtom, *Schilbeodes mollis*. Lower, Mud Minnow, *Umbra pygmaea*.

PLATE 13

Upper, Flagfish, *Jordanella floridae*. Middle, Florida Gold-spotted Killifish, *Floridichthys carpio carpio*. Lower, Southern Sheepshead Killifish, *Cyprinodon variegatus variegatus*.

PLATE 14

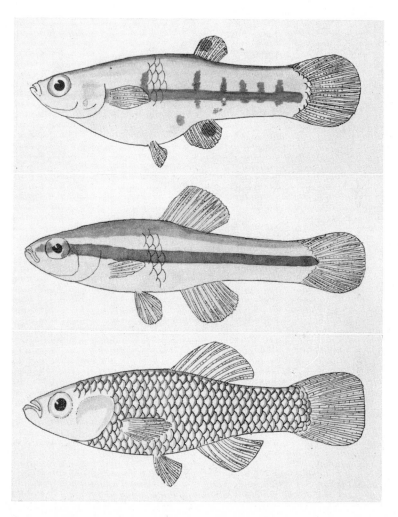

Upper, Least Killifish, *Heterandria formosa*. Middle, Red-finned Killifish, *Lucania goodei*. Lower, Rainwater Killifish, *Lucania parva*.

PLATE 15

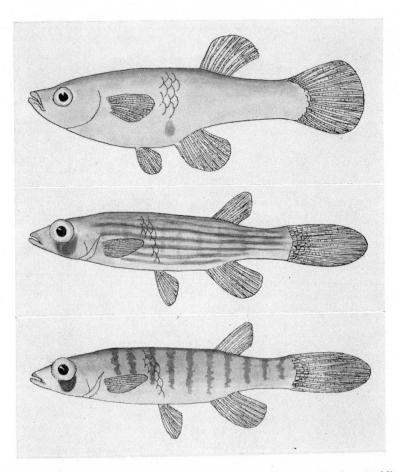

Upper, Eastern Mosquito-fish, *Gambusia affinis holbrooki*, female. Middle, Eastern Star-headed Topminnow, *Fundulus notti lineolatus*. Lower, Southern Star-headed Topminnow, *Fundulus notti notti*.

PLATE 16

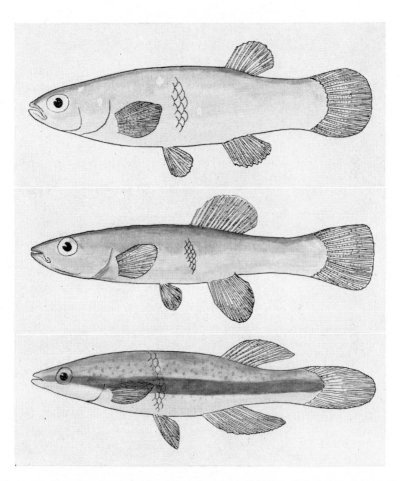

Upper, Golden Topminnow, *Fundulus chrysotus*. Middle, Caledonian, *Fundulus seminolis*. Lower, Streaked Topminnow, *Fundulus olivaceus*.

PLATE 17

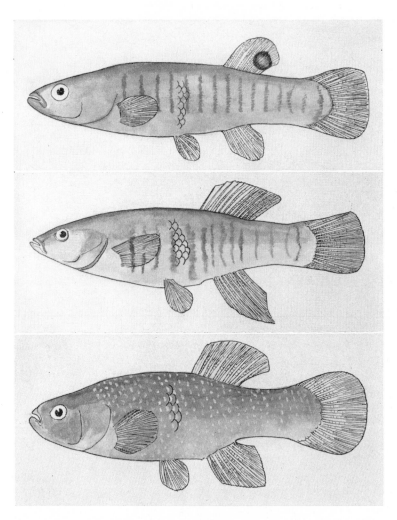

Upper, Spotfin Killifish, *Fundulus confluentus confluentus*. Middle, Striped Killifish, *Fundulus majalis*. Lower, Southern Common Killifish, *Fundulus heteroclitus heteroclitus*.

Plate 18

Upper, Everglade Pigmy Sunfish, *Elassoma evergladei.* Middle, Pirate Perch, *Aphredoderus sayanus.* Lower, Black-banded Sunfish, *Enneacanthus chaetodon elizabethae.*

PLATE 19

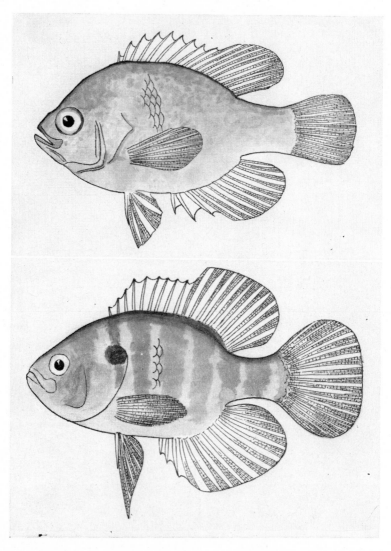

Upper, Blue-spotted Sunfish, *Enneacanthus gloriosus.* Lower, Banded Sunfish, *Enneacanthus obesus.*

PLATE 20

Upper, Mud Perch, *Acantharchus pomotis.* Lower, Southern Rock Bass, *Ambloplites rupestris ariommus.*

PLATE 21

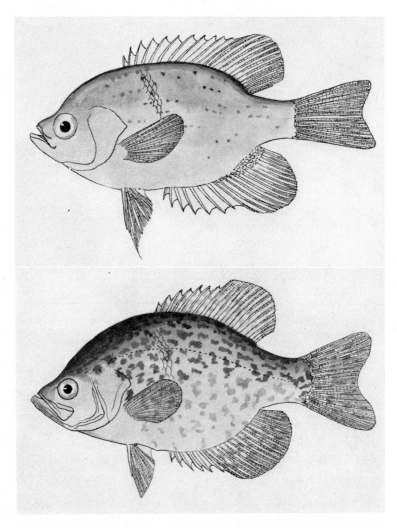

Upper, Flier, *Centrarchus macropterus*. Lower, Speckled Perch, *Pomoxis nigromaculatus*.

Plate 22

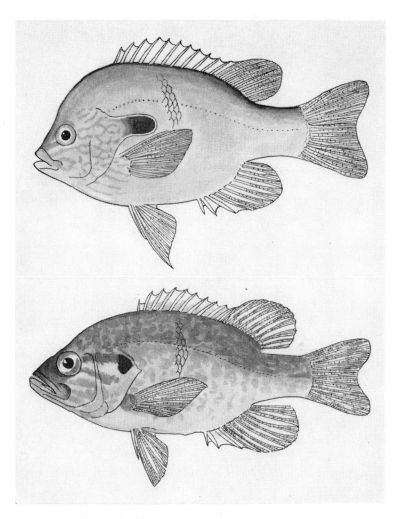

Upper, Long-ear Sunfish, *Lepomis megalotis megalotis.* Lower, Warmouth, *Chaenobryttus coronarius.*

Plate 23

Upper, Bluegill, *Lepomis macrochirus purpurescens*. Lower, Redbreast, *Lepomis auritus*.

PLATE 24

Upper, Spot, *Leiostomus xanthurus.* Lower, Pinfish, *Lagodon rhomboides.*

PLATE 25

Upper, Spot-tail Pinfish, *Diplodus holbrooki.* Lower, Sheepshead, *Archosargus probatocephalus.*

PLATE 26

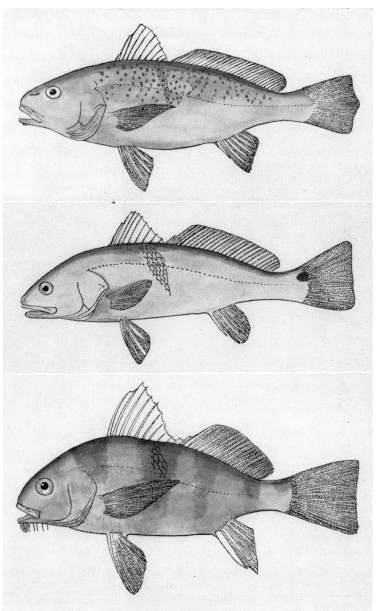

Upper, Croaker, *Micropogon undulatus.* Middle, Channel Bass, *Sciaenops ocellatus.* Lower, Sea Drum, *Pogonias cromis.*

PLATE 27

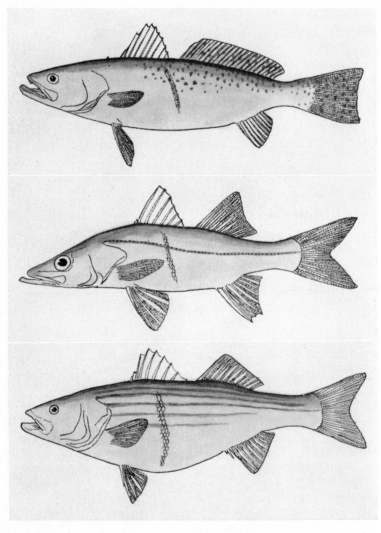

Upper, Speckled Trout, *Cynoscion nebulosus*. Middle, Snook, *Centropomus undecimalis*. Lower, Striped Bass, *Roccus saxatilis*.

PLATE 28

Upper, Mountain Mullet, *Agonostomus monticola*. Middle, Striped Mullet, *Mugil cephalus*. Lower, White Mullet, *Mugil curema*.

PLATE 29

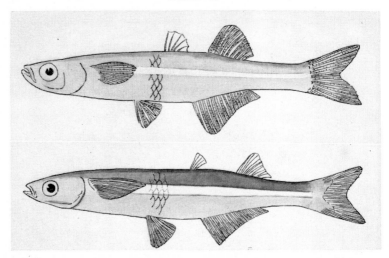

Upper, Freshwater Glass-minnow, *Menidia beryllina*. Lower, Rough Silverside, *Membras martinica*.

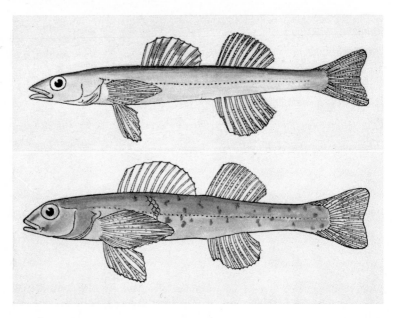

Upper, Naked Sand Darter, *Ammocrypta beani*. Lower, Eastern Johnny Darter, *Etheostoma nigrum olmstedi*.

PLATE 30

Upper, Okaloosa Darter, *Etheostoma okaloosae*. Middle, Florida Swamp Darter, *Etheostoma barratti*. Lower, Brown Darter, *Etheostoma edwini*.

PLATE 31

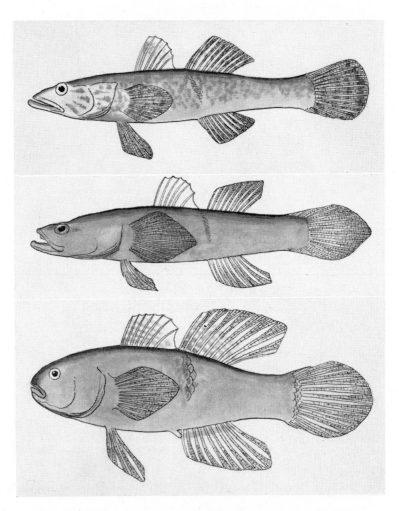

Upper, Sleeper, *Gobiomorus dormitor*. Middle, Slender Sleeper, *Eleotris abacurus*.
Lower, Fat Sleeper, *Dormitator maculatus*.

PLATE 32

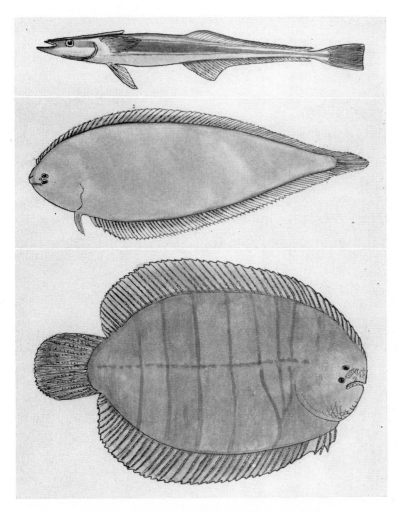

Upper, Shark Remora, *Echeneis naucrates*. Middle, Tonguefish, *Symphurus plagiusa*. Lower, Northern Round Sole, *Trinectes maculatus fasciatus*.

THE AMPHIBIANS

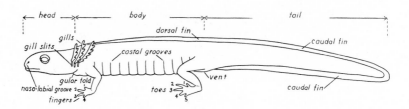

Fig. 15   Diagrammatic figure of a salamander, showing external structures.

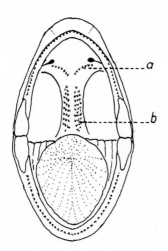

Fig. 16   View of open mouth of salamander, showing location of
(a) vomerine teeth; and (b)
parasphenoid teeth.

AMPHIBIAN GLOSSARY

ANAL WARTS—Small, white warts on each side of the anus in some frogs.

COSTAL GROOVES—A series of vertical grooves along the sides of the body between the fore and hind limbs of most salamanders.

CRANIAL CRESTS—Knobby protuberances on the top of the head of toads.

DIGITAL DISKS—Round adhesive pads on the tips of the fingers and toes of some frogs.

DORSOLATERAL FOLDS—Glandular folds of skin running from behind the eye to the region of the base of the hind leg in some frogs.

NARES—Nostrils.

NASO-LABIAL GROOVE—A groove running from the nostril to the edge of the upper lip on each side in some salamanders.

PALATINE TEETH—Teeth on the roof of the mouth.

PARASPHENOID TEETH—Teeth on the roof of the mouth of some salamanders, usually well behind the internal nares and arranged in longitudinal series.

PAROTOID GLANDS—Rounded or oval glandular protuberances on the back of the head in toads.

POSTFEMORAL—The back of the thigh.

TONGUE ON PEDICEL—Tongue mushroom-shaped and attached by a central stalk.

TYMPANUM—The ear drum of frogs, usually level with the surface of the head.

VOCAL POUCH—Skin sac underneath or at the side of the throat in some frogs.

VOMERINE TEETH—Teeth on the roof of the mouth between or just behind the internal nares, usually arranged in rounded patches or in transverse series.

KEY TO AMPHIBIANS

1	Adult with tail	2
1'	Adult without tail	29
2 (1)	Two pairs of legs present	3
2'	Only one pair of legs	25
3 (2)	Adult without external gills	4
3'	Adult with external gills and gill slits	
	Hog-nosed waterdog, *Necturus beyeri*, p.	160
4 (3)	Body eel-like; legs rudimentary	5
4'	Body not eel-like; with well-developed legs	6

5 (4)   Two toes on each foot...
....Two-toed Amphiuma, *Amphiuma means means,* p. 160
5′   Three toes on each foot..............................Three-
toed Amphiuma, *Amphiuma means tridactylum,* p. 161
6 (4)   No naso-labial groove; parasphenoid teeth lacking....   7
6′   Naso-labial groove and parasphenoid teeth present....   15
7 (6)   No costal grooves..   8
7′   Costal grooves present..   11
8 (7)   With a pair of dorsolateral red stripes............................
........................Striped Newt, *Diemictylus perstriatus,* p. 161
8′   Without dorsolateral red stripes......................................   9
9 (8)   Without a definite row of red spots along each side of
the back..   10
9′   With a definite row of black encircled bright red spots
along each side of the back...................................Red-
spotted Newt, *Diemictylus viridescens viridescens,* p. 163
10 (9)   Belly with but a few scattered black spots; found west
of the Apalachicola River....................................Louisi-
ana Newt, *Diemectylus viridescens louisianensis,* p. 163
10′   Belly with numerous tiny black dots; found east of the
Apalachicola River...
Florida Newt, *Diemictylus viridescens piaropicola,* p. 162
11 (7)   Teeth on jaws in more than 1 row..............................   12
11′   Teeth on jaws arranged in a single row......................   13
12 (11)   Vomerine teeth average 13 in each patch, arranged in 2
rows; salt and pepper ventral pattern................Reticu-
lated Salamander, *Ambystoma cingulatum bishopi,* p. 165
12′   Vomerine teeth average 15-16 in each patch; arranged
in 3 rows; ventral pattern of discrete white spots on a
dark ground color..Frosted
Salamander, *Ambystoma cingulatum cingulatum,* p. 164
13 (11)   Costal grooves less than 12; pattern not of irregular
yellow blotches...   14
13′   Costal grooves 12; pattern large irregular yellow
blotches...Eastern
Tiger Salamander, *Ambystoma tigrinum tigrinum,* p. 166
14 (13)   Costal grooves 11; back with broad light cross bars....
..............Marbled Salamander, *Ambystoma opacum,* p. 165
14′   Costal grooves 10; back dark brown or gray with small
gray dots...
.............Mole Salamander, *Ambystoma talpoideum,* p. 166
15 (6)   Five toes on hind foot...   16
15′   Four toes on hind foot..
........Dwarf Salamander, *Manculus quadridigitatus,* p. 168

16 (15) Tongue with a central pedicel, free all around............ 21
16′   Tongue attached in front, free at sides and behind only 17
17 (16) Light line from eye to angle of jaw............................. 18
17′   No light line from eye to angle of jaw; pattern of white
         and/or gold flecks on a black background......Southern
         Slimy Salamander, *Plethodon glutinosus grobmani,* p. 167
18 (17) Belly dark, at least posteriorly................................. 19
18′   Belly light... 20
19 (18) Head and body 1¾-2½ inches, tail as long as or longer
         than head and body............................Southern Dusky
         Salamander, *Desmognathus fuscus auriculatus,* p. 172
19′   Head and body length 1¼-1¾ inches; tail shorter than
         head and body length..............................Carr's
         Dusky Salamander, *Desmognathus fuscus carri,* p. 174
20 (18) Belly uniformly but lightly pigmented..Brimley's Dusky
         Salamander, *Desmognathus fuscus brimleyorum,* p. 173
20′   Belly light but mottled...........................Common
         Dusky Salamander, *Desmognathus fuscus fuscus,* p. 172
21 (16) Vomerine teeth continuous with parasphenoid teeth.... 22
21′   Vomerine teeth not continuous with parasphenoid teeth 24
22 (21) Costal grooves 16-18; belly with small, discrete, scat-
         tered black spots... 23
22′   Costal grooves 15-16; belly heavily spotted................
         Viosca's Red Salamander, *Pseudotriton ruber vioscai,* p. 171
23 (22) Ground color above dark; sides of body with short, dull
         yellow dashes sometimes forming irregular lines..Rusty
         Mud Salamander, *Pseudotriton montanus floridanus,* p. 170
23′   Ground color above light; small, discrete, well-scattered
         dark spots above and below...........................Gulf Coast
         Red Salamander, *Pseudotriton montanus flavissimus,* p. 170
24 (21) Black mid-dorsal stripe present.....................Three-
         lined Salamander, *Eurycea longicauda guttolineata,* p. 169
24′   No black mid-dorsal stripe.......................Southern
         Two-lined Salamander, *Eurycea bislineata cirrigera,* p. 168
25 (2)   Foot with 3 toes; body longitudinally striped.............. 26
25′   Foot with 4 toes; body not longitudinally striped.......... 28
26 (25) Head and snout broad and truncate...................... 27
26′   Head narrow and wedge-shaped; snout pointed............
         ....Narrow-headed
         Striped Siren, *Pseudobranchus striatus spheniscus,* p. 176
27 (26) Lateral light stripe pale gray........................Narrow-
         striped Siren, *Pseudobranchus striatus axanthus,* p. 176

27′   Lateral light stripe bright yellow or orange................
....Gulf Hammock
Striped Siren, *Pseudobranchus striatus lustricolus*, p. 177
28 (25)   Costal grooves 31-34..
..................Lesser Siren, *Siren intermedia intermedia*, p. 174
28′   Costal grooves 37-38....Great Siren, *Siren lacertina*, p. 175
29 (1)   Parotoid glands conspicuous, elevated.......................   30
29′   Parotoid glands lacking..   34
30 (29)   Pupil of eye vertical; parotoids rounded.....................   31
30′   Pupil of eye round, parotoids ellipsoidal.....................   32
31 (30)   Ground color gray, olive, or brownish.......................
Common Spadefoot, *Scaphiopus holbrooki holbrooki*, p. 178
31′   Ground color very pale..
....Key West Spadefoot, *Scaphiopus holbrooki albus*, p. 178
32 (30)   Parotoid with the long axis parallel to the long axis of
the body; cranial crests conspicuous.......................   33
32′   Parotoids with the long axes diverging posteriorly; cranial crests inconspicuous..Oak Toad, *Bufo quercicus*, p. 179

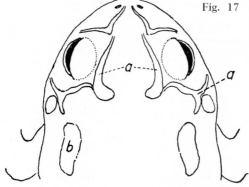

Fig. 17   Dorsal view of head of toad,
showing location of (a) cra-
nial crests; and (b) parotoid
glands.

33 (32)   Cranial crests not ending in knobs; crests in contact
with parotoid glands..
..................Fowler's Toad, *Bufo woodhousei fowleri*, p. 180
33′   Cranial crests ending in knobs; crests well separated
from the parotoids or connected only by a spur............
....................Southern Toad, *Bufo terrestris terrestris*, p. 180

34 (29)   Vomerine teeth in rounded patches............................ 35
34'   Vomerine teeth in transverse series....................Green-
           house Frog, *Eleutherodactylus ricordi planirostris*, p. 191

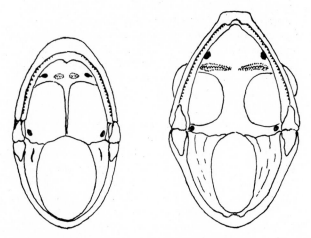

Fig. 18   View of open mouth of frog. Vomerine teeth in rounded patches
           (left); in transverse series (right).

35 (34)   Toes terminating in adhesive disks............................ 36
35'   Toes not terminating in adhesive disks...................... 50

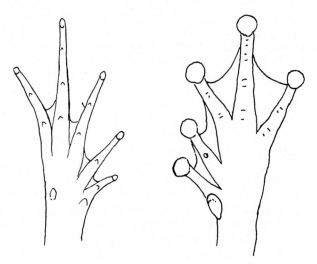

Fig. 19   Foot of frog with inconspicuous digital disks (left); with conspicuous
           digital disks (right).

36 (35)   Disks on fingers and toes large and conspicuous; length
          of adult more than ¾ inch......................................   37
36'   Disks on fingers and toes small and inconspicuous; *or*
          length of adults less than ¾ inch...........................   44
37 (36)   Fingers more or less webbed.................................   38
37'   Fingers entirely free of web.................................   41
38 (37)   Skin warty...   39
38'   Skin smooth, glandular or pustulate; not warty............   40
39 (38)   Warts very close and numerous...............................
          ....Common Tree Frog, *Hyla versicolor versicolor*, p.   190
39'   Warts few and scattered.....................................
          ....Cuban Tree Frog, *Hyla septentrionalis*, p.   191
40 (38)   Tympanum nearly or quite as large as eye; dorsal pat-
          tern often of rounded spots..Bell Frog, *Hyla gratiosa*, p.   189
40'   Tympanum small, diameter ⅓ or less than diameter of
          eye; dorsal pattern not of rounded spots.................Bird-
          voiced Tree Frog, *Hyla phaeocrypta phaeocrypta*, p.   186
41 (37)   Light line along upper jaw and usually along sides; dor-
          sal pattern either uniform or spotted...........................   42
41'   No light line along upper jaw; dorsal pattern of
          blotches, bars or heavy lines.................................   43
42 (41)   Light line along sides (if present) broad and with defi-
          nite borders; no transverse bar between the eyes.........
          ....Green Tree Frog, *Hyla cinerea cinerea*, p.   186
42'   Light line along sides wavy and without definite bor-
          ders; often with a transverse bar between the eyes.........
          ....Rain Frog, *Hyla squirella*, p.   189
43 (41)   Dorsal blotches irregular; hind surfaces of thighs with
          distinct yellow (white in preservative) markings.........
          ....Pine-woods Tree Frog, *Hyla femoralis*, p.   188
43'   Dorsal blotches forming a more or less oblique cross;
          no distinct yellow or white markings on thighs............
          Southern Spring Peeper, *Hyla crucifer bartramiana*, p.   187
44 (36)   Toes fully webbed; tympanum distinct; hind surface of
          thighs with distinct longitudinal stripes.....................   45
44'   Toes slightly webbed; tympanum distinct; hind surface
          of thighs without longitudinal stripes.....................   46
45 (44)   Two *distinct* dark postfemoral stripes on a light back-
          ground; no anal warts; size small, ¾ inch or less..........
          ....Florida Cricket Frog, *Acris gryllus dorsalis*, p.   182
45'   Only 1 distinct dark postfemoral stripe; a few anal
          warts generally present; size larger, generally exceeding
          ¾ inch in length..
          ....Common Cricket Frog, *Acris gryllus gryllus*, p.   181

ACCOUNTS OF SPECIES

Necturus beyeri Viosca
Hog-nosed Waterdog

General Appearance—A large, brownish salamander with external gills and 4 toes on each foot.

Distinguishing Characters.—Known by the large size, the brownish color and by having most of the belly mottled but with a few distinguishable small dark spots; external gills present; 4 toes on each foot.

Description.—Head widest in front of the gills, tapering gently to the angle of the jaws, then more rapidly to the truncate snout. Body somewhat flattened, with a shallow mid-dorsal groove. Tail strongly flattened, keeled above and below. Limbs moderate in size, the hind legs slightly larger than the front legs. Four toes on each foot, 3-2-4-1 in order of decreasing length. Costal grooves 16. Pterygoid and palatine teeth in a continuous series. Ground color of dorsum dark brown with small, irregular spots forming a vague, reticulated pattern. Belly somewhat lighter than dorsum, with numerous tiny dark spots superimposed. Length up to about 8 inches.

General Distribution.—The eastern Gulf coastal region.

Florida Range.—Western Florida.

Habitat.—Sand-bottomed streams.

Amphiuma means means Garden
Two-toed Amphiuma

General Appearance.—A large, eel-shaped salamander with 4 tiny, useless-looking legs.

Distinguishing Characters.—Two toes on each foot, costal grooves 57-60.

Description.—Head widest in front of the gills, tapering uniformly to a pointed snout. Eyes small and without lids. Body round and elongate. Tail nearly circular in cross section at base, keeled above and rounded below posteriorly. Limbs minute; 2 toes on each foot. Costal grooves, 57-60, average 58. Mouth large, angle of jaw about halfway between tip of snout and insertion of fore leg. Vomerine teeth in 2 long series arising at the margins of the posterior nares and converging to a point just behind the premaxillaries. Approximately 20 teeth in each series. Dorsal ground color dark grayish-brown, only slightly paler below. No sharp line of demarcation between dorsal and ventral colors. Maximum length, nearly 3 feet.

General Distribution.—The Atlantic coastal plain from Virginia to Florida.

Florida Range.—State-wide.

Habitat.—Large or small sloughs, marshes, prairies, muddy lakes, and streams.

Amphiuma means tridactylum Cuvier
Three-toed Amphiuma

General Appearance.—A large, eel-shaped salamander with 4 very tiny legs.

Distinguishing Characters.—Three toes on each foot, costal grooves 60-64.

Description.—Head widest in front of gills, tapering uniformly to a pointed snout. Eyes small and without lids. Body round and elongated. Tail nearly circular in cross section at base, keeled above and rounded below posteriorly. Limbs minute; 3 toes on each foot. Costal grooves 60-64, average 62. Mouth large, angle of jaw about halfway between tip of snout and insertion of fore leg. Vomerine teeth in 2 long series arising at the margins of the posterior nares and converging at a point just behind the premaxillaries; 16-22 teeth in each series. Dorsal ground color grayish-brown and ventral ground color light gray with a sharp line of demarcation between the two. Maximum length in excess of 3 feet.

General Distribution.—The Gulf Coast and the Mississippi Valley as far north as Arkansas.

Florida Range.—Probably a few streams in western Florida.

Habitat.—Calcareous streams.

Diemictylus perstriatus (Bishop)
Striped Newt *(Plate 33)*

General Appearance.—A small, reddish-brown salamander with a bright red stripe down each side of the back.

Distinguishing Characters.—No costal grooves; red markings on the back composed of a bright red stripe on each side from above the eye to the base of the tail.

Description.—Head widest at eyes, slightly converging posteriorly, anteriorly tapering to a rather blunt snout. No well-developed cranial ridges. Male with 3 pits on each side of head; pits lacking in the female. Body slender, slightly compressed. No distinct costal grooves. Gular fold normally well developed. Legs slender; 4 toes on front foot, 5 toes on hind foot. Tail compressed with a dorsal keel in aquatic adults. Skin somewhat granular. Tongue small and oval. Vomeropalatine teeth in 2 long series; arising opposite the posterior margins of the internal nares and extending posteriorly for ⅔ of their length, then diverging abruptly. Dorsal color brownish-red to olive with a bright red stripe on each side of the back running from above the eye to the base of the tail. Length from 2 to 3 inches.

General Distribution.—Southern Georgia and northern and central Florida.

Florida Range.—Northern and central Florida west to Leon County.

Habitat.—Ponds. An immature terrestrial stage occurs under logs in dry hammocks and pond margins.

Diemictylus viridescens piaropicola Schwartz and Duellman
Florida Newt

General Appearance.—A small, reddish-brown to blackish salamander.

Distinguishing Characters.—No costal grooves. Red markings on the back restricted to a few minute red dots, or absent. Belly with numerous small black dots.

Description.—Head widest at eyes, slightly converging posteriorly, anteriorly tapering to a rather blunt snout. No well-developed cranial ridges. Males with 3 pits on each side of the head; pits lacking in female. Body slender, slightly compressed. No distinct costal grooves. Gular fold normally developed. Legs slender; four toes on front foot, 5 toes on hind foot. Tail compressed with a dorsal keel in aquatic adults. Skin somewhat granular. Tongue small and oval. Vomeropalatine teeth in 2 long series; arising opposite the posterior margins of the internal nares and extending posteriorly for ⅔ of their length, then diverging abruptly. Dorsal color brownish-olive to blackish; red markings, when present, restricted to a few minute dots. Belly yellowish with small, often very numerous black spots. Length up to 3½ inches.

General Distribution.—Florida.

Florida Range.—East of the Apalachicola River Valley.

Habitat.—Practically any standing body of water. Immature individuals under logs.

Diemictylus viridescens louisianensis Wolterstorff
Louisiana Newt

General Appearance.—A small, greenish to brownish salamander.

Distinguishing Characters.—No costal grooves. Red markings on the back restricted to a few minute red dots, or absent. Belly with but a few scattered small black spots.

Description.—Head widest at eyes, slightly converging posteriorly, anteriorly tapering to a rather blunt snout. No well-developed cranial ridges. Males with 3 pits on each side of head; pits lacking in female. Body slender, slightly compressed. No distinct costal grooves. Gular folds normally developed. Legs slender; 4 toes on front foot, 5 toes on hind foot. Tail compressed with a dorsal keel in aquatic adults. Skin somewhat granular. Tongue small and oval. Vomero-palatine teeth in 2 long series; arising opposite the posterior margins of the internal nares and extending posteriorly for ⅔ of their length, then diverging abruptly. Dorsal color greenish to brownish; red markings, when present, restricted to a few minute dots. Belly yellowish with a few scattered black dots. Length up to about 4 inches.

General Distribution.—The Mississippi River Valley and the Gulf Coast.

Florida Range.—Found west of the Apalachicola River Valley.

Habitat.—Practically any standing body of water. The immature stage is found under rocks and logs.

Diemictylus viridescens viridescens (Rafinesque)
Red-spotted Newt

General Appearance.—A small, greenish to brownish salamander with a row of separate red spots down each side of the back.

Distinguishing Characters.—No costal grooves. Red markings consisting of a row of bright red dots along each side of the back; the red dots usually encircled with black. Belly with a few scattered small black dots.

Description.—Head widest at eyes, slightly converging posteriorly, anteriorly tapering to a rounded snout. No well-developed cranial ridges. Males with 3 pits on each side of the head; pits lacking in females. Body slender, slightly compressed. No distinct costal grooves.

Gular fold normally developed. Legs slender, 4 toes on front foot, 5 toes on hind foot. Tail compressed, with a dorsal keel in aquatic adults. Skin somewhat granular. Tongue small and oval. Vomero-palatine teeth in two long series; arising opposite the posterior margins of the internal nares and extending posteriorly for ⅔ of their length, then diverging abruptly. Dorsal color greenish to brownish with a series of black-encircled, bright red spots along each side of the back. Belly yellowish with scattered tiny black dots. Length up to about 4 inches.

General Distribution.—The eastern United States.

Florida Range.—The Apalachicola River Valley.

Habitat.—Quiet water. Immature stage under logs on land.

Ambystoma cingulatum cingulatum Cope
Frosted Salamander

General Appearance.—A dark, medium-sized salamander with lichen-like markings.

Distinguishing Characters.—Multiple rows of teeth on the jaws, vomerine teeth generally in 3 rows. Belly with discrete white spots on a black background.

Description.—Head somewhat elongate, sides nearly parallel behind the eyes, snout rounded. Eye moderate in size; distance from tip of snout just slightly exceeding length of eye. Body somewhat slender, very slightly flattened dorsoventrally. No pronounced constriction at neck. Limbs moderately stout; fingers 4, somewhat slender, unwebbed; toes 5, moderately slender, unwebbed. Costal grooves 13-16. A narrow mid-dorsal groove; a broad but shallow mid-ventral groove. Teeth in form of rounded knobs, in multiple rows on both upper and lower jaws. Vomerine teeth similar in form to jaw teeth; arranged in about 3 rows, 13-24 teeth in each patch. Ground color above, blackish; dorsal pattern of diffuse, lichen-like marks arising from and continuous with a lichenose band between axilla and groin. Ventral pattern of separate white marks on a black background. Adult size about 4 inches.

General Distribution.—The Atlantic coastal region from South Carolina to central Florida.

Florida Range.—Northeastern Florida southward to the vicinity of Gainesville.

Habitat.—A salamander of the pine flatwoods, especially near small cypress ponds.

Ambystoma cingulatum bishopi Goin
Reticulated Salamander *(Plate 33)*

General Appearance.—A dark, medium-sized salamander with lichen-like markings.

Distinguishing Characters.—Multiple rows of teeth on the jaws; vomerine teeth generally in 2 rows; belly with salt-and-pepper pattern.

Description.—Head somewhat elongate, the sides nearly parallel behind the eyes, snout rounded. Eye moderate in size, distance from tip of snout just slightly exceeding length of eye. Body somewhat slender, very slightly flattened dorsoventrally. No pronounced constriction at neck. Limbs somewhat stout; fingers 4, moderately slender, unwebbed. Toes 5, moderately slender, unwebbed. Costal grooves 15. A narrow mid-dorsal groove, and a broad but shallow mid-ventral groove present. Teeth in form of rounded knobs, in multiple rows on both upper and lower jaws. Vomerine teeth similar in form to jaw teeth; arranged in about 2 rows, 5-20 teeth in each patch. Ground color above, blackish. Dorsal pattern consisting of narrow vermiculations of creamy-yellow which arise from a band of lichen-like marks extending from the axilla to the groin. Ventral pattern of salt-and-pepper markings. Adult size about 4 inches.

General Distribution.—The Gulf Coast in Alabama, Georgia, and Florida.

Florida Range.—The western panhandle.

Habitat.—A salamander of the pine flatwoods, especially near small cypress ponds.

Ambystoma opacum (Gravenhorst)
Marbled Salamander

General Appearance.—A stout salamander about 4 inches long with white or silvery-white bars across the back.

Distinguishing Characters.—No naso-labial grooves; 11 costal grooves; light bars across the back.

Description.—Head and body stout; head moderately broad, widest above the angle of the jaw. Tail rounded, not keeled, thicker above than below. Limbs stout; fingers 4, moderately slender, unwebbed; toes 5, moderately slender, unwebbed. Costal grooves 11. Vomerine teeth in transverse sinuous series; interrupted at mid-point and behind each internal naris. Ground color of back dark grayish to black with a pattern of light markings (white in males, gray in females). The light markings are generally arranged in crossbands which are narrowest at the mid-dorsal line. Sometimes the widened lower ends of these crossbands unite to form dorsolateral light stripes. Belly gray or grayish-black. Adult size about 4 inches.

General Distribution.—The eastern United States.

Florida Range.—West and north Florida southward to the Tampa Bay region.

Habitat.—A salamander of low hammock lands and wooded flood plains.

Ambystoma talpoideum (Holbrook)
Mole Salamander

General Appearance.—A stout, gray or grayish-brown salamander, 3 to 4 inches long.

Distinguishing Characters.—No naso-labial grooves; 10 costal grooves; back dark brown or gray with small gray dots.

Description.—Head and body stout. Head broad, widest above the angle of the jaws; snout bluntly rounded. A very shallow mid-dorsal groove. Tail short, slightly keeled above, rounded below, compressed at tip. Fingers 4, toes 5, moderately slender, unwebbed; toes and fingers meeting or slightly overlapping when limbs are pressed along the side of the body. Costal grooves 10. Vomerine teeth in 3 transverse series, the middle series lying posterior to and between the internal nares, lateral series behind each internal naris. Grayish-brown above, bluish-gray on the sides and below; dorsal surface scattered with small bluish flecks. Maximum length about 4 inches.

General Distribution.—South Atlantic and Gulf states.

Florida Range.—Southward to the region of Orlando.

Habitat.—A burrowing salamander of hammock lands.

Ambystoma tigrinum tigrinum (Green)
Eastern Tiger Salamander *(Plate 33)*

General Appearance.—A good-sized, bluish-gray salamander with yellow or gold blotches.

Distinguishing Characters.—No naso-labial grooves; costal grooves 12; pattern of large, irregular yellow or gold blotches.

Description.—Head and body stout. Head broad, widest just back of the eyes, tapering to a bluntly rounded snout; neck distinct. Tail fairly long, thicker below than above, compressed at the tip. A prominent gular fold. Legs stout and moderately long. Fingers 4, toes 5, blunt-tipped, unwebbed. Costal grooves 12. Vomerine teeth in a single continuous transverse series lying behind and extending beyond the internal nares. Ground color above and on the sides dull black; belly olive-yellow. Top of head, dorsum, and tail covered with numerous yellowish or golden irregular blotches. In some individuals the blotches tend to fuse along the sides to form bands. Adults average 7 or 8 inches in total length.

General Distribution.—The eastern United States.

Florida Range.—Known from as far west as Jackson County and as far south as Hernando County.

Habitat.—A burrowing salamander of hammock lands and fields.

Plethodon glutinosus grobmani Allen and Neill
Southern Slimy Salamander *(Plate 34)*

General Appearance.—A small, blue-black salamander with scattered whitish or golden flecks on the back.

Distinguishing Characters.—Naso-labial grooves present; no fin on tail; tongue attached only at anterior margin; no light line from eye to angle of the jaw.

Description.—Head moderately broad, widest just behind the eyes; the sides nearly parallel. Snout bluntly rounded; naso-labial grooves present. Body rounded in cross section, slightly depressed along mid-dorsal line. Tail nearly circular and tapering to a slender tip, not keeled. Legs fairly stout, 4 toes on front feet, slightly webbed at base; 5 toes on hind feet. Costal grooves about 15; usually 1 costal fold between tips of adpressed toes. Tongue broad and flat, attached along its anterior margin, free along the sides and posteriorly. Vomerine teeth well separated from the parasphenoid teeth. Color bluish-black with a band of whitish, lichen-like markings between the fore and hind limbs. Dorsum sprinkled with whitish or golden flecks or both. About 4 inches in total length.

General Distribution.—The lower coastal plain of the southeastern United States.

Florida Range.—Southward to Hillsborough County.

Habitat.—Dry to swampy hammock lands; usually under logs.

Manculus quadridigitatus (Holbrook)
Dwarf Salamander

General Appearance.—A small, slender, long-tailed, yellow to brownish salamander.

Distinguishing Characters.—Naso-labial grooves present; 4 toes on hind foot.

Description.—Head and body long and slender. Head widest behind the eyes; sides of head converging abruptly before the eyes to a very short and bluntly rounded snout. Naso-labial grooves present, produced into short cirri in the males. Eyes large for such a small salamander, markedly protuberant. Body slender, rounded, slightly flattened below. Tail long and slender, slightly keeled above and compressed distally. Legs small, 4 fingers on fore leg, 4 toes on hind leg, unwebbed. Sixteen costal grooves. Vomerine teeth in 2 short series behind the internal nares, the series scarcely separated. Parasphenoid teeth in 2 patches, widely separated from the vomerines but scarcely separated from each other. Ground color above yellowish or brownish, in the form of a broad, rather sharply limited, longitudinal band. Some individuals with a median row of small dark spots. Sides lighter brown than the dorsum, merging into a golden-yellow belly. Average length nearly 3 inches.

General Distribution.—The Atlantic and Gulf coastal plain.

Florida Range.—South to the Everglades.

Habitat.—A somewhat ubiquitous salamander, found in all sorts of wet places.

Eurycea bislineata cirrigera (Green)
Southern Two-lined Salamander *(Plate 34)*

General Appearance.—A slender, yellowish salamander with 2 lines down the back.

Distinguishing Characters.—Naso-labial grooves present; 5 toes on hind foot; no black mid-dorsal stripe; vomerine teeth not continuous with parasphenoid teeth; tongue with a central pedicel, its edges free all around.

Description.—Head rather long, with parallel sides behind the eyes. Snout bluntly pointed, naso-labial grooves extending into cirri in the males. Eyes moderate in size and slightly protuberant. Body slender, nearly cylindrical but with a faintly impressed median dorsal depression. Tail long and slender, somewhat sharp-edged above, without fins.

Limbs slender, 4 toes on front feet, 5 toes on hind feet. Costal grooves 14. Tongue mounted on a central pedicel, with unattached edges. Vomerine teeth separated from parasphenoid patches. General color yellowish, with a broad median pale stripe along the dorsum and upper surface of tail. This light dorsal band bordered on each side by a narrow brownish-black stripe. Sides below the dark stripes brown and yellow mottled. Belly yellowish. Adults slightly less than 4 inches in total length.

General Distribution.—The southeastern states.

Florida Range.—Northern and western Florida, southward through the Gulf Hammock region to Dixie County.

Habitat.—In and near spring-runs and lime-rock streams; river swamps; under rocks and logs.

Eurycea longicauda guttolineata (Holbrook)
Three-lined Salamander *(Plate 34)*

General Appearance.—A long, slender, yellowish salamander with 3 dark lines down the back.

Distinguishing Characters.—Naso-labial grooves present; 5 toes on hind feet; a black mid-dorsal stripe; vomerine teeth not continuous with parasphenoid teeth; tongue with a central pedicel and free edges all around.

Description.—Head widest behind the eyes, its sides gently converging posteriorly. Eyes large and protuberant. Snout slightly rounded; naso-labial grooves present. Body somewhat flattened above and below. Tail long and slender, tapering to a slender tip; no fins on tail. Legs moderately stout, 4 toes on front feet, 5 toes on hind feet. Toes of hind feet slightly webbed at base. Costal grooves 14. Tongue mounted on a central pedicel, its edges completely free. Vomerine teeth usually separated from the parasphenoid teeth. Ground color yellowish with a bold mid-dorsal dark stripe of deep brown or black from the top of the head to the base of the tail and a similar stripe on each side, originating behind the eye and running posteriorly, parallel to the mid-dorsal stripe, to the tip of the tail. Belly and lower surfaces of the legs and tail heavily mottled on a yellowish background. Large adults sometimes exceed 7 inches in total length.

General Distribution.—Virginia to Tennessee and Louisiana.

Florida Range.—The western panhandle as far east as Leon County.

Habitat.—Low hammocks, gum swamps, and ravines; usually under logs or in crevices.

Pseudotriton montanus floridanus Netting and Goin
Rusty Mud Salamander (Plate 35)

General Appearance.—A dark, reddish-brown salamander with an orange to red belly.

Distinguishing Characters.—Dorsum rusty or dark red; belly with scattered, round, dark spots on an orange or reddish background. Naso-labial groove present. Costal grooves 17-18.

Description.—Head and body moderate. Head widest just behind the eyes, tapering slightly to a rounded snout. Naso-labial grooves present. Eyes of moderate size, slightly protuberant. Body nearly circular in cross section, a faint depression along the mid-ventral line. Tail shorter than head and body. Tail laterally compressed, with a dorsal fin on the posterior half and a ventral fin on the posterior third. Legs stout, 4 toes on fore feet and 5 toes on hind feet. Toes of hind foot minutely webbed. Costal grooves 18, rarely 17. Vomerine and parasphenoid teeth in continuous series. Tongue nearly circular, attached by a central pedicel. Color above a rusty brown, mottled slightly with darker areas. A series of short dashlike marks, somewhat pinkish in color, extending along the side between the limbs. Venter orange-buff to red with scattered, small, round, dark spots. Attains a length of nearly 5 inches but averages smaller.

General Distribution.—Southern Georgia and northern Florida.

Florida Range.—Westward to Jackson County and southward to Seminole County.

Habitat.—Seepage areas, particularly those leading from low places in pine woods; bogs with sphagnum or begonias.

Pseudotriton montanus flavissimus Hallowell
Gulf Coast Red Salamander (Plate 35)

General Appearance.—An orange or orange-red salamander with scattered, small, round, dark spots.

Distinguishing Characters.—Naso-labial grooves; 16-18 costal grooves; orange or pale red in color with scattered, small, black dots both above and below.

Description.—Head and body moderate. Head widest just behind the eyes, tapering gently to a buntly rounded snout. Naso-labial grooves present. Eyes of moderate size, slightly protuberant. Body nearly circular in cross section, slightly compressed ventrally. Tail shorter than head and body. Tail laterally compressed, with an indistinct dorsal fin posteriorly. Legs short and moderately stout, 4 toes on fore limbs, 5 toes on hind limbs. Toes of hind feet minutely webbed. Costal grooves 16-18, generally 17-18 in Florida specimens. Vomerine and parasphenoid teeth in continuous series. Tongue nearly circular, attached by a central pedicel. Color ranging from salmon or orange to pale red, slightly paler below than above. Dorsum, tail, and (usually) venter with scattered, small, rounded, dark spots. Adults range in length from 3 to 4 inches.

General Distribution.—The Southeast from South Carolina to Louisiana, except in the Florida peninsula.

Florida Range.—The western panhandle.

Habitat.—Probably bogs and seepage areas and the borders of small streams.

Pseudotriton ruber vioscai Bishop
Viosca's Red Salamander *(Plate 34)*

General Appearance.—A stout-bodied, rusty brown, mottled salamander, with a speckled belly.

Distinguishing Characters.—Naso-labial grooves present; dorsum rusty or dark red with numerous coalescing black spots, venter paler but heavily flecked. Costal grooves usually 16.

Description.—Head and body stout. Head widest at angle of jaws, the sides nearly parallel posterior to this point. Anterior to the eyes the sides of the head converge abruptly to a bluntly rounded snout. Naso-labial grooves present. Eye moderate in size, protuberant. Body stout, nearly circular in cross section with a shallow mid-dorsal depression. Tail shorter than head and body, broadly oval in cross section at base, strongly compressed posteriorly. Legs stout, 4 toes on fore feet, 5 toes on hind feet. Costal grooves 15-16. Vomerine and parasphenoid teeth in continuous series. Tongue circular, attached by central pedicel. Ground color rusty brown above, somewhat paler below. Above, this ground color is overlain by numerous rather large dark spots, a few of which may tend to flow together. Ventrally on both the body and tail there are numerous tiny brown spots and specks. Adults average about 5 inches in total length.

General Distribution.—The Gulf Coast area from Louisiana to Georgia.

Florida Range.—The western panhandle.

Habitat.—Ravines and river valleys, under logs or debris.

Desmognathus fuscus fuscus (Rafinesque)
Common Dusky Salamander

General Appearance.—A rather small, brownish salamander with a light streak from the eye to the angle of the jaw.

Distinguishing Characters.—Naso-labial grooves present; a distinct light line from the eye to the angle of the jaw; belly pale, lightly mottled.

Description.—Head and body moderately stout. Adult males generally with the head somewhat swollen behind the angles of the jaws. Sides of head curving smoothly from the angles of the jaws to the rounded snout. Eyes moderately large and somewhat protuberant. Naso-labial grooves present. Body rounded in cross section with a shallow mid-dorsal depression. Tail triagonal in cross section at base, tapering to a slender tip; sharply keeled above posteriorly. Legs relatively stout, 4 toes on fore feet, 5 toes on hind feet. Costal grooves generally 14. Vomerine teeth separated from the parasphenoid teeth; vomerines usually absent in adult males. Tongue attached in front, free at the sides and behind. Color variable but ground color usually yellowish-brown to dark brown, venter much paler and usually lightly but definitely mottled. A light streak runs from the eye to the angle of the jaw on each side of the head. Florida specimens are generally less than 4 inches in length.

General Distribution.—The eastern United States from Maine to Florida.

Florida Range.—The Apalachicola River basin.

Habitat.—The cool ravines of the Apalachicola River Valley; under logs and sticks near the water's edge.

Desmognathus fuscus auriculatus (Holbrook)
Southern Dusky Salamander *(Plate 33)*

General Appearance.—A rather small, brownish to blackish salamander with a light streak from the eye to the angle of the jaws.

Distinguishing Characters.—Naso-labial grooves present; a light line from the eye to the angle of the jaw; belly dark, throat region not much lighter than rest of belly; tail about ½ of total length.

Description.—Head and body moderately stout. Adult males generally with the head somewhat swollen behind the angles of the jaws. Sides of head curving smoothly from the angles of the jaws to the rounded snout. Eyes large, protuberant. Naso-labial grooves present.

Body rounded in cross section with a shallow mid-dorsal depression. Tail triagonal in cross section at base, tapering to a slender tip; sharply keeled above posteriorly. Tail equal or nearly equal to ½ the total length. Legs relatively stout, 4 toes on fore feet, 5 toes on hind feet. Costal grooves generally 14. Vomerine teeth separated from the parasphenoid teeth, vomerines usually absent in adult males. Tongue attached in front, free at the sides and behind. Ground color dark brown or black; venter generally black with light stippling. A light streak from the eye to the angle of the jaw on each side of the head. Adult length about 4 inches.

General Distribution.—From Dismal Swamp, Virginia, southward to Alachua County, Florida.

Florida Range.—Westward to Apalachicola River and southward to Alachua County.

Habitat.—Swamps, muddy shores, and wet places generally; under logs and sticks.

Desmognathus fuscus brimleyorum Stejneger
Brimley's Dusky Salamander

General Appearance.—A rather small, brownish salamander with a light streak from the eye to the angle of the jaw.

Distinguishing Characters.—Naso-labial grooves; a light line from the eye to the angle of the jaw; belly uniformly pale, not mottled.

Description.—Head and body rather stout. Adult males with the head somewhat swollen behind the angles of the jaws. Sides of head curving smoothly from the angles of the jaws to the rounded snout. Body rounded in cross section with a shallow mid-dorsal depression. Tail stout, triagonal in cross section at base, tapering to a slender tip; sharply keeled above posteriorly. Legs relatively stout, 4 toes on fore feet, 5 toes on hind feet. Costal grooves generally 14. Vomerine teeth separated from the parasphenoid teeth; vomerine teeth usually absent in adult males. Tongue attached in front, free at the sides and behind. Color variable, but dorsal ground color some shade of brown, belly much paler and uniform rather than mottled. Florida specimens average about 4 inches in total length.

General Distribution.—The Mississippi Valley.

Florida Range.—The western panhandle west of the Apalachicola River Valley.

Habitat.—Under logs or sticks near water.

Demognathus fuscus carri Neill
Carr's Dusky Salamander

General Appearance.—A small, blackish salamander with a light streak from the eye to the angle of the jaw.

Distinguishing Characters.—Naso-labial groove; a light streak from the eye to the angle of the jaw; belly light to dark but throat region invariably pale; tail less than ½ of total length.

Description.—Head and body moderate in stoutness. Adult males generally with the head somewhat swollen behind the angles of the jaws. Sides of head curving smoothly from the angles of the jaws to the rounded snout. Eyes moderately large and somewhat protuberant. Naso-labial grooves present. Body rounded in cross section with a shallow mid-dorsal depression. Tail triagonal in cross section at base, tapering to a slender tip; sharply keeled above posteriorly. Tail definitely less than ½ the total length. Legs relatively stout, 4 toes on fore feet, 5 toes on hind feet. Costal grooves generally 14. Vomerine teeth separated from the parasphenoid teeth; vomerine teeth usually absent in adult males. Tongue attached in front, free at the sides and behind. Color variable, but dorsal ground color usually very dark brown to black; coloration of venter variable, but lighter anteriorly than posteriorly. Gular region always light. Adult size generally slightly under 3 inches.

General Distribution.—Restricted to Florida.

Florida Range.—The peninsula from Putnam to Hillsborough Counties.

Habitat.—Under logs and sticks around wet places, particularly near springs and spring-runs.

Siren intermedia intermedia Le Conte
Lesser Siren *(Plate 35)*

General Appearance.—A large, eel-shaped salamander with external gills, 2 tiny front legs and no hind legs.

Distinguishing Characters.—Only front legs present, each with 4 toes; 31-34 costal grooves along the sides between legs and anus.

Description.—Head elongate, the sides nearly straight but converging to the broadly rounded snout. Eyes small, about halfway between tip of snout and base of first gill. Mouth crescent-shaped, subterminal in position. External gills conspicuous, slightly above and anterior to the legs. Three gill slits. Legs short and stout, 4 toes on each foot, the third the longest. Body ovate in cross section, generally not quite so wide as the head. Shallow mid-dorsal, mid-ventral, and lateral depressions along the body. Tail compressed, with definite fins above and below, tapering to a pointed tip. Costal grooves 31-34, generally 32. Color dark above, slightly lighter below. Usually with a pattern of minute dark dots sprinkled on the back, sides, and tail. Adults usually between 8 and 12 inches in length.

General Distribution.—Coastal lowlands from South Carolina to Louisiana.

Florida Range.—All of northern and western Florida, southward to Pasco County.

Habitat.—Ponds and swampy areas, particularly in pine flatwoods.

Siren lacertina Linnaeus
Great Siren

General Appearance.—A large, eel-shaped salamander with external gills, 2 small front legs and no hind legs.

Distinguishing Characters.—Front legs only, each with 4 toes; 38 costal grooves along the sides between legs and anus.

Description.—Head elongate, the sides nearly straight but converging to the bluntly rounded snout. Eyes small, much closer to tip of snout than to base of first gill. Mouth crescent-shaped, subterminal in position. External gills conspicuous, slightly above and anterior to the legs. Three gill slits. Legs short and stout, 4 toes on each foot, the third the longest. Body oval in cross section, generally slightly wider than the head. A shallow lateral depression along each side from the leg to a point above the anus. Tail compressed, with definite fins above and below posteriorly; tapering to broadly rounded tip. Costal grooves generally 38. Color dark, with a series of yellowish dashes along the side and often with indistinct dark dots or mottlings above. Venter slightly paler than the back, with numerous light flecks. Attains a length of 3 feet, but adults generally average smaller.

General Distribution.—From the District of Columbia southward to the Everglades of Florida.

Florida Range.—Throughout the state east of the Apalachicola River.

Habitat.—Hyacinth-covered lakes, marshes, rivers, and ditches.

Pseudobranchus striatus axanthus Netting and Goin
Narrow-striped Siren *(Plate 35)*

General Appearance.—An eel-shaped salamander about the size of a pencil, with external gills, 2 little front legs and no hind legs.

Distinguishing Characters.—Each of the single pair of legs with 3 toes; about 35 costal grooves along the sides between the legs and anus; snout blunt-tipped; without bright yellow or orange stripes.

Description.—Head elongate, the sides nearly straight but converging gently to a broad, blunt snout. Eyes small, much nearer tip of snout than base of gills. Mouth crescent-shaped, subterminal in position. External gills conspicuous, slightly above and anterior to the legs. A single gill opening present. Legs short and slender, 3 toes on each foot, the middle toe the longest. Body oval in cross section, about as wide as head. Tail compressed, with a low fin present on posterior third of tail; tip of tail pointed. Costal grooves along side between leg and anus 34 to 36, usually 35. Ground color rather somber tones of gray, somewhat darker above than below. Marked with a lateral stripe of pearl gray, a slightly darker dorsolateral stripe and sometimes with an indistinct mid-dorsal stripe. Maximum length about 8 inches.

General Distribution.—Extreme southern Georgia and the Florida peninsula.

Florida Range.—The peninsula from Okefinokee Swamp southward to Lake Okeechobee, except the Gulf Hammock region along the West Coast.

Habitat.—Marshes, lakes, and ditches, especially those with water hyacinths.

Note.—Since the manuscript was completed, Schwartz (Nat. Hist. Misc., No. 115, 1952) has described *Pseudobranchus s. belli* from Dade County, Florida. It differs from *P. s. axanthus* in having a narrower head, distinct, buffy lateral stripes, and an average of only $31\frac{1}{2}$ costal grooves.

Pseudobranchus striatus spheniscus Goin and Crenshaw
Narrow-headed Striped Siren

General Appearance.—An eel-shaped salamander, smaller than a pencil, with external gills, 2 little front legs and no hind legs.

Distinguishing Characters.—Each of the single pair of legs with 3 toes, about 34 costal grooves along sides between legs and anus; snout sharply pointed; marked with tannish-brown to yellowish-gray stripes.

Description.—Head elongate, the sides nearly straight but converging rapidly to a sharply pointed snout. Eyes small, much nearer tip of snout than base of gills. Mouth crescent-shaped, subterminal in position. External gills conspicuous, slightly above and anterior to the legs. A single gill opening. Legs short and slender, 3 toes on each foot, the middle toe the longest. Body nearly circular in cross section, wider than the head. Tail compressed, low tail fins present on posterior third of tail; tip of tail pointed. Costal grooves along side between leg and anus usually 34. Ground color of dorsum brownish, venter somewhat lighter. Lateral and dorsolateral light stripes tannish-brown, not sharply distinct from ground color. Mid-dorsal stripe lacking or very inconspicuous. Maximum length about 6 inches.

General Distribution.—Southwestern Georgia and northern Florida.

Florida Range.—The northern portion of the state between Baker County on the east and Gulf and Leon counties on the west.

Habitat.—Low places and ponds in pine flatwoods.

Pseudobranchus striatus lustricolus Neill
Gulf Hammock Striped Siren

General Appearance.—An eel-shaped salamander about the size of a pencil, with external gills, 2 little front legs and no hind legs.

Distinguishing Characters.—Each of the single pair of legs with 3 toes, about 34 costal grooves along the sides of the body between the legs and anus; snout blunt tipped; marked with bright yellow or orange stripes.

Description.—Head elongate, the sides nearly straight but converging gently to a broad blunt snout. Eyes small, nearer to tip of snout than to base of gills. Mouth crescent-shaped, subterminal in position. External gills conspicuous, slightly above and anterior to the legs. A single gill opening. Legs short and slender, 3 toes on each foot, the middle toe the longest. Body oval in cross section. Body about as wide as head. Tail compressed, low tail fins present on posterior third of tail. Tip of tail pointed. Costal grooves along side between leg and anus usually 34. Dorsal ground color gray to chocolate-brown, venter slightly lighter. Three indistinct stripes on dorsum, a very distinct dorsolateral stripe of yellow, yellowish-tan, or orange, and a lateral stripe of yellowish or silvery-white. Maximum length about 8 inches.

General Distribution.—Restricted to Florida.

Florida Range.—The Gulf Hammock area along the upper West Coast from about Citrus County to Taylor County.

Habitat.—Low wet places in Gulf Hammock.

Scaphiopus holbrooki holbrooki (Harlan)
Common Spadefoot *(Plate 36)*

General Appearance.—A squat, brownish, big-eyed toad.

Distinguishing Characters.—Parotoid gland conspicuous, elevated, and rounded rather than oblong; pupil of eye vertical; color dark brown or olive.

Description.—Head about as broad as body, snout rounded. Eyes protuberant, with pupils vertical; tympanum much smaller than the eye. Rounded parotoid glands posterior to but not in contact with the eyes. Dorsum somewhat rugose. Fore limbs short and stout; fingers very slightly webbed. Hind limbs stout; toes fully webbed. A sharp, black, horny structure, the "spade," present on the inner margin of the inner toe. Belly skin smooth with scattered pustules. Male with subgular vocal sac. Teeth present on upper jaw, although poorly developed. Tongue oval, not notched behind. Two small rounded patches of vomerine teeth between the internal nares. Ground color brownish-tan to dirty brown with a dorsal light stripe running from behind the eye to the vent on each side; these stripes tannish to lemon-yellow in color. Belly pale. Breeding voice a snarling nasal *naarh* repeated at intervals. Adults 2-3 inches in snout-to-vent length.

General Distribution.—The eastern United States from Massachusetts and Indiana southward to Texas and Florida.

Florida Range.—State-wide except for extreme southern Florida and the Keys.

Habitat.—A burrowing toad of the hammock lands.

Scaphiopus holbrooki albus Garman
Key West Spadefoot

General Appearance.—A squat, pale-colored, big-eyed toad.

Distinguishing Characters.—Parotoid glands conspicuous, elevated, and rounded rather than oblong; pupil of eye vertical; ground color a pale dirty gray to nearly white.

Description.—Head about as broad as body, snout rounded. Eyes protuberant, with vertical pupils; tympanum smaller than eye. Rounded parotoid glands posterior to but not in contact with eyes.

Dorsum somewhat rugose. Fore limbs short and stout; fingers very slightly webbed. Hind limbs short and stout, toes fully webbed. A sharp, black, horny digging structure present on the inner margin of the inner toe. Belly skin smooth with scattered pustules. Male with subgular vocal sac. Teeth present on upper jaw, but poorly developed. Tongue oval, not notched behind. Two small rounded patches of vomerine teeth between the internal nares. Ground color tan to pale dirty gray; sometimes nearly white. Stripes from eye to vent on each side of dorsum dirty yellow. Breeding voice a snarling nasal *naarh* repeated several times.

General Distribution.—Restricted to Florida.

Florida Range.—Extreme southern Florida and the Keys.

Habitat.—Burrowing in wooded places, especially in open hammocks.

Bufo quercicus Holbrook
Oak Toad *(Plate 36)*

General Appearance.—A tiny toad, usually with a thin light line down the middle of the back.

Distinguishing Characters.—Parotoid glands diverging posteriorly rather than parallel; cranial crests inconspicuous; upper jaw toothless; adult size less than 1½ inches.

Description.—Head about as broad as body, snout broadly obtuse. Eyes moderate in size, protuberant, pupil horizontal. Tympanum small, inconspicuous. Parotoid glands elongate, diverging posteriorly, finely spinose. Posterior ends of parotoids connected by a transverse series of raised warts. Dorsum finely rugose. Fore limbs short, fingers not webbed. Hind limbs shorter than snout-to-vent length, somewhat weak. Toes short, webbed for about ⅓ their length. Skin of belly somewhat granular, but not warty. Male with a dark subgular pouch. Mouth entirely toothless. Tongue elongate, free behind. Ground color, grayish, reddish, or blackish, with a light line generally along dorsum from tip of snout to anus; 3 to 5 pairs of unconnected dark blotches on each side of light line along back. Belly dirty white; throat of male much darker. Breeding voice a single, high-pitched whistle with a slight descending inflection. The smallest of the toads, breeding at ¾-1¼ inches in length.

General Distribution.—North Carolina to Louisiana.

Florida Range.—State-wide.

Habitat.—Pine flatwoods and oak scrub.

Bufo terrestris terrestris (Bonnaterre)
Southern Toad

General Appearance.—A fair sized, fat toad, with prominent parotoid glands and head crests.

Distinguishing Characters.—Cranial crests terminating in pronounced knobs in the adults; parotoid glands well-separated from the cranial crests or connected only by spurs extending from the crests.

Description.—Head broad, snout rounded. Eyes protuberant, pupils horizontal. Tympanum about ½ the diameter of the eye. Parotoid glands elongate, parallel, well-separated from cranial crests or connected only by a spur from the latter. Cranial crest very prominent, terminating posteriorly in a prominent knob in adults. Dorsum very warty. Fore limbs short, fingers unwebbed; hind limbs short, toes about ⅓ webbed. Skin of belly granular. Male with a dark subgular pouch. Mouth entirely toothless. Tongue about twice as long as wide, free posteriorly. Ground color variable, but generally some shade of gray, red, or brown. Belly whitish, with dark spots in the pectoral region. Breeding call a melodious trill continued for several seconds. Length up to 3¾ inches (snout-to-vent).

General Distribution.—North Carolina to Louisiana.

Florida Range.—State-wide.

Habitat.—Widely distributed, but perhaps most abundant in dry, rather open woods, congregating about houses and artificial lights.

Bufo woodhousei fowleri Hinckley
Fowler's Toad

General Appearance.—A short, fat toad with prominent parotoid glands and head crests.

Distinguishing Characters.—Cranial crests not terminating in pronounced knobs in the adults; parotoid glands in contact with the posterior margins of the cranial crests.

Description.—Head broad, snout more pointed than rounded. Eyes protuberant, pupils horizontal. Tympanum ½ or slightly less than ½ the diameter of the eye. Parotoid glands elongate, parallel, and in direct contact with the cranial crests. Cranial crests prominent but not terminating in rounded knobs in adults. Back very warty. Fore limbs short, fingers not webbed; hind limbs longer than snout-to-vent length; toes about ⅓ webbed. Skin of belly granular. Male with a dark subgular pouch. Mouth entirely toothless. Tongue about twice as long as wide, posterior half the widest; free posteriorly. Ground color grayish with 2 parallel series of darker spots along each side of back. Belly gray-buff. Breeding call a brief droning burr, not a musical trill. Size up to about 3 inches in Florida specimens.

General Distribution.—Eastern United States.

Florida Range.—The western portion of the western panhandle.

Habitat.—Woods or open country in deep sand areas.

Acris gryllus gryllus (Le Conte)
Common Cricket Frog

General Appearance.—A tiny, sharp-headed, very active frog with a dark stripe down the back of the thigh.

Distinguishing Characters.—Back of thigh with a single distinct dark stripe; a few warts generally present around the anus; length of adult ¾ inch or slightly more.

Description.—Head narrow, snout rather pointed. Eye moderate, not particularly protuberant. Tympanum small and inconspicuous. Dorsum somewhat rugose, but not warty. Fore limbs slender, fingers not webbed. Hind limbs long and slender, toes webbed, webbing continuing as a very narrow margin to the tip of the longest toe. Skin of belly smooth anteriorly, slightly granular posteriorly and beneath the thighs. A few scattered wartlike pustules around the anus. Male with a darkened subgular pouch. Vomerine teeth in 2 tiny, rounded patches between the internal nares. Tongue somewhat heart-shaped, free behind and on the sides. Ground color very variable; generally grayish, brownish, or blackish. A mid-dorsal stripe, from between the eyes to the vent, is quite variable in color but usually a paler tone than the ground color. Pattern on rear portion of thighs composed of a broad black stripe on a white background; this white background sharply defined above and below. Breeding voice a metallic *ik*, repeated several times in succession. Adult length ¾ inch or a little more.

General Distribution.—Along the coastal plain from Dismal Swamp, Virginia, to Louisiana.

Florida Range.—The western panhandle from Leon County westward.

Habitat.—The margins of lakes, ponds, and streams, and all sorts of wet places.

Acris gryllus dorsalis (Harlan)
Florida Cricket Frog *(Plate 36)*

General Appearance.—A tiny, active, sharp-headed frog with dark stripes along the back of the thigh. Good fish bait.

Distinguishing Characters.—Back of thigh with two distinct dark stripes; no warty pustules around the anus; adult size ¾ inch or less.

Description.—Head narrow, snout rather pointed. Eyes moderate in size, not particularly protuberant. Tympanum small and inconspicuous. Dorsum somewhat rugose, but not warty. Fore limbs slender, fingers not webbed; hind limbs long and slender, toes webbed, the webbing continuing as a narrow margin to the tip of the longest toe. Skin of belly smooth anteriorly, slightly granular posteriorly and beneath the thighs. No warty pustules about the anus. Male with a dark subgular pouch. Vomerine teeth in 2 tiny, rounded patches between the internal nares. Tongue somewhat heart-shaped, free behind and on the sides. Ground color very variable; but generally grayish, brownish, or blackish. A stripe originates on the posterior margin of each eye, fuses with its fellow from the opposite side on the posterior margin of the head and continues along the mid-dorsal line as a broad light band, sometimes greenish, sometimes reddish. Two distinct dark stripes along the posterior margin of thigh on a white background. This white background sharply delimited above but not below. Breeding voice a metallic *ik,* repeated several times. Adult length ¾ inches or less.

General Distribution.—Okefinokee Swamp to southern Florida.

Florida Range.—State-wide, except the western panhandle.

Habitat.—Practically any wet place.

Pseudacris nigrita nigrita (Le Conte)
Black Chorus Frog *(Plate 36)*

General Appearance.—A small, narrow, rough frog about an inch long with 3 dark stripes on the back.

Distinguishing Characters.—Back with dark spots arranged in 3 irregular rows; no triangular or transverse mark between the eyes; an unbroken whitish maxillary stripe; skin of dorsum rough.

Description.—Head slender, snout pointed. Eye prominent, protuberant. Tympanum inconspicuous, less than ½ the diameter of the eye. Body slender. Dorsum rough and warty. Fore limb slender; fingers slender and delicate, without pronounced digital pads; hind limbs long and slender; toes thin and delicate, slightly webbed at base, with inconspicuous digital pads at tips. Belly granular. Male with subgular pouch. Skin on throat of male slightly folded. Two rounded patches of vomerine teeth between the internal nares. Tongue elongate ovoid, free behind. Ground color, gray, olive, or blackish, with 3 longitudinal rows of dark spots down the back. Upper surface of hind limbs barred. Belly whitish. Throat region of male often yellowish-gray. Light line along margin of upper jaw unbroken. Breeding voice, a series of 4 or 5 rapidly repeated, nonmusical, staccato "clicks," "pips," or "ticks," voiced with a rising cadence: *tick-tick-tick-tick, tick-tick-tick-tick...*, and repeated each second or so. Snout-to-vent length of adult about an inch.

General Distribution.—The coastal plain from North Carolina to Florida.

Florida Range.—Northern Florida east of the Apalachicola River basin and southward to Alachua County.

Habitat.—Pine flatwoods and around grassy ponds.

Pseudacris nigrita verrucosa (Cope)
Florida Chorus Frog

General Appearance.—A small, narrow, rough frog about an inch in length, with 3 rows of dark spots down the back.

Distinguishing Characters.—Back with dark spots arranged in 3 irregular rows; no triangular or transverse mark between the eyes; light maxillary stripe interrupted at intervals with darker markings; back rough.

Description.—Head slender, snout pointed. Eyes prominent, protuberant. Tympanum inconspicuous, less than $\frac{1}{2}$ the diameter of the eye. Body slender. Dorsum rough and warty. Fore limbs slender; fingers thin and delicate, without pronounced digital pads. Hind limbs long and slim; toes thin and delicate, slightly webbed at base, with very inconspicuous digital pads at tips. Belly granular. Male with subgular pouch. Skin on throat of male slightly folded. Two rounded patches of vomerine teeth between the internal nares. Tongue elongate ovoid, free behind. Ground color gray, olive, or blackish, with 3 longitudinal rows of dark spots down the back. Upper surfaces of hind limbs barred. Belly whitish; throat region of male yellowish-gray. Light line along margin of upper jaw interrupted. Breeding voice like that of *n. nigrita* with the tempo perhaps somewhat slower. Snout-to-vent length of adults about an inch.

General Distribution.—Restricted to Florida.

Florida Range.—From the region of Alachua County southward throughout the peninsula.

Habitat.—Pine flatwoods and around grassy ponds.

Pseudacris feriarum (Baird)
Eastern Chorus Frog

General Appearance.—A small, often pinkish, frog about an inch long, with 3 dark stripes down its back.

Distinguishing Characters.—Back with 3 longitudinal stripes; a dark triangular or transverse mark between the eyes; ground color often pinkish or tannish.

Description.—Head slender, snout pointed. Eyes prominent, protuberant. Tympanum inconspicuous, less than ½ the diameter of the eye. Body slim. Dorsum rough and warty. Fore limbs slender; fingers slender and delicate, without pronounced digital pads. Hind limbs long and weak; toes thin and delicate, slightly webbed at base, with inconspicuous digital pads at tips. Belly granular. Male with subgular pouch. Skin on throat of male slightly folded. Two rounded patches of vomerine teeth between the internal nares. Tongue elongate ovoid, free behind. Ground color gray, tannish, or pinkish, with 3 longitudinal dark stripes down the back. Upper surfaces of hind limbs barred. Belly whitish; throat region of male yellowish-gray. Breeding voice an often repeated, very rapidly voiced, burring trill: *i-i-i-i-k, i-i-i-i-k, i-i-i-i-k,* perhaps representing the "ticks" of *nigrita* run together. Snout-to-vent length of adults about an inch.

General Distribution.—Eastern United States.

Florida Range.—Known only from Liberty and Gadsden counties.

Habitat.—River and creek flood plains and swamps.

Pseudacris ornata (Holbrook)
Ornate Chorus Frog *(Plate 37)*

General Appearance.—A small, handsome, reddish-brown frog, 1-1¼ inches in length, with about 3 very dark marks along each side.

Distinguishing Characters.—Toes but slightly webbed; hind surface of thigh without longitudinal stripes; muzzle rounded in profile; skin smooth; a very dark stripe over each eye, another along each side, and a rounded spot just anterior to the groin.

Description.—Head relatively broad, snout rounded. Eye prominent, protuberant. Tympanum small and inconspicuous. Body moderately stout; back smooth. Fore limbs fairly stout, fingers pointed, without pronounced digital pads; hind limbs moderately long and slender, toes thin, with only a trace of a web at the base, and with no conspicuous digital pads. Belly granular. Male with subgular pouch. Skin on throat of male slightly folded. Two rounded patches of vomerine teeth between the internal nares. Tongue elongate ovoid, free behind. Ground color above chestnut-brown. The most conspicuous markings are chocolate-brown to black markings along each side as follows: a stripe from the snout through the eye and tympanum to above the shoulder; a stripe about midway of the body; a short stripe or rounded spot just anterior to the groin. The belly is dirty white with spotting in the pectoral region. The throat of males is yellowish to olive. Breeding voice a sharp, short, shrill, whistled single note repeated 60-80 times per minute. Adult size in snout-to-vent length 1-1¼ inches.

General Distribution.—The southeastern Coastal Plain from North Carolina to Alabama.

Florida Range.—Southward to Lake County and westward to Leon County.

Habitat.—Pine flatwoods and mixed hammocks.

Hyla ocularis Bosc and Daudin
Little Grass Frog *(Plate 37)*

General Appearance.—A tiny, tan frog with a dark stripe on the side of the head.

Distinguishing Characters.—Toes slightly webbed; tympanum distinct, hind surface of thigh without longitudinal stripes; muzzle truncate in profile; adults less than ¾ inch long.

Description.—Head slender, snout pointed, truncate in lateral profile. Eyes prominent, slightly protuberant. Tympanum inconspicuous. Body slender. Dorsum with faint scattered rugosities. Fore limbs slender; fingers thin, without webs but with small digital pads. Hind limbs and toes slender, slightly webbed at base, with small but distinct digital pads. Belly slightly granular. Male with subgular pouch. Skin on throat of male slightly folded. Two rounded patches of vomerine teeth between the internal nares. Tongue elongate, ovoid, free behind. Ground color tannish, pinkish, or grayish. Usually with a distinct brown stripe from the snout, through the eye, and over the shoulder on each side. Breeding voice a high, shrill, cricket-like chirp, something like *set-see, set-see.* The call is so high in pitch that it is difficult for some people to hear. Adult length less than ¾ inch; the smallest North American frog.

General Distribution.—The coastal plain from North Carolina to Texas.

Florida Range.—State-wide.

Habitat.—Moist, grassy places, the grassy edges of cypress ponds in particular.

Hyla phaeocrypta phaeocrypta Cope
Bird-voiced Tree Frog

General Appearance.—A medium-sized, gray tree frog with lichen-like, dark marks on the back.

Distinguishing Characters.—Tympanum a third the diameter of the eye or less; skin glandular but not warty; fingers with webs; fingers and toes with large, conspicuous digital pads; length of adult greater than ¾ inch.

Description.—Head short, broader than long. Muzzle truncate in profile. Eyes large and protuberant. Tympanum a third the diameter of eye or less. Body fairly slender. Dorsum smooth, without warts or pustulations. Forelimbs somewhat stout. Fingers with distinct digital disks, webbed at base. Hind limbs moderately stout; toes with distinct digital disks; fully webbed. Belly somewhat granular. Male with subgular pouch. Skin on throat of male slightly folded. Two rounded patches of vomerine teeth between the internal nares. Tongue orbicular, slightly notched behind. Ground color gray or olive-gray with broad blotches of dark, lichen-like marks on the dorsum. Rear surface of thigh with spots or vermiculations of green. Belly white, throat dark in males. Breeding voice a rapidly repeated series of musically whistled, single, unslurred notes. Voice to some reminiscent of the red-bellied woodpecker, to others of young ducks. Adult size up to 1¾ inches.

General Distribution.—The Mississippi Valley and the Gulf Coast.

Florida Range.—The panhandle.

Habitat.—River and creek swamps.

Hyla cinerea cinerea (Schneider)
Green Tree Frog (*Plate* 38)

General Appearance.—A slim, long-legged, bright green tree frog, usually with a white line down the side.

Distinguishing Characters.—Light line along side straight and with definite borders; no dark bar between the eyes; fingers entirely free of webs; conspicuous disks on fingers and toes; adult size 1½-2½ inches.

Description.—Head as long as or slightly longer than broad. Muzzle rounded in profile. Eye moderately large and protuberant. Tympanum about ⅔ the diameter of the eye. Body rather slender with the sides nearly parallel. Dorsum smooth. Fore limbs slender, fingers without webs, terminating in conspicuous disks. Hind limbs slender, toes fully webbed, terminating in distinct disks. Belly somewhat granular. Male with subgular pouch. Skin on throat of male slightly folded. Two rounded patches of vomerine teeth between the internal nares. Tongue elongate oval, widest posteriorly, slightly notched behind. Color bright green above, whitish below. A distinct white line along the edge of the upper lip usually continuing without interruption over the shoulder and along the side. Throat of male dark. Individuals occasionally brown or dark olive-green instead of green. Scattered golden spots may occasionally be present on the back. Call a not unmelodious (but not bell-like) *quank, quank,* or yelplike note, repeated about once per second for varying intervals of time. These frogs call only around permanent bodies of water. Size 1½-2½ inches.

General Distribution.—Virginia to Texas and up the Mississippi Valley to southern Illinois.

Florida Range.—State-wide.

Habitat.—Low shrubs, particularly palmettos, most often near permanent water.

Hyla crucifer bartramiana Harper
Southern Spring Peeper (*Plate 38*)

General Appearance.—A small, tan tree frog with blotches of brown on its back.

Distinguishing Characters.—Dorsal blotches forming a more or less oblique cross; no spots on thighs; no light line along jaw; fingers entirely free of web; disks on toes conspicuous; adult length 1-1⅓ inches.

Description.—Head about as broad as long; muzzle somewhat pointed in profile. Eyes not large but somewhat protuberant. Tympanum ¼-⅓ the diameter of the eye. Body moderately stout, widest in the belly region. Dorsum smooth, without warts or pustulations. Fore limbs slender, fingers without webs, terminating in conspicuous disks. Hind limbs slender, toes about ⅓ webbed, terminating in conspicuous disks. Belly somewhat granular. Male with subgular pouch. Skin on throat of male slightly folded. Vomerine teeth in 2 rounded patches between internal nares. Tongue an elongate oval, slightly notched behind. Color tan or light brown above with darker brown markings, usually in the shape of an oblique cross on the back. Belly whitish or tinged with yellow. Throat of male dark. No distinct rounded yellow spots on the rear of the thighs. Voice a single, rather melodious, short whistle with a slight rising inflection; about two octaves above middle C. Adult length 1-1⅓ inches.

General Distribution.—Southern Georgia and northern Florida.

Florida Range.—Southward to Lake County, westward to Liberty County.

Habitat.—Hammock land in leaf mold or on low shrubs, calling about wooded pools.

Hyla femoralis Latreille
Pine-woods Tree Frog *(Plate 39)*

General Appearance.—A gray, medium-sized, rather slender tree frog with orange spots on the backs of the thighs.

Distinguishing Characters.—Hind surfaces of thighs with big yellow spots; dorsal blotches irregular; no light line along upper jaw; fingers entirely free of web.

Description.—Head about as broad as long. Muzzle rounded in profile. Eyes moderately large and protuberant. Tympanum about ½ the diameter of the eye. Body moderately slender, the sides nearly parallel. Dorsum smooth. Fore limbs slender. Fingers thin, without webs but with distinct digital disks. Hind limbs and toes slender, the latter webbed for about ½ their length, with distinct digital pads. Belly granular. Male with subgular pouch. Skin on throat of male slightly folded. Two rounded patches of vomerine teeth between the internal nares. Tongue broadly oval, slightly notched behind. Ground color gray to olive-gray with darker irregular blotches on the dorsum. Posterior margins of thighs with large, rounded, bright orange spots. Belly whitish. Throat of male dark. Breeding voice very like the clicking of a telegraph key. Length up to 1⅗ inches.

General Distribution.—The coastal lowlands from Dismal Swamp, Virginia, to Louisiana.

Florida Range.—The entire state north of the Okeechobee region.

Habitat.—Pine flatwoods.

Hyla gratiosa Le Conte
Bell Frog *(Plate 37)*

General Appearance.—A large, fat, handsome tree frog with a fancy color pattern.

Distinguishing Characters.—Tympanum nearly as large as eye; skin above with numerous tiny wartlike pustulations; fingers more or less webbed.

Description.—Head broader than long. Muzzle rounded in profile. Eyes large and protuberant. Tympanum about as large as eye. Body stout, widest in the belly region. Dorsum granular. Fore limbs moderately stout, fingers webbed at base, ending in conspicuous digital disks. Hind limbs rather slender, toes about ¾ webbed, with distinct digital disks. Belly granular. Male with subgular pouch. Skin on throat of male slightly folded. Two rounded patches of vomerine teeth between the internal nares. Tongue broadly rounded, slightly notched behind. Coloration very variable, but usually of bright shades of green or brown with a dorsal pattern of distinct rounded spots. Belly whitish; throat of male dark. Voice a melodious single note, bell-like at a distance. Adult length 2-2¾ inches.

General Distribution.—North Carolina to Louisiana.

Florida Range.—South to St. Lucie County, westward to Leon County.

Habitat.—Pine flatwoods.

Hyla squirella Latreille
Rain Frog *(Plate 38)*

General Appearance.—A variously, but not strikingly, marked tree frog, 1-1½ inches in length.

Distinguishing Characters.—Light line along side wavy and without definite borders; often with a dark bar between the eyes; fingers entirely free of web; conspicuous digital pads on fingers and toes; adult length 1-1½ inches.

Description.—Head about as broad as long. Muzzle truncate in profile. Eyes moderately large, protuberant. Tympanum about ⅓ the diameter of the eye. Body moderately slim, widest in the belly region. Dorsum smooth, without warts or pustulations. Fore limbs moderately stout. Fingers slender, entirely free of webs, with distinct digital disks. Hind limbs moderately slender. Toes thin, about ⅓ webbed, terminating in distinct digital disks. Belly granular. Male with subgular pouch.

Skin on throat of male slightly folded. Two rounded patches of vomerine teeth between the internal nares. Tongue ovate, slightly notched behind. Color very variable: brown, green, and either uniform or with dorsal blotches. Usually there is a white margin along the upper jaw, which continues over the arm and onto the side as a wavy white line without distinct margins, and there is often a dark bar between the eyes. Belly white, throat of the male darker. Voice, a rasping unmusical *waaaaak*. Length of adults 1-1½ inches.

General Distribution.—Virginia to Texas and up the Mississippi Valley to southern Indiana.

Florida Range.—Statewide.

Habitat.—Trees, particularly oaks and hollies, and about houses in drains and under eaves. Common about lighted windows at night.

Note.—This is one of the most difficult of the Florida tree frogs to define. If a tree frog cannot be identified definitely as another species, it is probably the rain frog.

Hyla versicolor versicolor Le Conte
Common Tree Frog

General Appearance.—A fat, warty-looking, gray mottled tree frog with yellow spots on the backs of the thighs.

Distinguishing Characters.—Dorsum with numerous, minute, warty granulations; fingers with webs at the base; disks on fingers and toes large and conspicuous; size greater than ¾ inch.

Description.—Head short, broader than long. Muzzle truncate in profile. Eyes moderately large and protuberant. Tympanum about ½ the diameter of the eye. Body stout, dorsum covered with numerous minute warty granulations. Fore limbs fairly stout. Fingers with distinct digital disks, webbed at base. Hind limbs moderately stout, the toes with distinct digital disks, fully webbed. Belly granular. Male with subgular pouch. Skin on throat of male slightly folded. Two rounded patches of vomerine teeth between the internal nares. Tongue ovoid, broadest behind, but little or not at all notched. Ground color pale gray with broad lichen-like marks of dark gray or black above. Rear of thighs with distinct dots or vermiculations of yellow. Belly whitish. Throat of male dark. Breeding voice a loud, resonant, uninflected trill of about a second's duration, given at the rate of 10-12 calls per half-minute. Adult length 1½-2¼ inches.

General Distribution.—The eastern half of the United States.

Florida Range.—Southward to Marion County, westward to Jackson County.

Habitat.—Low hardwood hammocks; swamps, bayheads, and river bottoms.

Hyla septentrionalis Boulenger
Cuban Tree Frog *(Plate 37)*

General Appearance.—A big, fairly rough-skinned tree frog with very large digital pads on the fingers.

Distinguishing Characters.—Warts on dorsum tiny and scattered; fingers with webs at the base; digital disks on fingers as large as the tympanum; skin on top of head fused to the skull.

Description.—Head large, broader than long. Muzzle rounded in profile. Eyes large and protuberant. Tympanum about ⅔ the diameter of the eye. Body stout, widest in the belly region. Dorsum with scattered tiny warts. Fore limbs moderately stout, fingers webbed at base, terminating in digital pads that are as large as the tympanum. Hind limbs somewhat slender, toes ⅔ webbed, terminating in broad distinct digital pads. Belly granular. Male with subgular vocal pouch. Skin on throat of male slightly folded. Skin on top of head solidly fused to skull. Vomerine teeth in a single series behind the internal nares. Tongue broader than long, not notched behind. A gray, green, or brown frog with longitudinal blotches on the back. Belly whitish, throat of male dark. The voice is a rasping snarl that has been likened to the noise made by an ungreased pulley. The males begin calling when quite small, and the range in pitch in a chorus is striking. Length up to 4 inches.

General Distribution.—Cuba, the Isle of Pines, and the Bahamas.

Florida Range.—Miami and the lower Keys.

Habitat.—Old cisterns and similar situations.

Eleutherodactylus ricordi planirostris (Cope)
Greenhouse Frog *(Plate 39)*

General Appearance.—A small, active, brownish frog an inch or less in length.

Distinguishing Characters.—Vomerine teeth in crescent-shaped, transverse series rather than in rounded patches.

Description.—Snout blunt, upper jaw projecting beyond lower. Eyes prominent, slightly protuberant. Tympanum inconspicuous, ⅓ to ⅔ diameter of eye. Head and body moderately slender. Dorsum smooth. Fore limbs and fingers slender, the latter unwebbed, ending in slightly expanded tips. Hind limbs moderately stout, toes slender, unwebbed, ending in slightly expanded tips. Belly somewhat granular. Vomerine teeth in 2 arched series extending laterally to the level of the outer margins of the internal nares. Tongue oval, free behind. There are 2 distinct color patterns in this species. In both the ground color is tannish brown. In one phase the pattern consists simply of mottlings of darker and lighter browns; in the other the pattern consists of 2 pale dorsal stripes on the brownish background. These stripes originate behind each eye and continue, without interruption, to the region of the groin. The belly is whitish, sometimes flecked with tiny brown marks. The breeding voice is a faint cheep repeated 1 to 4 times. Adult length less than 1 inch.

General Distribution.—Many of the islands in the West Indies. Introduced into Florida.

Florida Range.—Widely distributed in southern Florida, in the northern portion of the state restricted to populated areas.

Habitat.—Leaf mold, flower beds, and moist litter generally.

Rana capito Le Conte
Gopher Frog (Plate 40)

General Appearance.—A big-headed, short-bodied, pale frog with dark spots on the back.

Distinguishing Characters.—No digital pads; upper jaw with teeth; dorsolateral folds present, low and wide and usually not extending to the hips; spotted pattern above; head short and broad.

Description.—Head and body stout, head as broad as long. Muzzle sloping in profile. Tympanum not quite so large as the eye. Sides of body tapering abruptly to a very slender waist. A distinct dorsolateral fold originating behind each eye and continuing posteriorly $\frac{1}{2}$ to $\frac{2}{3}$ the distance to the hips; each of these folds is low and wide rather than high and narrow. Fore limbs stout, fingers not webbed and not terminating in digital disks. Hind limbs moderately slender; last 2 joints of longest toe and last joint of other toes unwebbed. Toes not ending in digital disks. Belly smooth. Vocal pouch of male a sausage-shaped sac at the angle of each jaw; not conspicuous except in calling frogs. Two rounded patches of vomerine teeth between the internal nares and maxillary teeth along the upper jaw. Tongue broadly ovate with 2 low lobes and a median notch behind. Color generally quite pale with numerous rounded brownish spots on the dorsum. Whitish below with flecks of brown in the throat region. Breeding voice a deep, resonant, snorelike sound. Length 2¾-4⅓ inches.

General Distribution.—North Carolina to Florida.

Florida Range.—North Florida and the peninsula.

Habitat.—The burrows of the gopher tortoise; thus, usually longleaf pine, turkey oak, or sand scrub terrain.

Rana catesbeiana Shaw
Bullfrog *(Plate 40)*

General Appearance.—A very large, dark mottled bullfrog.

Distinguishing Characters.—No digital pads; upper jaw with teeth; no dorsolateral folds; web not extending to the tip of the longest toe; chin light, with irregular and at times indistinct dark blotches.

Description.—Head and body stout. Muzzle broadly sloping in profile. Tympanum as large as or larger than the eye, rough in the center. Body broad, widest in the region of the belly. No dorsolateral folds. Dorsum smooth or slightly warty. Fore limbs stout, fingers not webbed, not terminating in digital pads. Hind limbs long and stout; toes fully webbed except for the terminal joint of the longest toe. Toes not terminating in digital pads. Belly smooth. Vocal pouches of male not apparent externally. Two rounded patches of vomerine teeth between the internal nares and maxillary teeth along the upper jaw. Tongue oval, with 2 lobes and a median notch posteriorly. Color moderately dark with indistinct mottlings above. Chin light, mottled with smoky gray. Breeding voice 2 consecutive sonorous bass notes. Adults up to about 7 inches in length.

General Distribution.—Native in the eastern United States; introduced throughout the West.

Florida Range.—North and west Florida, southward to Lake County.

Habitat.—Edges of ponds and lakes in hammock regions; creek and river swamps.

Rana clamitans Latreille
Bronze Frog *(Plate 39)*

General Appearance.—A moderate sized (3-inch) frog with uniform bronze coloration above.

Distinguishing Characters.—No digital pads; upper jaw with teeth; dorsolateral folds present; uniform bronze-colored above.

Description.—Head and body moderately stout, head slightly longer than wide. Muzzle sloping in profile. Tympanum about the size of the eye. Body with sides nearly parallel. A distinct dorsolateral fold originating behind each eye and continuing to the small of the back. Forelimbs moderately stout; fingers slightly webbed at base, without digital disks. Legs rather long. Toes slender, webbed to the next to the last joint of the longest toe, other toes webbed to tips. No digital pads on tips of toes. Belly smooth. Vocal pouches of males not apparent externally. Two rounded patches of vomerine teeth between the internal nares and maxillary teeth along upper jaw. Tongue ovate, with a pair of low lobes and a median notch posteriorly. Color above and on the sides bronzy, whitish below with spots and vermiculations of gray or black. Voice a single, low, explosive note (occasionally repeated 2 or 3 times in rapid succession), somewhat similar to the plucking of a string of a bass viol. Size up to 3 inches.

General Distribution.—The eastern half of the United States from Canada to the Gulf Coast.

Florida Range.—Southward to Lake County.

Habitat.—Wooded springs, seepage areas, and small streams, particularly in hammock regions.

Rana heckscheri Wright
River-swamp Frog *(Plate 40)*

General Appearance.—A large, very dark bullfrog.

Distinguishing Characters.—No digital pads; upper jaw with teeth; no dorsolateral folds; web not extending to the tip of the longest toe; chin and edge of lower jaw slate-colored or smoky with small, irregular light, nearly white, blotches.

Description.—Head and body stout. Muzzle broadly sloping in profile. Tympanum as large as or larger than the eye, rough in the center. Body broad, widest in the region of the belly. No dorsolateral folds. Dorsum smooth or somewhat warty. Fore limbs stout, fingers not webbed, not ending in digital pads. Hind limbs long and stout. Toes fully webbed except the last joint of the longest toe. Toes not ending in digital pads. Belly smooth. Vocal pouches of male not apparent externally. Two rounded patches of vomerine teeth between internal nares and maxillary teeth along the upper jaw. Color quite dark, with indistinct mottlings above; belly pattern a mottling of gray or smoky and light. Hind margin of thigh dark with mottlings of lighter color. Chin and edge of lower jaw smoky with small, irregular white blotches. Breeding voice an explosive snort or grunt. Adults up to 5 inches in length.

General Distribution.—Coastal lowlands from South Carolina to Mississippi.

Florida Range.—Southward to Marion County, westward to Leon County.

Habitat.—Rivers in hammock regions; fluvial swamps.

Rana grylio Stejneger
Southern Bullfrog *(Plate 40)*

General Appearance.—A large, tan or green, often yellow-bellied bullfrog.

Distinguishing Characters.—No digital pads; upper jaw with teeth; no dorsolateral folds; web extending to the tip of the longest toe; rear of thigh with a longitudinal yellow stripe bordered by dark stripes.

Description.—Head and body stout. Muzzle somewhat pointed as seen from above and sloping in profile. Tympanum as large as or larger than the eye, rough in the center. Body broad, widest in the region of the belly. No dorsolateral folds. Dorsum smooth. Fore limbs stout, fingers not webbed nor ending in digital pads. Hind limbs long and stout. Toes fully webbed, even to the tip of the longest toe, not ending in digital pads. Belly smooth. Vocal pouches apparent at the angles of the jaws in males only in strongly calling individuals. Two rounded patches of vomerine teeth between the internal nares, maxillary teeth in the upper jaw. Tongue oval, with a pair of lobes and a median notch posteriorly. Color light brown or tan, often greenish around the head. Rear of thigh with a longitudinal yellow stripe bordered by black or dark brown. Call a short, guttural note reminiscent of the grunt of a pig. Length of adults 3-6½ inches.

General Distribution.—Georgia to eastern Texas.

Florida Range.—State-wide, except for the Keys.

Habitat.—Marshes and prairies.

Note.—This is the most succulent of the Florida frogs and is the species commonly taken by professional frog hunters. It is probably well on the way toward extermination in the larger prairies.

Rana pipiens sphenocephala Cope
Southern Leopard Frog *(Plate 39)*

General Appearance.—A slim, narrow-headed, long-legged, spotted frog.

Distinguishing Characters.—No digital pads; upper jaw with teeth; dorsolateral folds present, high and narrow and extending nearly to the hips; spotted pattern above; head slender and pointed.

Description.—Head narrow and pointed, longer than broad; muzzle rather truncate in profile. Tympanum about the size of the eye. Body slender, widest in the region of the belly. A distinct but narrow dorsolateral fold originating behind each eye and continuing posteriorly to or nearly to the hips; often with smaller, less extensive, longitudinal folds between the dorsolateral folds. Fore limbs moderately slender; fingers with very narrow webs at the base; not ending in digital pads. Hind limbs long and moderately slender; $2\frac{1}{2}$ joints of the longest toe free of web, 1 joint of the other toes free of web. Toes not terminating in digital pads. Belly smooth. Vocal pouches of males sausage-shaped sacs at the angles of the jaws; usually not conspicuous save in calling individuals. Two rounded patches of vomerine teeth between the internal nares and maxillary teeth along the upper jaw. Tongue an elongate oval with 2 well-developed lobes and a median notch posteriorly. Color green or brown with distinct rounded white dark spots on the back and sides. Belly whitish. Usually a rounded white dot in the center of each tympanum. Breeding call very harsh, guttural croaks suggestive of the sound made by rubbing the stretched rubber of a toy balloon. Adults 2-5 inches in length.

General Distribution.—The southeastern states.

Florida Range.—State-wide.

Habitat.—All sorts of wet places; a ubiquitous frog.

Microhyla carolinensis carolinensis (Holbrook)
Narrow-mouth Toad *(Plate 39)*

General Appearance.—A small, squat, smooth-skinned frog with a tiny head and a fold of skin across the back of its neck.

Distinguishing Characters.—Tympanum concealed; upper jaw toothless; a fold of skin across the back of the neck, head very small.

Description.—Head extremely small and pointed. Eye small, slightly protuberant. Tympanum concealed. A fold of skin across the back of the head posterior to the eyes. Dorsum smooth. Fore limbs moderate, fingers delicate, not webbed. Hind limbs short and stout; toes slender and delicate, not webbed. Belly smooth. Male with subgular pouch. Skin on throat of male slightly folded. Tongue elongate ovoid, free behind. Mouth devoid of teeth. Color pale to dark gray. Sometimes with a pale light stripe running from the eye to the groin on each side of the back. The breeding voice can best be described as similar to the bleat of a forlorn lamb. Adult size up to 1⅖ inches.

General Distribution.—Maryland southward and westward to Texas and Missouri.

Florida Range.—State-wide.

Habitat.—Under rocks, logs, and piles of debris, usually in moist soil.

PLATE 33

CONANT

Upper, Reticulated Salamander, *Ambystoma cingulatum bishopi;* near Pensacola, Santa Rosa County. Lower, Eastern Tiger Salamander, *Ambystoma tigrinum tigrinum;* 10 miles south of McRae, Telfair County, Georgia.

CONANT

Upper, Striped Newt, *Diemictylus perstriatus;* 3 miles east of Gainesville, Alachua County. Lower, Southern Dusky Salamander, *Desmognathus fuscus auriculatus;* 3 miles north of Gainesville, Alachua County.

PLATE 34

CONANT

Upper, Southern Slimy Salamander, *Plethodon glutinosus grobmani;* 3 miles north of Gainesville, Alachua County. Lower, Viosca's Red Salamander, *Pseudotriton ruber vioscai;* 4 miles east of McBean, Burke County, Georgia.

CONANT

Upper, Southern Two-lined Salamander, *Eurycea bislineata cirrigera;* DeBruce, Georgia. Lower, Three-lined Salamander, *Eurycea longicauda guttolineata;* near Jesup, Wayne County, Georgia.

PLATE 35

CONANT

Upper, Rusty Mud Salamander, *Pseudotriton montanus floridanus;* 3 miles north of Gainesville, Alachua County. Lower, Gulf Coast Red Salamander, *Pseudotriton montanus flavissimus;* Augusta, Richmond County, Georgia.

CONANT

Upper, Narrow-striped Siren, *Pseudobranchus striatus axanthus;* Payne's Prairie, Alachua County. Lower, Lesser Siren, *Siren intermedia intermedia;* 6 miles east of Gainesville, Alachua County.

PLATE 36

CONANT

Left, Common Spadefoot, *Scaphiopus holbrooki holbrooki;* Gainesville, Alachua County. Right, Oak Toad, *Bufo quercicus;* Alachua County.

CONANT

Left, Florida Cricket Frog, *Acris gryllus dorsalis;* Gainesville, Alachua County. Right, Black Chorus Frog, *Pseudacris nigrita nigrita;* 11 miles southwest of Jesup, Wayne County, Georgia.

PLATE 37

CONANT

Left, Ornate Chorus Frog, *Pseudacris ornata;* 6 miles east of Gainesville, Alachua County. Right, Little Grass Frog, *Hyla ocularis;* Gainesville, Alachua County.

CONANT

Left, Cuban Tree Frog, *Hyla septentrionalis;* Key West, Monroe County. Right, Bell Frog, *Hyla gratiosa;* Micanopy, Alachua County.

PLATE 38

CONANT

Left, Southern Spring Peeper, *Hyla crucifer bartramiana;* Gainesville, Alachua
County. Right, Green Tree Frog, *Hyla cinerea cinerea;* Gainesville,
Alachua County.

CONANT

Left, Rain Frog, *Hyla squirella* (spotted phase); Gainesville, Alachua County.
Right, *Hyla squirella* (striped phase); Gainesville, Alachua County.

PLATE 39

CONANT

Narrow-mouth Toad, *Microhyla carolinensis carolinensis;* Corapeake, North Carolina.

CONANT

Left, Greenhouse Frog, *Eleutherodactylus ricordi planirostris;* Gainesville, Alachua County. Right, Pine-woods Tree Frog, *Hyla femoralis;* 8 miles east of Gainesville, Alachua County.

CONANT

Left, Bronze Frog, *Rana clamitans;* Gainesville, Alachua County. Right, Southern Leopard Frog, *Rana pipiens sphenocephala;* Florida City, Dade County.

PLATE 40

CONANT

Left, Southern Bullfrog, *Rana grylio;* Everglades National Park. Right, Bullfrog, *Rana catesbeiana;* Silver Springs, Marion County.

CONANT

Left, River-swamp Frog, *Rana heckscheri;* near Boulogne, Nassau County. Right, Gopher Frog, *Rana capito;* Micanopy, Alachua County.

THE REPTILES

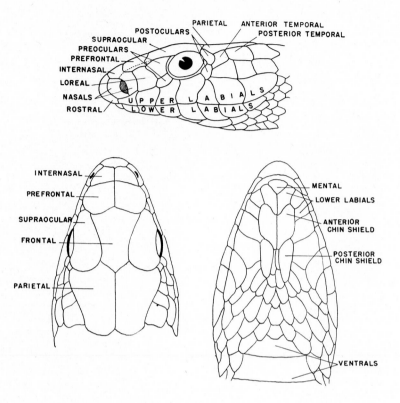

Fig. 20   Lateral, dorsal, and ventral views of head of snake, showing terminology of head scales.

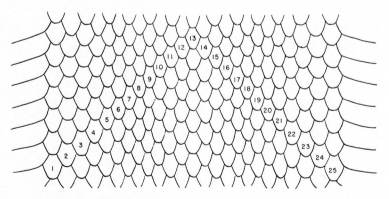

Fig. 21   Method of counting rows of scales of snake.

REPTILE GLOSSARY

Alveolar Surface—The crushing surface of the jaw of a turtle.

Anal Plate—The single or divided scale lying just in front of the anus.

Azygous—Single, not divided, median in position.

Canthals—Scales forming the edge of a ridge extending from the eye to the nostril.

Carapace—The upper shell of a turtle.

Centrals—The median row of laminae of a turtle carapace.

Cusp—A toothlike projection.

Frontal—A single median plate on top of the head between the eyes.

Imbricate—Overlapping, like shingles.

Inframarginals—Short rows of laminae between the plastrals and marginals in a turtle shell.

Intercalary—Something inserted or interpolated.

Internasal—One or two scales on top of the head just behind the rostral.

Interparietal—A single median scale on the head behind the frontal.

Keel—A sharp ridge.

Labials (upper and lower)—Scales bordering the jaw.

Lamellae—The plates forming pads on the feet of some lizards.

Laminae—The scales of a turtle's shell.

Laterals—The row of enlarged laminae on each side of the centrals in a turtle's shell.

Loreal—A small scale between the nasal and preocular.

Lorilabials—An irregular group of scales arranged longitudinally between the loreal and labials or posteriorly between the subocular and labials.

Mandible—The lower jaw.

Marginals—The laminae forming the edge of a turtle's shell.

Maxillary—Pertaining to the upper jaw.

Nasal—The scale in which the nostril lies.

Pectorals—The second paired laminae on the plastron of a turtle.

Plastrals—The laminae covering the plastron.

Plastron—The lower shell of a turtle.

Postlabials—Scales behind and in line with the upper labials.

Postnasal—One or two scales just behind the nasal.

Postoculars—One or more small scales directly behind the eye.

Precentral—The single lamina preceding the centrals.

Prefrontals—One or two pairs of scales on top of the head in front of the frontal.

Preocular—One or more small scales directly in front of the eye.

Rostral—Plate at the tip of the snout.

Seam—The furrow separating the laminae of the shell of a turtle.

Serrate—Saw-toothed.

Subcaudals—The scales on the under side of the tail.

Submarginals—A few small scales between the marginals and the plastrals of the alligator snapping turtle.

Suboculars—Scales between the eye and the labials.

209

SUPRAOCULARS—Scales above the orbits.

SUPRAORBITAL SEMICIRCLES—Scales forming paired arcs on top of the head between the eyes.

SUTURE—The line where two bones meet.

SYMPHYSIS—The place where two bones meet.

TEMPORALS, ANTERIOR—One or two longitudinal, elongated scales, lying one above the other, behind the postoculars and between the parietals and upper labials.

TEMPORALS, POSTERIOR—One, or more, longitudinal, elongated scales, lying one over the other, behind the anterior temporals and between the parietals and upper labials.

TOMIUM—The horny covering of the jaws.

TUBERCLE—A wartlike projection.

VENTRALS—The laterally enlarged scales on the lower surface of a snake.

KEY TO THE REPTILES

1   Body elongate, covered with scales, not encased in rigid armor; jaws with teeth; lizards, snakes and crocodilians.... 37

1′   Body short and wide, encased in more or less complete bony armor; jaws with horny cutting edges; turtles........ 2

2 (1)   Limbs not paddle-like, the wrist and ankle joint movable except in *Gopherus* in which the fore limbs are stiffened as shovel-like digging implements; land and freshwater turtles.. 3

2′   Limbs paddle-like, the wrist and ankle joint not movable; sea turtles.. 33

3 (2)   Shell covered with horny plates (laminae); cutting edge of upper jaw not concealed by fleshy lips......................... 5

3′   Shell covered with a leathery skin and with pliable edges; cutting edge of upper jaw concealed by fleshy lips............ 4

4 (3)   Bones of the carapace coarsely granular above, with more or less distinct longitudinal ridges that run together; young with the leathery surface of the carapace with longitudnial rows of tubercles, with a light shell margin but no marginal dark lines, and with the dorsum covered by large dark spots separated by narrow light lines.................
........Southern Soft-shelled Turtle, *Amyda ferox ferox*, p. 249

4′   Bones of the carapace finely granular above, with no longitudinal ridges; young usually with two or more dark lines around edge of carapace, or with dark ocelli, and without a pattern of large, solid dark spots.......................Southern Spiny Soft-shelled Turtle, *Amyda ferox aspera*, p. 250

5 (3) Tail more than half the length of shell; plastron small and cross-shaped, not nearly covering the soft parts below......... 6

5′ Tail less than half the length of shell; plastron not small and cross-shaped (except in *Sternotherus carinatus minor*), forming an almost complete covering for the soft parts below.. 8

6 (5) Eyes located dorsolaterally, readily seen from above; no supramarginals.. 7

6′ Eyes located on the sides of the head, not visible from above; a row of supramarginal laminae above the marginals at each side..
......Alligator Snapping Turtle, *Macrochelys temmincki*, p. 230

7 (6) Width of the third central lamina less than ⅓ of the length of the 5 centrals; knobs of dorsal keels well back of centers of the laminae; lateral caudal tubercles much less conspicuous than median tubercles; extreme northern Florida northward.......................................Common Snapping Turtle, *Chelydra serpentina serpentina*, p. 230

7′ Width of the third central ⅓ of the length of the 5 centrals; knobs of dorsal keels located near centers of the laminae; lateral caudal tubercules not much less conspicuous than median tubercles; the peninsula......................
..Florida Snapping Turtle, *Chelydra serpentina osceola*, p. 231

8 (5) Laminae of the plastron 12, the pectorals in contact with the marginals.. 14

8′ Laminae of the plastron 10 or 11, the pectorals not in contact with the marginals; mud and musk turtles............ 9

9 (8) Pectoral laminae nearly triangular, the seam between them very short; plastron with the anterior and posterior portions nearly equal in size and movable on a transverse hinge.. 11

9′ Seam between the pectorals not shortened, the laminae oblong; plastron with the anterior part shorter than the posterior part and only slightly movable if at all............ 10

10 (9) Sides of head with light stripes, or if no light stripes then ground color lustrous black.......................................
...........Common Musk Turtle, *Sternotherus odoratus*, p. 232

10′ Sides of head with dark dots or spots, not striped; ground color of soft parts gray or brownish-gray........................
Loggerhead Musk Turtle, *Sternotherus carinatus minor*, p. 231

11 (9) Carapace with three longitudinal light stripes, these either distinct and continuous or broken or intercepted by other light bars or blotches.. 12

11′ Carapace plain, not striped... 13

12 (11)　Laminae of carapace thick and opaque, not showing sutures between bony plates beneath; peninsular Florida except in the extreme south............:...................
..........Striped Mud Turtle, *Kinosternon bauri bauri,* p. 233

12′　Laminae of carapace thin and translucent, showing sutures of the underlying bony plates; extreme southern Florida...Paradise Key Mud Turtle, *Kinosternon bauri palmarum,* p. 233

13 (11)　Bridge wide, its breadth usually half the length of the fore lobe of plastron or more; northern Florida..........
....Common Mud Turtle, *Kinosternon subrubrum subrubrum,* p. 234

13′　Bridge narrower, its breadth usually contained $2\frac{1}{2}$-3 times in length of fore lobe of plastron; peninsular Florida...Florida Mud Turtle, *Kinosternon subrubrum steindachneri,* p. 234

14 (8)　Feet not shovel-like or elephantine; toes more or less webbed.. 15

14′　Fore feet shovel-like and hind feet elephantine; toes not webbed....Gopher Tortoise, *Gopherus polyphemus,* p. 246

15 (14)　Plastron in one rigid piece, not hinged, attached to the carapace by rigid joints..................................... 16

15′　Plastron hinged near middle, its halves movable, attached to carapace only by ligaments; box turtles........ 30

16 (15)　Neck not strikingly long, the distance along extended neck to shoulder about equal to $\frac{1}{2}$ the length of the plastron... 17

16′　Neck markedly elongate, the distance from tip of snout along extended neck to shoulder about equal to length of plastron..Chicken Turtle, *Deirochelys reticularia,* p. 246

17 (16)　Alveolar surface of upper jaw with a ridge or row of tubercles parallel to its margin.................................. 18

17′　Alveolar surface of upper jaw very broad, smooth or undulating, not ridged or toothed............................. 25

18 (17)　Carapace usually with longitudinal wrinkles, a more or less complete keel, or both; its hind margin serrate...... 19

18′　Carapace very smooth, not wrinkled longitudinally and without a keel, its hind margin not serrate.................
........Eastern Painted Turtle, *Chrysemys picta picta,* p. 241

19 (18)　Alveolar surface of upper jaw usually not narrower anteriorly than posteriorly; alveolar ridge coarsely and irregularly tuberculate; general outline of horny upper beak rounded and obtuse in both anterior and ventral aspects, although rarely with a median notch that may

or may not be bounded on each side by a toothlike cusp; under side of mandible flat, head always with light stripes.. 20

19'   Alveolar surface of upper jaw usually narrower anteriorly than posteriorly and with the ridge smooth or finely serrate; general outline of fore part of cutting edge or upper jaw angular from anterior and ventral aspects; under side of mandible rounded; head either with a broad yellow patch behind eye or without any light markings at all..

....Yellow-bellied Turtle, *Pseudemys scripta scripta*, p. 242

20 (19)   Upper jaw smooth or slightly serrate, without a notch or cusps at the tip.. 21

20'   Upper jaw with a median notch bordered by cusps........ 24

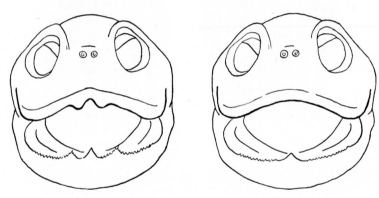

Fig. 22   Upper jaw of turtle with median notch bordered by cusps (left); smooth upper jaw of turtle (right).

21 (20)   Plastron without dark markings.............................. 22

21'   Plastron with a more or less extensive dusky figure roughly superimposed on the seams, at least in juveniles and young adults.. 23

22 (21)   Two prominent stripes on dorsolateral area of head and neck joining behind eye, or nearly so, to continue forward along top of head to snout as a single line; lower marginal blotches solid, smudgelike; plastron greenish-white or greenish-yellow in live individuals; peninsular Florida..

Peninsular Turtle, *Pseudemys floridana peninsularis*, p. 244

22′   The two prominent stripes on dorsolateral area of head
           and neck not convergent but separately continuous
           along top of head to snout; blotches on lower marginals
           ringlike, inclosing light centers; plastron in life yellow
           or orange-yellow; northern Florida.............................
           Coastal Plain Turtle, *Pseudemys floridana floridana*, p. 243

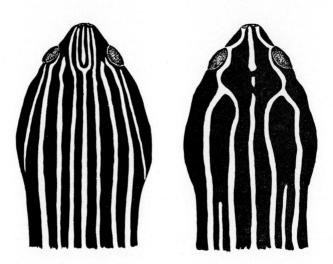

Fig. 23   Head pattern of Coastal Plain Turtle (left); of Peninsular Turtle
           (right).

23 (21)   Ground color of carapace, limbs and head light to dark
           brown, the stripes and reticulations yellow, orange-
           yellow or reddish; four or more lines on outer surface
           of fore limbs; outer surface of hind limbs striped;
           usually 7 or more lines between eyes; extreme western
           Florida westward..
           ....Mobile Turtle, *Pseudemys floridana mobilensis*, p. 244

23′   Ground color of carapace, legs and head deep black,
           the stripes and reticulations light greenish-yellow; outer
           surface of fore leg with 2 or 3 lines; outer surface of
           hind leg not striped; 5 lines between the eyes; rivers
           and brackish waters of the western coast of peninsula
           ....Suwan-
           nee Turtle, *Pseudemys floridana suwanniensis*, p. 245

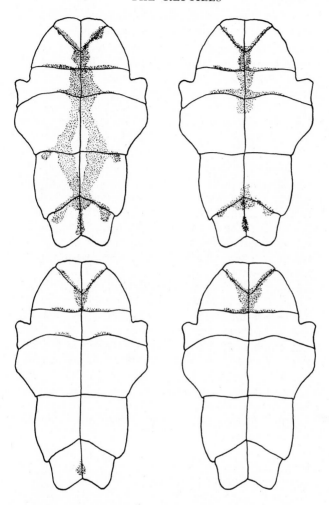

Fig. 24   Variations in extent of dark markings on plastron of the Suwannee Turtle.

24 (20)   Carapace with a many-lined, more or less reticulate pattern; plastron always marked; lower marginals with black rings, bands or circles; rivers and brackish or salt waters of Gulf Coast only; the *"alabamensis"* phase of *P. f. suwanniensis* and *P. f. mobilensis;* return to couplet... 23

24′ Carapace plain black or with broad transverse light bands dominating the pattern or (rarely) marked by irregularly scattered red and black mottling; plastron often marked in young but rarely in adults; lower marginals with large, solid, black, smudgelike spots; the peninsula...

........Florida Red-bellied Turtle, *Pseudemys nelsoni*, p. 242

25 (17) Laminae of the carapace smooth, not concentrically striated or ridged; head and neck light striped; fresh-water turtles.. 26

25′ Laminae of the carapace usually with concentric ridges or striations; head and neck plain, spotted or mottled, without longitudinal stripes; salt- and brackish-water turtles.. 27

26 (25) Each lateral lamina with a thin-lined, U-shaped figure turned on its side and with its open end against the posterior seam of the lamina; chin with transverse markings only..

......Barbour's Sawback Turtle, *Graptemys barbouri*, p. 239

26′ Laterals not marked as above; chin with a short, median longitudinal stripe; in Florida known only from Escambia River...

........Alabama Sawback Turtle, *Graptemys pulchra*, p. 240

27 (25) Keels of centrals with bulbous terminal expansions...... 28

27′ Central keels of carapace not terminally expanded; Cape Hatteras to southern Florida.........Southern Diamondback Terrapin, *Malaclemys terrapin centrata*, p. 237

28 (27) Laminae of the carapace with conspicuous light yellow centers; Gulf Coast of the peninsula.............................

....Florida Diamondback Terrapin, *Malaclemys terrapin macrospilota*, p. 237

28′ Laminae without (or with desultory) light centers...... 29

29 (28) Seams of lower marginals and of plastrals usually black bordered; shell strongly oblong; Florida Keys......Mangrove Terrapin, *Malaclemys terrapin rhizophorarum*, p. 238

29′ Seams not regularly black bordered; shell usually more oval; coast of the panhandle to Louisiana............................

....Mississippi Diamondback Terrapin, *Malaclemys terrapin pileata*, p. 238

30 (15′) Carapace with its highest point at middle; pattern on laterals usually not composed of long lines radiating eccentrically; side of head usually spotted or unmarked 31

30′ Carapace with its highest point usually posterior to middle; pattern on laterals usually comprising long

yellow lines radiating from postero-dorsal corners; side
of head usually with two stripes; the peninsula........
......Florida Box Turtle, *Terrapene carolina bauri*, p. 235

31 (30) Hind foot with four claws (usually); face and anterior
surface of fore limbs usually without numerous small
light spots; no white blotches..................................... 32

31' Hind foot usually with three claws; face and anterior
surface of fore limbs usually with numerous small
orange or yellow spots and often with white blotches;
the Tallahassee-Thomasville (Ga.) area northwestward
....Three-
toed Box Turtle, *Terrapene carolina triunguis*, p. 236

32 (31) Shell elongate; markings frequently obscured by black
or horn color in adults, the plastron, especially, often
with much black; hind margin of carapace usually distinctly flaring; Gulf Coast of the panhandle westward
..Gulf Coast Box Turtle, *Terrapene carolina major*, p. 236

32' Shell short, broad; markings usually not obscured by
black or horn color; posterior marginals usually almost
vertical; extreme northern Florida northward...............
..Common Box Turtle, *Terrapene carolina carolina*, p. 235

33 (2) Shell covered with horny scales (laminae)................. 34

33' Shell covered with leathery skin......................Atlantic
Leatherback Turtle, *Dermochelys coriacea coriacea*, p. 250

34 (33) Head with two pairs of prefrontal scales; tomium of
lower jaw smooth or only feebly toothed; that of upper
jaw without strongly elevated vertical ridges on its
inner surface; laterals 4-9.................................... 35

34' One pair of prefrontal scales on head; tomium of lower
jaw coarsely toothed, that of the upper jaw with vertical ridges on its inner surface; lateral laminae usually 4
......Atlantic Green Turtle, *Chelonia mydas mydas*, p. 247

35 (34) Laterals in 5 or more pairs; precentral in contact with
first laterals; snout relatively short and broad, the
mandibular symphysis toothed terminally or blunted
by wear; anterior part of roof of mouth not deeply
excavated; laminae of carapace not conspicuously imbricated except occasionally in very young.................. 36

35' Laterals in 4 pairs; precentral not in contact with first
laterals; snout elongate, narrow, not terminally toothed;
the roof of the mouth deeply excavated at the mandibular symphysis; laminae usually conspicuously imbricated...Atlantic
Hawksbill Turtle, *Eretmochelys imbricata imbricata*, p. 247

36 (35)   Bridge with 4 enlarged inframarginals; color gray to olive-green; maxillary bones of the skull separated by the vomer......Atlantic Ridley, *Lepidochelys kempi,* p. 249

36′   Bridge with 3 enlarged inframarginals; color brown or reddish-brown; maxillary bones of the skull in contact with each other..
Atlantic Loggerhead Turtle, *Caretta caretta caretta,* p. 248

37 (1)   Anal opening a longitudinal slit; alligators and crocodiles.. 63

37′   Anal opening a transverse slit; lizards and snakes........ 38

38 (37)   Ventral scales nearly as wide as width of body; bones of lower jaw loosely joined in front by an elastic ligament; snakes.. 64

38′   Ventral scales not nearly so wide as width of body; bones of lower jaw rigidly joined in front; lizards...... 39

39 (38)   Legs present.. 40

39′   Legs lacking.. 60

40 (39)   Eyelids lacking; eye always open; geckos...................... 41

40′   Eyelids present; eye capable of being closed................ 44

41 (40)   Toes expanded.. 42

41′   Toes not expanded..
................Yellow-headed Gecko, *Gonatodes fuscus,* p. 252

42 (41)   Back not warty; toes with a single rounded pad at tip of each.. 43

42′   Back with warts; toe pads elongate, extending almost the whole length of toe..
......Warty Gecko, *Hemidactylus turcicus turcicus,* p. 253

43 (42)   Dorsal scales big (10-12 equal to distance from snout to ear), keeled, imbricate and distinctly larger than ventral scales..Reef Gecko, *Sphaerodactylus notatus,* p. 253

43′   Dorsal scales small and granular, not so big as ventral scales............Ashy Gecko, *Sphaerodactylus cinereus,* p. 254

44 (40)   Body not markedly flat; tail longer than width of body; head without long, heavy spines.............................. 45

44′   Body greatly flattened, wider than tail is long; head with long, heavy spines..
........Texas Horned Lizard, *Phrynosoma cornutum,* p. 259

45 (44)   Toes laterally broadened, with padlike dilations; scales minute; body without 6 longitudinal stripes.............. 46

45′   Toes not laterally dilated; scales big and rough, big and shiny, or very tiny and granular, but if the latter, then body with 6 well-marked longitudinal stripes............ 50

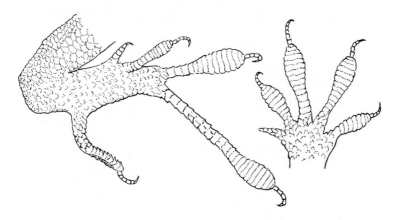

Fig. 25   Hind foot (left) and front foot (right) of an Anole, showing laterally broadened toes.

52 (51)   Tail round in cross section or flattened above, not com-
          pressed or keeled above..   53
52'   Tail laterally compressed and keeled dorsally..............
          ....Bahamian
          Crested Lizard, *Leiocephalus carinatus virescens*, p. 257
53 (52)   Side without a distinct brown stripe; dorsal scale rows
          usually fewer than 38; first canthal scale rarely in con-
          tact with the lorilabials.................................South-
          ern Fence Lizard, *Sceloporus undulatus undulatus*, p. 258
53'   Side with a distinct brown stripe; dorsal scale rows
          usually 40 or more; first canthal scale usually in con-
          tact with lorilabials..
          ....Scrub Pine Lizard, *Sceloporus woodi*, p. 258
54 (51)   Limbs not rudimentary; toes 5.............................   55
54'   Limbs rudimentary; toes 1 or 2.............................
          ....Florida Sand Skink, *Neoseps reynoldsi*, p. 265

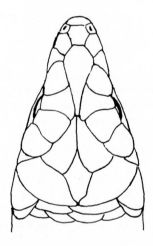
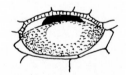

Fig. 26   Top of head (left) and eye showing transparent lower eyelid (right)
of brown skink.

55 (54)   Anterior margin of ear toothed; lower eyelid scaly, not
          transparent; palate with teeth.............................   56
55'   Anterior margin of ear smooth; lower eyelid partly
          transparent; palate without teeth.........................
          ....Brown Skink, *Lygosoma laterale*, p. 262
56 (55)   Head with 3 supraocular scales.............................   57
56'   Head with 4 supraocular scales.............................   58

57 (56) Dorsolateral light line short or if extending full length of body then its inner border on third scale row posteriorly; 2 mid-dorsal scale rows only slightly larger than adjacent rows..............................

..........Brown Red-tailed Skink, *Eumeces onocrepis,* p. 263

57' Dorsolateral light line extending the full length of the body, its inner border on second scale row; 2 mid-dorsal rows much larger than adjacent rows..................

..........Striped Red-tailed Skink, *Eumeces egregius,* p. 262

58 (56) Median row of scales beneath tail distinctly wider than adjacent rows; lines on head usually confluent with median line.. 59

58' Median row of scales under tail not wider than adjacent rows or only slightly so; lines on head usually not confluent with median line............................

......Florida Five-lined Skink, *Eumeces inexpectatus,* p. 264

59 (58) Two relatively large postlabials; an intercalary row of scales on the side of fourth toe not extending onto next-to-last phalanx; maximum snout-to-vent length about 3⅛ inches...............................

........Common Five-lined Skink, *Eumeces fasciatus,* p. 265

59' No postlabial scales, or only 1; or, if 2, then these very small; the intercalary row of scales on side of fourth toe extending onto next-to-last phalanx; maximum snout-to-vent length about 5 1/16 inches...........

...........Greater Five-lined Skink, *Eumeces laticeps,* p. 263

60 (39) Eyes and a deep lateral fold present; not whitish, ringed or worm-like, tail very long....................... 61

60' Blind, whitish, pink or lavender, earthworm-like, with rings around body and very short tail; no lateral fold....

..............Florida Worm Lizard, *Rhineura floridana,* p. 266

61 (60) Two frontonasal scales present; 1 or 2 upper labials in contact with orbit; side with a single dark stripe on scale rows 4 and 5 only............................

........Coastal Glass Snake, *Ophisaurus compressus,* p. 261

61' One frontonasal scale present; upper labials separated from orbit by lorilabials; side either with more than 1 dark stripe or with 1 which encroaches on the sixth scale row as well as the fourth and fifth....................... 62

62 (61) White markings of adults on posterior corners of scales, not in their centers; no distinct mid-dorsal stripe; ventral surface not dark striped.............................

..........Common Glass Snake, *Ophisaurus ventralis,* p. 260

62'   White markings of adults on center of scales and often aligning to form stripes; distinct mid-dorsal stripe usually present in adults and always in young; scale rows 1 and 2 of ventral surface often with dark stripes.... ....Eastern Long-tailed Glass Snake, *Ophisaurus attenuatus longicaudus*, p. 260

63 (37) Snout broad, straight-sided; fourth tooth in lower jaw not exposed when mouth closed............................... ....Alligator, *Alligator mississippiensis*, p. 251

63'   Snout pointed; fourth tooth in lower jaw exposed when mouth closed.. ....American Crocodile, *Crocodylus acutus*, p. 251

64 (38) Face without a pit between eye and nostril................. 65

64'   Face with pit between eye and nostril....................... 125

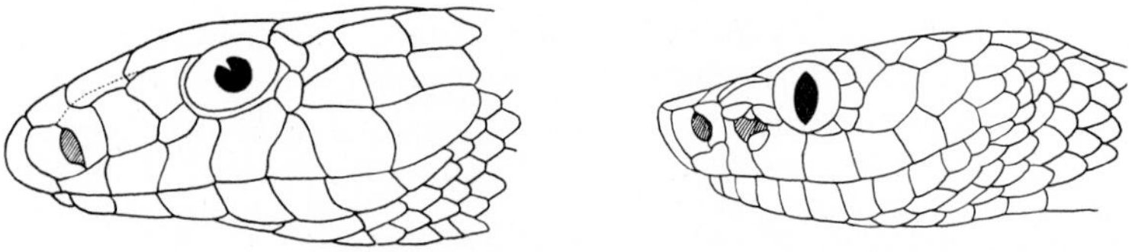

Fig. 27   Side of head of snake without pit (left); with pit (right).

65 (64) Snout with a single internasal..................................... 66

65'   Two internasals present... 71

66 (65) Upper labials 5, lower labials 6.................................. 67

66'   Upper labials 7 or 8, lower labials 8-10.................... 68

67 (66) Scales keeled.. ....Rough Ground Snake, *Haldea striatula*, p. 292

67'   Scales smooth, or with only a few on the posterior part of body weakly keeled.. ......Eastern Ground Snake, *Haldea valeriae valeriae*, p. 292

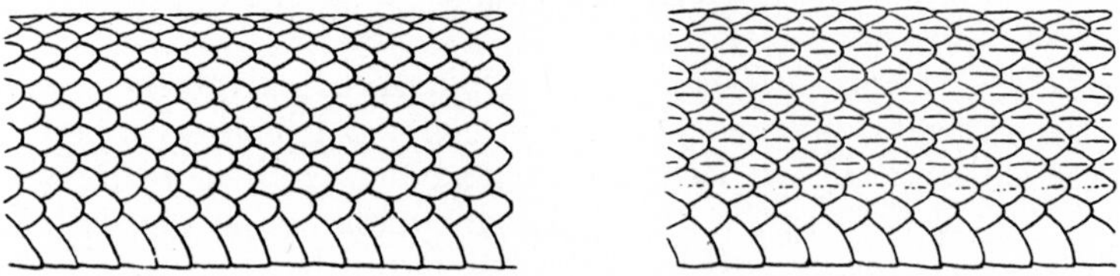

Fig. 28   Snake with smooth scales (left); with keeled scales (right).

68 (66) Preocular lacking, loreal reaching eye........................... 69

68'   Preocular present, between loreal and eye.................... 70

69 (68)   Each side of body with 53 or more triangular red
          markings which on the neck come to within 3 or 4
          scale rows of each other; most of Florida..................
          ....Horn Snake, *Farancia abacura abacura*, p. 267
69'   Each side of body with 52 or fewer triangular red
          markings; on the neck those of the two sides are sepa-
          rated above by 8 or 9 scale rows; extreme western
          Florida.............................
          Western Horn Snake, *Farancia abacura reinwardti*, p. 268
70 (68)   Belly without a regular mid-ventral row of distinct
          black spots or line; peninsular Florida except south-
          ward of Lake Okeechobee..........................
          ....Allen's Swamp Snake, *Liodytes alleni alleni*, p. 293
70'   Belly with a mid-ventral row of distinct black spots
          or a mid-ventral line; Florida southward of Lake Okee-
          chobee...............................
          Everglades Swamp Snake, *Liodytes alleni lineapiatus*, p. 293
71 (65)   Dorsal scales keeled, at least faintly so, on uppermost
          row and on hind part of body...........................   72
71'   Dorsal scales smooth................................. 103
72 (71)   Anal plate divided.................................   73
72'   Anal plate single................................. 100

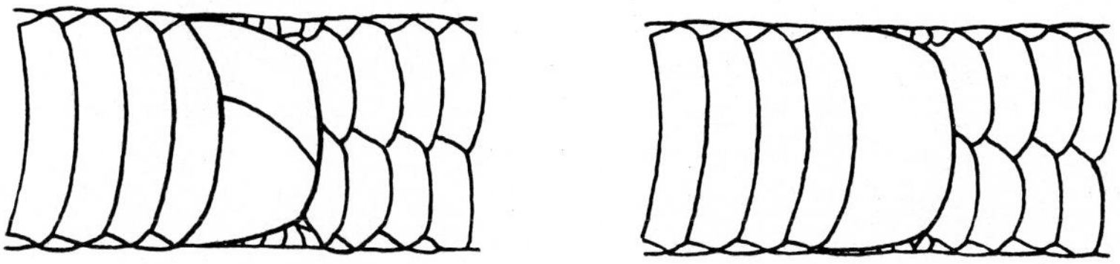

Fig. 29   Anal plate divided (left); anal plate single (right).

73 (72)   Rostral turned up and keeled...........................   74
73'   Rostral normal, not turned up.........................   75
74 (73)   Under side of tail not conspicuously lighter than belly;
          prefrontals separated by small scales...................
          ....Southern Hog-nosed Snake, *Heterodon simus*, p. 270
74'   Under side of tail conspicuously lighter than belly;
          prefrontals in contact, at least behind...................
          Common Hog-nosed Snake, *Heterodon platyrhinos*, p. 269
75 (73)   Loreal present...........................   78
75'   Loreal lacking...........................   76
76 (75)   Scales in 15 rows...........................   77
76'   Scales in 17 rows...........................
          Wright's Brown Snake, *Storeria dekayi wrightorum*, p. 290

77 (76) Belly red, without a row of dark spots on either side....
....Florida
Red-bellied Snake, *Storeria occipitomaculata obscura,* p. 291

77′ Belly light, with a row of dark spots on either side of it
............Florida Brown Snake, *Storeria dekayi victa,* p. 291

78 (75) No preoculars, the loreal in contact with eye............ 79

78′ One or 2 preoculars present, blocking the loreal from
the eye.. 80

79 (78) Upper labials 5 or 6; *Haldea;* return to couplet.......... 67

79′ Upper labials 7 (scales only faintly keeled)................
..............Rainbow Snake, *Abastor erythrogrammus,* p. 267

80 (78) Scale rows 17.. 81

80′ Scale rows more than 17... 83

81 (80) Subcaudals fewer than 60... 82

81′ Subcaudals more than 100..
................Rough Green Snake, *Opheodrys aestivus,* p. 271

82 (81) Ventral pattern not of short triangular markings; ventrals usually more than 118; north of Polk County....
......Black Swamp Snake, *Seminatrix pygaea pygaea,* p. 289

82′ Ventral pattern of short triangular markings; ventrals
usually fewer than 118; peninsular Florida south of
Polk County..South
Florida Swamp Snake,, *Seminatrix pygaea cyclas,* p. 290

83 (80) Body rough; dorsal scales strongly keeled...................... 84

83′ Body nearly smooth; dorsal scales weakly keeled, several lower lateral raws smooth.. 94

84 (83) Scales in 19 rows at mid-body.. 85

84′ Scale rows at mid-body more than 19.......................... 86

85 (84) Each side of belly with a light stripe............................
............................Queen Snake, *Natrix septemvittata,* p. 288

85′ Side of belly without light stripe...................................
........................Striped Water Snake, *Natrix rigida,* p. 288

86 (84) Scale rows 27 or more; lower labials usually 11-13.... 87

86′ Scale rows 21-25; lower labials usually 10.................. 89

87 (86) A single anterior temporal present; no squared mid-
dorsal spots.. 88

87′ Two anterior temporals present; body with 21-25
squared mid-dorsal spots..
................Brown Water Snake, *Natrix taxispilota,* p. 287

88 (87) Lateral bars on body 41-49..
......Green Water Snake, *Natrix cyclopion cyclopion,* p. 285

88′ Lateral bars on body 50-57............................Florida
Green Water Snake, *Natrix cyclopion floridana,* p. 286

89 (86) Belly with a median row of more or less regular light spots.. 90

89' Belly variously marked or plain but with no regularly arranged median light spots.................................... 92

90 (89) Back longitudinally striped, at least mid-dorsally...... 91

90' Back crossbanded, spotted or plain, not striped long-wise except sometimes on neck............................Flat-tailed Water Snake, *Natrix sipedon compressicauda*, p. 284

91 (90) A continuous lateral stripe present.............................
..........Clark's Water Snake, *Natrix sipedon clarki*, p. 283

91' Lateral stripe broken to form a row of diamond-shaped blotches..East Coast Striped Water Snake, *Natrix sipedon taeniata*, p. 285

92 (89) Dorsal surface of body with crossbands; ventrals usual-ly fewer than 140.. 93

92' Dorsal surface of body plain, not banded; ventrals more than 140...Red-bellied Water Snake, *Natrix erythrogaster erythrogaster*, p. 286

93 (92) Dorsal bands on body about 24 (19-33); ventrals 126-137; belly with quadrate spots............................
..........Banded Water Snake, *Natrix sipedon fasciata*, p. 282

93' Dorsal bands on body about 29 (24-35); ventrals 120-129; ventrals often red- or black-bordered an-teriorly...Florida Banded Water Snake, *Natrix sipedon pictiventris*, p. 283

94 (83) Body with longitudinal stripes well defined; dorsal blotches present or absent.. 97

94' Body blotched or spotted only, without stripes............ 95

95 (94) Dorsal ground color reddish or pink; neck bands cross-ing parietals and uniting on frontals.............................. 96

95' Dorsal ground color grayish; no neck bands crossing parietals and uniting on frontals; the panhandle........
..........Whiteoak Snake, *Elaphe obsoleta spiloides*, p. 276

96 (95) Belly extensively marked with black; throughout main-land Florida......Corn Snake, *Elaphe guttata guttata*, p. 274

96' Belly plain or with very little black; the Keys............
..........Pink Rat Snake, *Elaphe guttata rosacea*, p. 274

97 (94) Ground color yellow to olive; the peninsula and the Keys.. 98

97' Ground color light gray or whitish; dorsal blotches prominent; between the lower Suwannee and the lower Withlacoochee rivers...Gulf Ham-mock Whiteoak Snake, *Elaphe obsoleta williamsi*, p. 277

108'   Body speckled, crossbands not or but vaguely dis-
        cernible; southern tip of the peninsula...................
        Brooks' King Snake, *Lampropeltis getulus brooksi*, p. 280
109 (108)   Crossbands fewer than 50; northern Florida.......... 110
109'   Crossbands more than 50; central Florida south-
        ward to the Everglades...............................Florida
        King Snake, *Lampropeltis getulus floridana*, p. 280
110 (109)   Crossbands usually 25-50; no more than 2 or 3
        scales wide dorsally; northern Florida generally
        except Gulf and Calhoun counties...................Com-
        mon King Snake, *Lampropeltis getulus getulus*, p. 279
110'   Crossbands usually about 21, 4 to 8 scales in width
        dorsally; Gulf and Calhoun counties.......................
        Chipola King Snake, *Lampropeltis getulus goini*, p. 281
111 (107)   Red rings around body.....................................
        Scarlet King Snake, *Lampropeltis doliata doliata*, p. 278
111'   Back with black-edged reddish or brown blotches that
        do not extend onto belly......................Brown King
        Snake, *Lampropeltis calligaster rhombomaculata*, p. 279
112 (103)   Scales in fewer than 19 rows.................... 113
112'   Scales in more than 19 rows.................... 121
113 (112)   Loreal present.................... 114
113'   Loreal absent.................... 122
114 (113)   One or more preoculars present.................... 115
114'   No preocular, loreal reaching eye.................... 120
115 (114)   One preocular present.................... 116
115'   Preoculars 2 or 3.................... 117
116 (115)   Subcaudals more than 60; upper labials 7..........
        ....Yellow-lipped Snake, *Rhadinaea flavilata*, p. 269
116'   Subcaudals fewer than 60; upper labials usually 8;
        Seminatrix...............................return to couplet 82
117 (115)   Anterior temporals 2 or 3; a small lower preocular
        between labials..................... 118
117'   Anterior temporal single; no small lower preocular
        ....Southern Ring-
        necked Snake, *Diadophis punctatus punctatus*, p. 268
118 (117)   Scales in 15 rows at posterior end of body.......... 119
118'   Scales in 11-13 rows at posterior end of body........
        Eastern Coachwhip, *Coluber flagellum flagellum*, p. 272
119 (118)   Dorsal color deep blue black; belly usually slaty-blue
        ....South-
        ern Black Racer, *Coluber constrictor priapus*, p. 272

119′   Dorsal color gray, blue-gray, or tan; belly white or
            yellowish..
            Everglades Racer, *Coluber constrictor paludicolus,* p. 271
120 (114)   Nasal plate divided; upper labials 6; dorsal scale
            rows 15 or 17; *Haldea*................return to couplet   67
120′   Nasal plate not divided; upper labials 5; dorsal scale
            rows 13..
            ......Worm Snake, *Carphophis amoena amoena,* p. 266
121 (112)   Dorsal pattern of longitudinal stripes........................
            ....Rainbow Snake, *Abastor erythrogrammus,* p. 267
121′   No dorsal pattern of longitudinal stripes................   69
122 (113)   Color pattern of red, black and yellow rings around
            body.. 124
122′   Body plain, without ringed color pattern.................. 123
123 (122)   Light band on back of head well defined although
            often interrupted on midline; ventrals 131-144 in
            males, 139-148 in females; subcaudals 42-51 in
            males, 41-46 in females..
            ....Crowned Snake, *Tantilla coronata coronata,* p. 295
123′   Light line on back of head usually indistinct or lack-
            ing; ventrals 119-129 in males, 123-145 in fe-
            males; subcaudals 50-67 in males, 41-59 in fe-
            males..Florida
            Crowned Snake, *Tantilla coronata wagneri,* p. 295
124 (122)   Red rings sprinkled with black dorsally; all but
            southernmost Florida..
            Common Coral Snake, *Micrurus fulvius fulvius,* p. 296
124′   Red rings with little or no black markings; southern-
            most Florida..South
            Florida Coral Snake, *Micrurus fulvius barbouri,* p. 296
125 (64)   Tail without a rattle.. 126
125′   Tail with a rattle.. 127
126 (125)   Upper labials entering orbit; loreal present............
            ....Cottonmouth
            Moccasin, *Ancistrodon piscivorus piscivorus,* p. 297
126′   Upper labials excluded from orbit by small scales;
            loreal absent..Southern
            Copperhead, *Ancistrodon contortrix contortrix,* p. 297
127 (125)   Top of head covered with small scales except for
            2 big plates over the eyes................................ 128
127′   Top of head covered with about 9 big scales........
            ....Florida
            Ground Rattlesnake, *Sistrurus miliarius barbouri,* p. 298

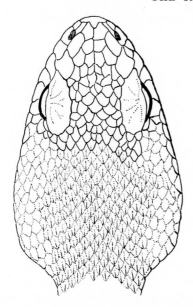
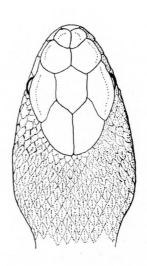

Fig. 30   Top of head covered with small scales (left); top of head covered
with about 9 big scales (right).

ACCOUNTS OF SPECIES

Macrochelys temmincki (Troost)
Alligator Snapping Turtle

General Appearance.—A very large, rough-shelled, big-headed, mean-looking turtle with a long tail.

Distinguishing Characters.—Shell highly ridged; tail more than ½ the length of shell; supramarginals present; eye sockets lateral.

Description.—Shell about ⅔ as wide as long. Carapace with 3 high keels and a serrate hind margin. Three to 8 supramarginal scales between the laterals and marginals. Plastron small and cross-shaped. Head large and pointed, the upper jaw terminally hooked. Color of shell and soft parts brownish, sometimes with vague dark spots on the latter. Shell length up to 2 feet and more; weights of 50-100 pounds are regularly attained and an occasional individual becomes much heavier.

General Distribution.—Mississippi Valley eastward to Florida.

Florida Range.—The panhandle eastward and southward to the Suwannee River drainage and the Okefinokee area.

Habitat.—Rivers.

Chelydra serpentina serpentina (Linnaeus)
Common Snapping Turtle

General Appearance.—A big, dark, long-tailed, big-headed, and ill-natured brute of a turtle, with a hard, fast strike and no color pattern.

Distinguishing Characters.—The three-keeled shell, long tail, small, cross-shaped plastron and dorsolaterally placed eyes (visible from above) set the snapper off from all other turtles. The very slight points of distinction between the common snapper and the Florida snapper are given in the account of the latter race.

Description.—Shell broad, widest and serrate posteriorly, rough and three-keeled above, the knobs of the keels located well behind centers of the laminae. Plastron cruciform, falling far short of covering the soft parts. Carapace dark, often nearly black; plastron light yellowish. Head very large, the eyes placed dorsolaterally and far forward, both being evident from directly above. Tail long and armed above with 3 rows of tubercles, the central row much the more prominent. Soft parts unmarked, dark above, lighter below. Sexes without notable differences in form. Maximum size represented by lengths of about 14 inches and weights of 50 to 70 pounds.

General Distribution.—Eastern North America from Canada (Nova Scotia to Saskatchewan) southward to northern Florida and northeastern Mexico, where it is replaced by other races.

Florida Range.—The panhandle and northernmost part of the peninsula, where it intergrades with the Florida snapper in a broad area.

Habitat.—Nearly any aquatic situation. Perhaps partial to lakes and ponds with muddy bottoms and submerged timber.

Chelydra serpentina osceola Stejneger
Florida Snapping Turtle *(Plate 41)*

General Appearance.—A big, dark, long-tailed, big-headed and ill-natured turtle, with a hard, fast strike and no color pattern.

Distinguishing Characters.—Very poorly differentiated from the common snapper. The features that have been said to separate the two are as follows: knob on dorsal keels located near centers of laminae in *osceola,* farther back in *serpentina;* lateral rows of tubercles on top of tail not much less conspicuous than the mid-dorsal row in *osceola,* much less so in *serpentina;* width of third central usually ⅓ the length of the 5 centrals in *osceola,* and less than ⅓ their length in *serpentina.* In most of the upper peninsula these characters are found in all stages of intergradation. Shell length of adult about 12-14 inches.

General Distribution.—Confined to Florida.

Florida Range.—Central and southern Florida, beginning to merge with the northern form in Alachua County and extending from there to the tip of the peninsula.

Habitat.—Nearly any body of water, with little or no habitat preference discernible.

Sternotherus carinatus minor (Agassiz)
Loggerhead Musk Turtle

General Appearance.—A small turtle with a big, spotted or mottled head.

Distinguishing Characters.—The high, usually three-keeled shell with radiating shell pattern, the lack of light head markings and the presence of a gular lamina.

Description.—Shell deep and, except in old worn individuals, with the slope from the sharp central keel interrupted by a lateral keel. Laminae of carapace of immature individuals and young adults with dark seam borders and with dark, narrow, radiating lines. Head very large, especially in old males, with much expanded crushing surfaces in the jaws and with no light stripes but with dark dots or spots on a brown background. In old eroded individuals with smooth, unmarked, and keelless shells, the enlarged heads will distinguish the form. Maximum shell length appears to be just under 5 inches.

General Distribution.—Southern Georgia, coastal Alabama, and northern Florida.

Florida Range.—The panhandle and upper part of the peninsula southward to Lake County.

Habitat.—Swamp-shore streams, floodplain sloughs, oxbow lakes, and spring-runs.

Sternotherus odoratus (Latreille)
Common Musk Turtle

General Appearance.—A small, dark, often black turtle with a high shell.

Distinguishing Characters.—The black ground color of shell and soft parts; the light (white or yellow) head stripes; the small size and the oblong pectoral laminae.

Description.—Shell somewhat highly arched and usually keeled sharply above except in very old individuals. Carapace usually unmarked in Florida specimens. Plastron small, light in color and with much skin exposed between the seams. Ground color head and limbs usually black, the side of the head with a pair of light lines that begin on the snout and extend backward, one above the other, below the eye. Maximum length about 5 inches.

General Distribution.—Eastern North America from Ontario and Michigan southward to Florida.

Florida Range.—Throughout Florida except the Keys.

Habitat.—Shows little habitat preference, being found in streams, lakes, and ditches alike.

Kinosternon bauri bauri (Garman)
Striped Mud Turtle

General Appearance.—A small, brown turtle with a striped back.

Distinguishing Characters.—This turtle may be known by its low, broad, keelless shell which is marked by 3 longitudinal light stripes, and by the light stripes on the side of the head.

Description.—Shell low, smoothly globular, usually with the highest (and sometimes the widest) point behind the middle; occasionally depressed along centrals. Dorsal laminae smooth; marginals steeply inclined behind and at sides, with no sign of flare. Plastron large, with freely movable anterior and posterior lobes. Head small and tapering. Male with conspicuous patches of tilted scales on hind surface of hind leg. Young with a row of light spots along shell margin. Length about 3 inches or slightly more.

General Distribution.—Restricted to Florida.

Florida Range.—Peninsular Florida, from Leon, Alachua, and Clay counties southward to Key West, except where replaced by a slightly divergent population in the southern Everglades.

Habitat.—Small or quiet bodies of water, often wandering on land.

Kinosternon bauri palmarum Stejneger
Paradise Key Mud Turtle

General Appearance.—A small, brown turtle with a cross-striped shell.

Distinguishing Characters.—This race, which is only very slightly different from the Striped Mud Turtle, shares all the characteristics of that except the pattern of the carapace. Because the laminae of the shell of *palmarum* are very thin and translucent, the yellowish areas along the sutures of the bony shell show through. Since these sutures are predominately transverse, the shell appears to be cross-striped. Any other points of divergence between the two striped mud turtles have yet to be pointed out.

General Distribution.—Restricted to Florida.

Florida Range.—The Everglades, northward to Collier County, West Palm Beach, and Lake Okeechobee. The curious occurrence of typical *bauri* south of the range of this form is hard to explain, but has a parallel in the distribution of the racers.

Habitat.—Ditches, canals, and flooded glades, ranging into brackish water.

Kinosternon subrubrum subrubrum (Lacépède)
Common Mud Turtle

General Appearance.—A small mud turtle with a smooth, unmarked shell.

Distinguishing Characters.—Carapace smooth, keelless, and without light stripes, side of head plain or mottled but not clearly striped. Bridge wider than in *steindachneri,* a closely related subspecies.

Description.—Shell low, oval, or straight-sided, with steep hind margin. No central keel in adult; centrals sometimes depressed and shell bilobed. Anterior lobe of plastron shorter than posterior and the width of the bridge ⅔ or more of the length of the interabdominal seam. Head medium. Carapace yellowish, olive, or nearly black, without decoration; plastron yellowish or brownish. Head brownish or olive, with lighter mottling, which sometimes is arranged to form one or two vague bands on the neck. Length about 4½ inches.

General Distribution.—Eastern United States.

Florida Range.—Northern Florida, intergrading with *steindachneri* in Alachua County and with *hippocrepis* in extreme western Florida.

Habitat.—Most frequently seen in quiet water with abundant vegetation.

Kinosternon subrubrum steindachneri Siebenrock
Florida Mud Turtle *(Plate 41)*

General Appearance.—A small, smooth-shelled mud turtle with no distinctive markings.

Distinguishing Characters.—Some specimens of this mud turtle are very big-headed and look like a *Sternotherus;* they may be distinguished by the nearly triangular pectoral laminae, in which there is only a very short fourth side (these laminae oblong in *Sternotherus*). From *bauri* this mud turtle differs in having no light stripes on either the shell or the head, in the narrow bridge (its width contained in length of interabdominal seam 2½-3 times), its posteriorly forked nasal scale, and in the somewhat smaller plastron, in which the fore lobe is as long as or longer than the hind lobe.

General Distribution.—Restricted to Florida.

Florida Range.—Peninsular Florida from the Alachua County area southward to Cape Sable. It intergrades with *subrubrum* north of Alachua County and in the eastern part of the panhandle.

Habitat.—Ditches, sloughs, and marshes. Very aquatic.

Terrapene carolina carolina (Linnaeus)
Common Box Turtle

General Appearance.—A medium-sized land turtle with a dark brown shell usually marked with yellow dots or lines and capable of closing up completely.

Distinguishing Characters.—This subspecies may be usually distinguished by the combination of a closable shell which is broad, of medium height, with a slight keel, with its highest point near the middle, and the rear margins deep and not flaring; the small size as compared with the other subspecies; the 4 toes on the hind foot; and the lack of stripes on the side of the head.

Description.—Shell comparatively short, broad, and oval to nearly oblong in dorsal aspect; highest point of the carapace is nearly always about the middle of the long axis and the central keel is almost always evident; back margin slightly flaring or not at all; concentric growth rings discernible in young specimens but tending to disappear with old age; carapace brown or yellowish, nearly always with yellow markings, but these extremely variable; in a majority of specimens however showing some radial arrangement; plastron yellowish to dark brown with or without darker smudges or rayed blotches and sometimes with a dark area in the middle sending out branches along the borders of the seams. Average size probably between 5 and $5\frac{1}{2}$ inches.

General Distribution.—Most of the eastern part of the United States.

Florida Range.—The northernmost counties of the Florida peninsula, occurring as variants as far south as Alachua County.

Habitat.—Open woodlands and sometimes fields and meadows, usually in the vicinity of brooks or ponds.

Terrapene carolina bauri Taylor
Florida Box Turtle (Plate 41)

General Appearance.—A medium-sized box turtle with a high, narrow, yellow-rayed shell.

Distinguishing Characters.—This subspecies is very closely related to *T. c. carolina* and *T. c. major,* in some respects being intermediate between the two. The following combination of characters will distinguish a majority of specimens from all other box turtles: shell comparatively narrow and highly domed, with the highest point often back of the middle; hind foot usually with 3 toes; side of head with 2 usually complete yellow stripes; carapace brown or olive with yellow stripes which are usually distinct, narrow, and on the laterals radiate from the upper rear part of the laminae. Male with the plastron strongly concave below, and narrower than that of the female. Young spotted, with a yellow keel on the carapace. Length of mature specimens about 5½ inches.

General Distribution.—Peninsular Florida.

Florida Range.—Northeastern Florida, where it intergrades with *T. c. carolina,* southward through the Keys, intergrading with *T. c. major* of the Gulf counties of the upper part of the peninsula through a somewhat poorly defined area.

Habitat.—Hammocks, pinelands, and fields. Most numerous in Dade County limestone flatwoods.

Terrapene carolina major (Agassiz)
Gulf Coast Box Turtle

General Appearance.—A good-sized box turtle often dark to nearly black in color, with a high, keeled shell.

Distinguishing Characters.—Although this subspecies is very closely related to both *bauri* and *triunguis,* a majority of specimens can be recognized by the combination of large size, a four-toed hind foot, the elongate, highly domed shell with its highest point in the middle and with its sides nearly straight in lateral outline; by the usually reduced dorsal pattern which only occasionally shows any radial arrangement of yellow dots or broken lines; and by the lack of definite yellow stripes on the sides of the head. Length 6 or 7 inches.

General Distribution.—The upper Gulf Coast of the United States.

Florida Range.—Coast of the Florida panhandle from about the region of Cape San Blas westward.

Habitat.—Pine flatwoods and upland hammocks.

Terrapene carolina triunguis (Agassiz)
Three-toed Box Turtle

General Appearance.—A small, narrow-shelled, rather strikingly colored box turtle.

Distinguishing Characters.—This subspecies has not been well defined but it is probable that a majority of specimens may be identified by the combination of a narrow, keeled shell with a flaring posterior margin; the conspicuous, often very striking, spotting of the soft parts of the head; the three-toed hind foot; and the usually yellow, unmarked plastron. Length about 5½ inches.

General Distribution.—The Mississippi Valley eastward and southward into southwestern Georgia.

Florida Range.—The Tallahassee area northward to the Georgia line.

Habitat.—Found in a wide variety of habitats but perhaps most numerous in the edges of open woodlands preferably near water.

Malaclemys terrapin centrata (Latreille)
Southern Diamondback Terrapin

General Appearance.—A medium-sized, usually rough-shelled, salt-water turtle with no light head stripes.

Distinguishing Characters.—Recognized by the broadly ovoid shell as seen from above, the slightly convergent sides of the posterior lobe of the plastron, the lack of terminal expansions on the keels of the centrals and the lack of yellow spots on the shell and of black borders on the submarginal laminae.

Description.—Shell rather broad, sometimes nearly straight-sided as seen from above, or if not, then the widest point at about the middle; dorsal laminae usually marked by deep growth ridges and the central keel not strong, the individual sections never terminating in a bulb. Head relatively large and flat-topped. Color of shell black to brown or slightly grayish, unmarked except for vague light concentric rings sometimes on the dorsal laminae. Head and soft parts black to gray green, lighter specimens usually sporadically marked with dark dots and irregular short lines. Lips and top of head either uniform white or dusky. Plastron either uniform yellowish or greenish or blotched with irregular dark pigment. In size the males are much smaller than the females (average size for males being about 5 inches and average length of females about 7 inches).

General Distribution.—Cape Hatteras to southern peninsular Florida where it meets and intergrades with the Mangrove Terrapin.

Florida Range.—The East Coast.

Habitat.—Salt marshes and estuaries.

Malaclemys terrapin macrospilota (W. P. Hay)
Florida Diamondback Terrapin *(Plate 42)*

General Appearance.—A medium-sized salt-water turtle with bulbous projections along the central keel and a spotted shell.

Distinguishing Characters.—This striking subspecies may be recognized by the combination of a large yellow spot in the center of each dorsal lamina, a central keel in which the individual sections terminate with a strong bulb, and by the lack of dark borders along the submarginal and plastral laminae. The yellow spots on the upper shell make this the most easily recognized of all the races of diamondbacks. Size about as in *centrata*.

General Distribution.—Restricted to Florida.

Florida Range.—Gulf Coast of peninsular Florida, intergrading with *pileata* in the panhandle and with the Mangrove Terrapin in Florida Bay.

Habitat.—Passes and mangrove-bordered lagoons and estuaries. It is perhaps significant that the northern limit of the range of this subspecies coincides fairly closely with that of the Red Mangrove.

Malaclemys terrapin rhizophorarum Fowler
Mangrove Terrapin

General Appearance.—A strongly keeled salt-water turtle of medium size and no striking color pattern on the upper shell.

Distinguishing Characters.—Although in a way intermediate between the adjacent subspecies of terrapins, this race may be recognized in a majority of specimens by its terminally expanded dorsal keels, the lack of yellow centers in the dorsal laminae, and the presence of black borders along the submarginal seams and also along some of the plastral seams. Nothing is known about the size range of this form, but it is hardly likely that it shows any differences from the annectent races in this respect.

General Distribution.—Restricted to Florida.

Florida Range.—The Florida Keys westward at least as far as the Marquesas Keys.

Habitat.—Mangrove swamps and mangrove-bordered waters of Florida Bay.

Malaclemys terrapin pileata (Weed)
Mississippi Diamondback Terrapin

General Appearance.—A medium-sized salt-water turtle with no dorsal shell pattern.

Distinguishing Characters.—The relatively minor features by which this form is distinguished are: the central keel in which the individual sections end in marked expansions; the uniform dark color of the carapace which is not marked with large yellow central spots on the laminae; and the usually dark upper lip and upper surface of the head. Shell perhaps somewhat narrower and even more straight-sided than the Southern Diamondback and the size a little larger. The largest Diamondback on record is a Louisiana specimen of this race.

General Distribution.—Gulf Coast of the Florida panhandle where through a rather broad area it intergrades with the Florida Diamondback Terrapin westward to eastern Louisiana where it meets and intergrades with the Texas Diamondback.

Florida Range.—Gulf Coast of the Florida panhandle.

Habitat.—Brackish streams, estuaries, and salt marshes, appearing to favor the channels with moving water.

Graptemys barbouri Carr and Marchand
Barbour's Sawback Turtle *(Plates 43 and 45)*

General Appearance.—A medium-sized, high-keeled turtle with conspicuous head markings.

Distinguishing Characters.—This sawback may be recognized by the extensive yellow areas on the head; the high, tuberculate mid-dorsal keel; the simple or nonexistent plastral pattern; by the presence of a U-shaped, thin-lined figure on each dorsal lamina, the open edge of the U against the posterior seam; and by the presence on the lower surface of the chin of only transverse light markings.

Description.—Shell somewhat high, tapered posteriorly and with its highest point usually before the middle; hind margin serrate. The carapace is smooth except for the prominent central keel of which the various sections are inclined to be tuberculate, although decreasingly so in old females. Profile of anterior part of keel slightly concave outward. Head very large in old females, the crushing surfaces of the jaws so broad as almost to meet in the median line. The characteristic color pattern of the shell includes, besides the C- or U-shaped figure that ends against the posterior suture of each lateral, a thin-lined mark on each upper marginal extending from the lower fore corner to the upper hind corner. The central keel (especially the tips of the tubercles) is darker brown than the surrounding ground color of the shell. Plastron yellowish to whitish with or without a seam pattern of very narrow black bands, one along the posterior margin of each lamina except the anals. Ground color of soft parts very dark brown or black, the markings cream-colored or whitish. Head with 3 interconnected broad areas of light color, 1 on the snout between the eyes and 1 behind each eye. The median blotch continues forward as a sagittal stripe. Ventral horny surface of lower jaw marked by a broad transverse band. Size of female about 9 inches, male very much smaller.

General Distribution.—The western panhandle.

Florida Range.—Known only from the Apalachicola and Chipola rivers in Gadsden, Jackson, and Calhoun counties and from the Escambia River in Escambia County.

Habitat.—Creeks and rivers, preferably with clear water and rocky bottoms.

Graptemys pulchra Baur
Alabama Sawback Turtle

General Appearance.—A medium-sized, high-keeled turtle with conspicuous head markings.

Distinguishing Characters.—Although as yet poorly understood, this turtle is obviously closely related to *G. barbouri.* Most males and young specimens can be immediately distinguished, however, by the pattern of lines on the laterals (at least parts of 3 to 5 irregular cells on each lateral in *pulchra;* one big, roughly circular mark opening against the hind seam in *barbouri*). Chin usually with a median longitudinal stripe in *pulchra* and only with cross bands in *barbouri.* There are average differences in the head markings, the plastral markings, and in a number of other features.

Description.—Carapace short and broad, in the young highly keeled above and deeply serrated around the margin, the hind edge very strongly toothed. The dorsal keel, which is strongest in the young and in males, comprises a boss on each of the first four centrals, these being very sharp and high on the second and third centrals, somewhat weaker on the fourth, weak to nearly lacking on the first and completely lacking on the fifth. The head is broad—sometimes extremely so in old females in which the crushing surfaces may be so expanded as to occupy all the fore part of the roof of the mouth. Ground color of carapace olive, the juvenile pattern comprising a usually incomplete set of reticulate markings on the laterals. There are usually on each 3 to 5 connected cells of ground color bounded by thin yellow lines; these are clearer on the fore half of each lamina than on the hind half. The centrals are usually unmarked except for a varyingly intense middorsal stripe which begins on the precentral and continues, as dark tips on the tubercles, to the fourth central, sometimes appearing on the last central as a short spot. Each marginal with a heavily colored, yellow, irregularly C-shaped mark surrounding concentric rings that are discernible only in very young. Plastron light, with dark markings on the sutures, at least in the young. Head markings very variable but usually involving a heavy light mark behind each eye and one between the eyes. Lower jaw with at least a suggestion of a median stripe toward the symphysis. Size about 7 inches.

General Distribution.—Extreme western Florida to the Pearl River drainage of Louisiana.

Florida Range.—Known only from the Escambia River.

Habitat.—The deeper, slower reaches of creeks and rivers; basking on logs over deep holes.

Chrysemys picta picta (Schneider)
Eastern Painted Turtle

General Appearance.—A small, flat, smooth-shelled turtle usually with red markings.

Distinguishing Characters.—This Painted Turtle may usually be recognized by the combination of a notched upper jaw; the low, flat, smooth, unkeeled shell, without serrations at its posterior margin; and the arrangements of the seams between the second and third centrals.

Description.—Shell oval as seen from above, depressed, widest toward the rear and either wholly smooth or with very slight concentric wrinkles. Second and third centrals in line with the second and third laterals, their anterior and posterior seams nearly continuous across. Shell not serrate behind. Upper jaw notched at the tip with a cusp on each side of the notch; crushing surface of upper jaw narrow and with a low, even ridge. Carapace olive to dark brown in color, the laminae broadly edged with yellowish or reddish anteriorly. Marginals conspicuously marked with red bands or bars above and below. Plastron plain yellow or rarely marked with black. Ground color of head dark olive to brown with light stripes. Legs dark, streaked with yellowish or red. Shell length of mature individuals 5 or 6 inches.

General Distribution.—Eastern North America.

Florida Range.—An old record for northeastern Florida has never been substantiated.

Habitat.—Ponds, protected lake shores, ditches, and slow streams and marshes.

Pseudemys scripta scripta (Schoepff)
Yellow-bellied Turtle *(Plates 43, 44, and 45)*

General Appearance.—A short, rough-shelled, high-shelled turtle.

Distinguishing Characters.—The Yellow-bellied Turtle may be easily distinguished from all others in its range by the notched or vertically angular junction of the two sides of the upper jaw, the conspicuous yellow blotch on the side of the head behind the eye, and the markings of the plastron.

Description.—Shell short, broad, straight-sided or oval in lateral outline, and moderately deep. Carapace thick-boned and often quite rough. Ground color of carapace dark brown to black with a light bar sometimes very conspicuous on each lateral. Plastron bright yellow to orange-yellow; one or more pairs of the laminae marked each with a deep black smudge at the posterior edge. A broad yellow patch behind the eyes formed by the fusion of a dorsolateral and a lateral neck stripe with a piece of the dorsolateral stripe lacking just behind the patch. In old males, all head markings as well as those of the carapace and plastron either fade or are strongly modified by secondary deposition of dark pigment. Size of mature specimens from 5 to 8 inches.

General Distribution.—Coastal Virginia to Georgia and Florida.

Florida Range.—Northeastern Florida from Alachua and Levy counties westward to the Apalachicola drainage where intergradation with *Pseudemys scripta elegans* occurs.

Habitat.—Ponds and lakes.

Pseudemys nelsoni Carr
Florida Red-bellied Turtle *(Plate 45)*

General Appearance.—A medium-sized, dark-shelled turtle, often with red markings above or below (or both).

Distinguishing Characters.—*P. nelsoni* may be recognized by the notched and cusped upper jaw and by the presence on most specimens of red pigment either on the plastron, the lower marginals, or the carapace.

Description.—Shell somewhat similar in shape to that of *P. f. peninsularis*, but more highly elevated along the centrals and usually with more fine longitudinal wrinkles. Bridge deep. Hind margin of shell serrate. Upper jaw notched and cusped at the tip and usually somewhat serrate. Crushing surface of upper jaw with a strong tuberculate ridge. Ground color of carapace dark, usually black, and often with red markings which may either be arranged as broad transverse bars or may be wholly without order. Plastron yellowish or red, with or without a seam-following, dusky figure. Lower marginals blotched and often red. Stripes on head yellowish or greenish-yellow and relatively few in number. Length about a foot, although males mature at much smaller size.

General Distribution.—Restricted to Florida.

Florida Range.—Peninsular Florida from Alachua and Levy counties southward to Cape Sable.

Habitat.—No strict habitat preferences shown. Found in ditches, sloughs, marshes, lakes, ponds, and streams, occasionally entering brackish water.

Pseudemys floridana floridana (Le Conte)
Coastal Plain Turtle

General Appearance.—A good-sized, brown-shelled turtle with yellow markings on the shell and neck.

Distinguishing Characters.—The Coastal Plain Turtle is readily distinguished by its high shell, its separately continuous supratemporal and paramedian head stripes, the smooth, unnotched upper jaw, the light centered submarginal spots, and the absence of a plastral pattern.

Description.—Carapace moderately elevated, with its highest point at the middle. Shell often longitudinally wrinkled and serrate behind. Bridge fairly deep although much less so than in *peninsularis*. Jaws not notched and relatively smooth, the crushing surface with a strong tuberculate ridge parallel with the cutting edge. Ground color of carapace dark brown, usually with a complex series of concentric or linear light markings. Plastron bright yellow or orange-yellow and not marked with a median dusky figure. The blotches on the submarginal seams usually ringlike, with light centers. Ground color of soft parts and limbs brown, markings bright yellow. The larger females are somewhat more than a foot long, the males slightly smaller.

General Distribution.—Atlantic coastal plain from southeastern Virginia to Alabama and northern Florida.

Florida Range.—The northern part of the peninsula except for the lower streams of the Gulf Coast drainage; westward in the panhandle it meets and intergrades with *Pseudemys floridana mobilensis*. In the St. Johns River and in Alachua and adjacent counties, *floridana* intergrades with *peninsularis*.

Habitat.—Shows little habitat discrimination, being found in rivers, ponds, lakes, and swamps.

Pseudemys floridana peninsularis Carr
Peninsular Turtle *(Plate 46)*

General Appearance.—A very high-backed, good-sized turtle, with greenish yellow markings on the head and neck.

Distinguishing Characters.—This race is separated from all the others by the confluent dorsal and dorsolateral (supratemporal and paramedian) head stripes on the side of the head, by the solid, smudge-like markings at the submarginal seams, by the lack of a plastral pattern and of a notch in the upper jaw, by the shell contours, and by the peculiar greenish tint of the head markings.

Description.—Shell very highly domed, torpedo-shaped with the highest point usually noticeably anterior to the middle and with the bridge so deep as to be conspicuously evident from the side. Upper jaw not notched, relatively smooth, and with a tuberculate median ridge on the alveolar surface. Color pattern of carapace usually with 1 or 2 broad transverse bars on each lateral the most conspicuous features. No plastral dusky figure. Ground color of head and soft parts very deep black, the lines and stripes greenish-yellow or greenish-white. The larger females are usually somewhat more than a foot in shell length, the males slightly less.

General Distribution.—Restricted to Florida.

Florida Range.—Peninsular Florida from about the level of Alachua County and the upper (southern) third of the St. Johns River southward to the tip of the peninsula except for some of the West Coast rivers in which it is replaced by *Pseudemys floridana suwanniensis.*

Habitat.—Nearly any aquatic situation, preferably where there is submerged vegetation.

Pseudemys floridana mobilensis (Holbrook)
Mobile Turtle *(Plates 43 and 44)*

General Appearance.—A good-sized, high-shelled, brown turtle with yellow head and neck markings.

Distinguishing Characters.—This race may be easily distinguished from its southern relative, *suwanniensis*, by the brown color of the soft parts, the yellow color of the markings, the greater number of head stripes and of stripes on the legs, the more extensive markings of the hind feet, the less symmetrical plastral pattern and by the more extensive occurrence of reddish color on the soft parts of the head and shell. The only consistently reliable character that distinguishes this subspecies from *floridana*, however, appears to be the presence of a dusky, dendritic pattern on the plastron.

Description.—The shell is high with its highest point usually at the middle; the jaws are not notched or cusped in the majority of specimens, but a notched-jawed individual may turn up occasionally. Such notched-jawed specimens of *mobilensis* and of *suwanniensis* have in the past been given the name of *Pseudemys alabamansis*. The cutting edge of the upper jaw is often serrate and the ridge on the alveolar surfaces tuberculate. Head and soft parts brown in ground color with 4 or more lines on the outer surface of each fore limb and 7 or more lines between the eyes; the outer surface of the hind foot is striped. Females about a foot long, males a little smaller.

General Distribution.—Coast of the Florida panhandle westward to Texas.

Florida Range.—Rivers of the panhandle from the Apalachicola River drainage, into which the subspecies extends at least as far as southwestern Georgia, westward apparently through all the master stream systems of western Florida.

Habitat.—Lower coastal streams, occasionally ascending them to fast-moving or even rocky tributaries. Most abundant where there is submerged vegetation. Found also in brackish estuaries and on saltwater flats.

Pseudemys floridana suwanniensis Carr
Suwannee Turtle

General Appearance.—A good-sized, high-shelled river turtle with dark markings on the lower shell.

Distinguishing Characters.—Recognized by the high-domed shell with its highest point before the middle, the presence of a dusky plastral pattern, the deep black color of the soft parts, and the dilute, lemon-yellow color of the markings on the head and neck and limbs, the presence of only about 3 stripes on the anterior surface of the fore foot and of 5 stripes between the eyes, and by the lack of stripings on the hind foot.

Description.—Shell similar in contours to that of *peninsularis*, except more depressed along the median line and with even more of the streamlined torpedo shape of that race, although some of the mature malcs are noticeably flattened. Shell dark above with more or less evident reticulated markings. Plastron yellow or yellowish-white with a usually well-expressed dendritic seam pattern occupying either the anterior part of the shell or the entire seam system, and usually bilaterally symmetrical. The head stripes include none which run together as they extend from the neck onto the top of the head. The supratemporal stripe is expanded on the neck. Upper limit of shell length of females about 13 inches or slightly more, the males are smaller.

General Distribution.—Restricted to Florida.

Florida Range.—Gulf coastal rivers and inshore brackish and salt water from the vicinity of Cape San Blas southward to Pinellas County. In the region about the Apalachicola delta, *suwanniensis* and *mobilensis* intergrade.

Habitat.—Rivers, spring runs, and shallow vegetated flats along the Gulf Coast.

Deirochelys reticularia (Latreille)

Chicken Turtle *(Plate 42)*

General Appearance.—A small to medium-sized, long-necked turtle with a narrow shell.

Distinguishing Characters.—The Chicken Turtle is easily recognized by its very long neck, its finely wrinkled, elongate shell, and by the vertical stripes on the rump.

Description.—Shell long, narrow, rather low, usually keelless, finely grooved longitudinally, and not conspicuously serrate behind. Neck about as long as plastron. Carapace olive to brown with a large mesh, thin-lined, reticulate pattern. Plastron yellow, with black smudges on the bridge and sometimes on some of the plastral laminae. Head and neck olive brown with light stripes. Hind surface of hind limbs marked by conspicuous vertical stripes. Length about 6 inches.

General Distribution.—Southeastern States and Lower Mississippi Valley.

Florida Range.—Known from all parts of the state except the Keys.

Habitat.—Usually found in ponds, marshes, sloughs, and ditches.

Gopherus polyphemus (Daudin)

Gopher Tortoise

General Appearance.—A medium-sized land turtle with fore feet modified for digging.

Distinguishing Characters.—The Gopher can be distinguished from the other Florida turtles by its shovel-like front feet and stubby, elephantine hind feet.

Description.—Carapace somewhat elongate, rather low, oblong from dorsal view, and with growth furrows often evident on the laminae. Gulars usually strongly projecting. Head large and blunt. Fore limbs flattened as laterally sweeping shovels; hind feet elephantine. No stripes on head, neck, or legs. Carapace brown or tan, with or without light centers of the laminae.

General Distribution.—Southeastern States.

Florida Range.—Known throughout Florida to tip of peninsula.

Habitat.—High pine woods, dune terrain, and other deep sand areas are most frequently inhabited.

Chelonia mydas mydas (Linnaeus)
Atlantic Green Turtle (Plate 47)

General Appearance.—A large turtle with paddle-like fore feet, a moderate-sized head, and brownish soft parts.

Distinguishing Characters.—Distinguished from all other turtles in its range by the single pair of prefrontals, the four pairs of laterals; the strong vertical ridges on the inner surface of the upper jaw, and the side-by-side arrangement of the laminae, which do not overlap.

Description.—Shell broad, low, flattened, and slightly more elongate than heart-shaped. Carapace smooth, keelless, the laminae never imbricate. Four inframarginals present, these not perforated by pores at their posterior margins. Plastron double-keeled in young, which have also a mid-dorsal keel and traces of dorsolateral keels. Carapace light to dark brown, often shaded or mottled with blotches or radiating lines of darker color. Plastron whitish to light yellow. Top of head brown. Sides of head with brown scales light-margined. Length about 3 feet.

General Distribution.—This subspecies inhabits the warmer parts of the Atlantic Ocean, the Gulf of Mexico, and the Mediterranean Sea.

Florida Range.—Recorded from all parts of the Gulf and Atlantic shore line.

Habitat.—Shallow shore waters with abundant vegetation.

Eretmochelys imbricata imbricata (Linnaeus)
Atlantic Hawksbill Turtle (Plate 47)

General Appearance.—A paddle-footed sea turtle, smaller than most of the others, with a sometimes highly decorated shell.

Distinguishing Characters.—Distinguished from other turtles in its range by the combination of 4 pairs of laterals (the first separated from the precentrals by the first central), 2 pairs of prefrontals, smooth inner surface of upper jaw, and usually imbricate laminae.

Description.—Shell heart-shaped or shield-shaped, longer in old than in young specimens. Laminae nearly always strongly overlapped. A mid-dorsal keel usually present on posterior 4 centrals. Carapace reddish-brown, flecked and dashed with various other shades; plastron yellow. The "tortoise shell" coloration is usually not evident until the laminae are polished. Head scales chestnut brown, light-bordered. Length about 2 feet.

General Distribution.—Warm waters of the Atlantic, Gulf of Mexico, and Caribbean Sea, rarely reaching the coast of Europe, possibly by way of the Gulf Stream.

Florida Range.—Recorded from most of the shore waters of the peninsula.

Habitat.—The shallow coastal waters.

Caretta caretta caretta (Linnaeus)
Atlantic Loggerhead Turtle *(Plate 48)*

General Appearance.—A huge, big-headed, thick-shelled turtle with paddle-like feet.

Distinguishing Characters.—The Loggerhead differs from the other sea turtles in its range in the 2 pairs of prefrontals, the 3 enlarged, poreless inframarginals, the 5 or more pairs of laterals, the smooth inner surface of the upper jaw, and the reddish color.

Description.—Shell elongate—oval or heart-shaped—somewhat concave over shoulders and in front. First pair of lateral laminae in contact with precentral. Dorsal laminae not overlapping. Head very large, broad behind and abruptly tapering anteriorly, and covered by about 20 scales including the 2 pairs of prefrontals between the eyes. Carapace brown, shaded or mottled with olive, the laminae sometimes bordered with dull yellowish. Scales of head brown, fading to yellowish peripherally. Plastron and lower surfaces of neck, legs, and tail yellowish. Length of shell of adult often 3 feet or more, although mature at smaller sizes and sometimes reaching much greater shell lengths.

General Distribution.—Atlantic Ocean, Caribbean Sea, Gulf of Mexico, and the Mediterranean.

Florida Range.—Common in all Florida shore waters.

Habitat.—Ranges widely. Found in large estuaries, marsh creeks, and in the open sea far from land.

Lepidochelys kempi (Garman)

Atlantic Ridley *(Plate 48)*

General Appearance.—A short-shelled, gray, salt-water turtle with paddle-feet and a big head.

Distinguishing Characters.—Readily recognized by the gray color, the 4 perforated enlarged inframarginals, the short shell, and the 5 pairs of laterals. Skulls may be distinguished from those of *Caretta* by the sharp lateral processes (ectopterygoid processes) on the pterygoid bones.

Description —Carapace short, wide, and often nearly circular in lateral outline. Precentral usually in contact with laterals, which are very consistently 5 on each side. Four enlarged inframarginal laminae, each pierced by a pore at the posterior seam. Head wide, outer surface of jaws convex. Lower jaw with a strong median elevation at the posterior edge of the bony alveolar surface. Mandible covered by a single large scale. Color gray above, white or yellowish-white below. Size about 2 feet.

General Distribution.—Gulf of Mexico and the Florida Keys, northward to coast of Massachusetts and (rarely) the British Isles and the Azores.

Florida Range.—Known from all sections of the Florida coast. It appears not to cross the Gulf Stream into the Bahamas.

Habitat.—Shallow coastal waters, especially the mangrove-bordered bays of the southern half of the peninsula of Florida.

Amyda ferox ferox (Schneider)

Southern Soft-shelled Turtle *(Plate 49)*

General Appearance.—A flat turtle with a long, thin snout and a leathery shell.

Distinguishing Characters.—Recognized by the flattened shell with leathery edges and no laminae, the long, tubular snout, the fleshy lips, the usually longitudinally ridged shell, the lack of marginal dark lines, and the peculiar pattern of the carapace in the young.

Description.—Shell somewhat elongate, with blunt tubercles anteriorly. Surface of carapace intricately sculptured, but usually with at least a trace of longitudinal arrangement of the ridges. Coloration of young very distinctive, including a conspicuous reticulate pattern on the carapace in which narrow light lines separate big dark blotches, upper surface of head, neck, and legs mottled olive and yellowish. Side of head with 3 or 4 light bands usually discernible. Usual length of adult about 1 foot.

General Distribution.—Florida and southern Georgia.

Florida Range.—All of Florida east of the Apalachicola, except the Keys.

Habitat.—All kinds of aquatic situations. Perhaps most abundant in the Everglades canals and in swamp-shore lakes.

Amyda ferox aspera (Agassiz)
Southern Spiny Soft-shelled Turtle

General Appearance.—A flat, long-snouted turtle with a leathery shell.

Distinguishing Characters.—This race can be distinguished from all others in its range in Florida by the leathery shell and long, narrow snout, the 2 or 3 dark lines that extend around the edge of the carapace, the failure of the lateral head stripes (if present) to meet on the neck, and the lack of a reticulate light shell pattern like that of *ferox*. Adult size about 1 foot or slightly less.

General Distribution.—Louisiana eastward to southwestern Georgia and western Florida.

Florida Range.—Probably present in most of the larger streams of the panhandle.

Habitat.—Rivers and river swamps.

Dermochelys coriacea coriacea (Linnaeus)
Atlantic Leatherback Turtle

General Appearance.—An immense salt-water turtle with a ridged, leathery shell.

Distinguishing Characters.—The Leatherback is easily recognized by the smooth skin of the shell, not covered by laminae; the 7 longitudinal ridges of the upper shell and the 5 similar ridges of the plastron; the flipper-like feet; the notched and toothed upper jaw; and the predominately black-and-white coloration, most striking in the young. The young are covered with scales. A shell length of 5-6 feet is probably an average size for mature individuals.

General Distribution.—Atlantic Ocean, Caribbean Sea, Gulf of Mexico, and the Mediterranean, replaced by a very similar race in the Indo-Pacific.

Florida Range.—Known from points off all parts of the Florida shore line.

Habitat.—The open sea.

Alligator mississippiensis (Daudin)
Alligator

General Appearance.—A huge, rough-backed, lizard-shaped reptile with a broad, rounded snout.

Distinguishing Characters.—Recognized by the longitudinal anal opening and broad, spatulate snout and by the fact that the fourth mandibular tooth is not exposed when the mouth is closed.

Description.—Fourth tooth of the lower jaw fitting into a notch in the upper jaw, not evident when the jaw is closed. Back covered by several rows of keeled, bony scales placed end to end in longitudinal series; ventral scales smooth and flexible. Fingers about ½ webbed; outer toes about ⅔ webbed. Tail strongly compressed and crested dorsally. Snout broad, straight-sided, and bluntly rounded at the end. Color black or olive, light below. Young crossbanded with yellow. Maximum length between 14 and 16 feet.

General Distribution.—North Carolina westward in the coastal lowlands through Texas.

Florida Range.—Occurs throughout the state. Occasionally found in salt waters.

Habitat.—Very generally distributed, the habitat today is for the most part merely the places that offer the best protection from molestation by man.

Crocodylus acutus Cuvier
American Crocodile (Plate 49)

General Appearance.—A huge, rough-backed, lizard-shaped reptile with a sharp snout.

Distinguishing Characters.—Recognized by the longitudinal anal slit, the pointed snout, and the exposed fourth mandibular tooth.

Description.—Fifth tooth of lower jaw the largest, the fourth, which usually fits into a notch in the upper jaw, being exposed when the mouth is closed. Back covered by several rows of keeled, bony scales placed end to end in longitudinal series; belly scales smooth and flexible. Outer toes strongly webbed. Outer edge of leg with a serrate fringe. Snout tapering to a blunt, rounded point. Gray to black above, sometimes mottled; whitish or yellowish below; young olive dotted or mottled with black. Maximum length between 14 and 16 feet.

General Distribution.—Southernmost Florida, the Greater Antilles (except Porto Rico); Pacific and Caribbean coasts of Central America from Mexico to Ecuador and Colombia.

Florida Range.—Now much reduced, the range once extended from Volusia County on the East Coast southward through the Keys and northward on the Gulf Coast at least to Collier County.

Habitat.—Salt bays and mangrove bordered estuaries, ranging into the open sea.

Gonatodes fuscus (Hallowell)

Yellow-headed Gecko   *(Plate 51)*

General Appearance.—A small, grayish- or yellow-headed lizard with no toe-pads.

Distinguishing Characters.—The male is easily recognized by the yellow head and neck above; the female can be identified by the lack of toe-pads and of eyelids.

Description.—Scales on head, legs and body small and tuberculate, projecting from surface a distance as great as their lengths; scales on tail and belly flat, imbricate and bigger than dorsal scales. Tail with the dorsal scales irregular and with a median row of enlarged scales. Base of digits with slightly enlarged lamellae. Femoral and anal pores lacking. Males usually grayish-brown to nearly black with head and neck yellowish to orange. Female brownish or gray with varyingly regular dark and light markings usually including a white vertical line before the fore legs and a series of 4-6 dark spots along side back of shoulder. Tip of whole unregenerated tail light. Snout-to-vent length about 1½ inches.

General Distribution.—Greater Antilles, Central America, and Colombia; introduced in Florida.

Florida Range.—Key West.

Habitat.—Houses, outbuildings, and lumber piles.

Hemidactylus turcicus turcicus (Linnaeus)
Warty Gecko (Plate 51)

General Appearance.—A small, warty, house lizard.

Distinguishing Characters.—The lidless eyes and elongate toe-pads are enough to distinguish this lizard from all others.

Description.—Dorsal scalation granular except for 7 to 8 irregular rows of enlarged, keeled tubercles; these occur also on the upper surface of the hind leg, and there are 2 rows of them on each side of the tail. Belly scales flat, smooth, in size intermediate between enlarged tubercles and granular scales of back. Pupil vertical. Males with 2-10 anal pores. Ground color whitish to dark gray, usually mottled with darker color. Ventral surfaces white or cream, usually brown speckled. Snout-to-vent length about 2⅜ inches.

General Distribution.—Persian Gulf and Red Sea borders and adjacent coast of Indian Ocean; northward to Egypt and westward along Mediterranean to Canary Islands; Mexico from Yucatan around Gulf to Tamaulipas; Cuba; extreme southern Florida.

Florida Range.—Key West and the Miami area.

Habitat.—Houses, outbuildings, wharves, and lumber piles, congregating near lights at night.

Sphaerodactylus notatus Baird
Reef Gecko (Plate 50)

General Appearance.—A tiny, striped or speckled lizard with pads at the ends of the toes.

Distinguishing Characters.—The smallest Florida lizard; dorsal scales keeled and quite large (bigger than those of *cinereus*); toes pad-tipped; eyes lidless; neck with dark stripes or spots instead of rows of light dots.

Description.—Scales on back large, keeled, pointed behind, slightly imbricate, those on neck smaller and those on head very small and low-keeled. Labials much smaller behind than before. Pupil vertical. Ground color brownish or grayish with either scattered, rounded, dark dots on head and body (largest anteriorly, fading toward mid-body) or with 3 dark stripes on neck which fade toward mid-body but extend onto head. Snout-to-vent length about 1⅜ inches.

General Distribution.—Cuba, the Bahamas, and southernmost Florida.

Florida Range.—Collier and Dade counties through the Keys and to Key West.

Habitat.—Trash and rock piles; about houses; leaf mold in hammocks; drift along beaches.

Sphaerodactylus cinereus Wagler
Ashy Gecko (*Plate 50*)

General Appearance.—A tiny, bright-colored lizard with pad-tipped toes.

Distinguishing Characters.—One of the smallest Florida lizards, with rounded pads at the tips of the toes, no eyelids, tiny scales, and a vaguely linear light dorsal pattern.

Description.—Dorsal and lateral scales very small and weakly keeled, not or but slightly overlapping; ventral scales larger than dorsal, flattened, those under tail irregular in size. Pupil vertical. No preanal or femoral pores. Brownish to grayish dorsally with many small, light spots which tend to align themselves in stripes anteriorly. Cream or whitish below, finely speckled with brown. Young marked with red cross-bands. Snout-to-vent length hardly more than 1⅜ inches.

General Distribution.—Haiti, Cuba, Isla de Piños, and Florida Keys.

Florida Range.—Recorded only from Key West and Key Largo. Probably an introduced species.

Habitat.—Trash and rock piles around buildings or in hammocks.

Anolis carolinensis carolinensis Voigt
Carolina Anole

General Appearance.—A slim, arboreal lizard of unpredictable color, although usually some shade of brown or green.

Distinguishing Characters.—Distinguished from all other lizards in Florida by the following combination of characters: the elongate pads on the next-to-last joint of the toes; the presence of eyelids; the keeled, small scales that do not overlap; the rounded or slightly oval tail cross-section; and the presence of a dewlap in the male.

Description.—Dorsal scales tiny, with obtuse keels; ventral scales slightly larger, with stronger keels. Head long, flat, and tapered. Color brown, gray or green to nearly white; light below. Darker individuals show a light stripe along side of head below eye extending to shoulder. Dewlap of the male red.

General Distribution.—Southern United States from North Carolina to the Rio Grande.

Florida Range.—Throughout the state.

Habitat.—Arboreal; found also about buildings and logs and lumber piles.

Anolis distichus floridanus Smith and McCauley
Brickell Hammock Anole *(Plate 51)*

General Appearance.—A slim tree lizard of medium size.

Distinguishing Characters.—Recognized by the small, granular, smooth, unkeeled dorsal and ventral scales; the yellow dewlap; the presence on the snout of a median groove bordered by a row of sub-rectangular scales on each side; the 5-8 enlarged supraoculars; the separation of the supraorbital ridges from each other and from the occipital; and the wrinkled scales on the snout.

Description.—Head with 6 scales from rostral to prefrontal on each side; at least 4 scales across snout between posterior canthals; occipital of about the area of the ear opening. Supralabials and infralabials 5 to a point below middle of eye. Dorsal and lateral scales subequal, granular, protuberant; ventral scales larger than dorsals. Color dark brown or gray above, often with 4 dark chevrons on the back; the forelegs dimly barred; ventral surfaces sprinkled with dusky pigment; especially at sides of throat fan, on which the scales are also pigmented; top of head in life with a straight dark line across the crown and another line from the postparietal region to the eye on either side. Snout-to-vent length about 1¾ inches.

General Distribution.—Known only from the Miami area.

Florida Range.—As above.

Habitat.—Trees and bushes.

Anolis sagrei sagrei Dumeril and Bibron
Cuban Anole

General Appearance.—A medium-sized tree lizard.

Distinguishing Characters.—This race may be recognized by the large, overlapping, keeled dorsal scales, and granular lateral scales; the strongly compressed tail; the separated, paired supraorbital scales; the 16 or more scales from interparietal to rostral; and the orange-red or reddish-brown, usually gray-streaked, and sometimes yellow-edged throat fan of the male.

Description.—About 8 mid-dorsal rows of scales enlarged, more strongly keeled than adjacent scales and more strongly imbricated; ventrals larger than the largest dorsals, imbricate, and with strong continuous keels; supraorbital semicircles separated by one row of keeled scales; occipital about half the size of ear opening, separated from semicircle by 3 or 4 small, strongly keeled scales. Top of head with 2 bowed ridges, not closely converging anteriorly, separated by 4 scales at a point about halfway between eye and nostril. Color usually uniform blackish or brown, pale below. In young, a light mid-dorsal band or a series of variably distinct separated or confluent pale rhombic markings. Body stout for an *Anolis*. Length (snout-to-vent) of adult about 2 inches.

General Distribution.—Cuba and Isla de Piños. Introduced in Jamaica, Florida, and British Honduras.

Florida Range.—Tampa and St. Petersburg.

Habitat.—Trees, bushes, pilings, boards, and piles of timber or pipe.

Anolis sagrei ordinatus Cope
Bahama Anole

General Appearance.—A medium-sized, rather stout-bodied lizard often found on bushes.

Distinguishing Characters.—Distinguished by the large, keeled, overlapping dorsal scales; the granular lateral scales; the strongly compressed tail; the fact that the paired supraorbital scales are in contact; and the gray to nearly black dewlap.

Description.—The lateral dorsal scales are granular, and less than half the size of the ventrals. Ventrals large, keeled and imbricate. Head with 4-5 paired supraorbitals, 16-23 loreals, and 6-7 supralabials; lamellae 33-38 on fourth toe. Color grayish to brownish, somewhat darker than *stejnegeri*. Color either solid brown, gray or blackish, or with a wide, zigzag median stripe margined with brown. Canthal and frontal ridges well developed; supraorbital ridge low and rounded. Snout-to-vent length about 2 inches.

General Distribution.—The Bahamas, where it is the commonest reptile.

Florida Range.—Introduced at Lake Worth.

Habitat.—Widely distributed; found on trees, bushes, rocks, and on the open ground.

Anolis sagrei stejnegeri Barbour
Key Anole *(Plate 52)*

General Appearance.—A medium-sized tree lizard.

Distinguishing Characters.—Characterized by the large, imbricate, keeled dorsal scales and granular lateral scales; the laterally strongly compressed tail; the separation of the paired supraorbital scales; the presence of 15 or fewer scales from interparietal to rostral; and the burnt orange color of the dewlap of the male.

Description.—Ventral scales much larger than dorsal scales, all with keels. Head scales with one or more longitudinal keels; supraoculars 9-11. The lateral dorsal scales are larger, more sharply keeled, and more imbricate than in the other Florida races of *sagrei;* the crest on the tail is less prominent. Color uniform grayish to tan (lighter than other races of *sagrei*); throat fan with the mid-ventral scales at its anterior end when unexpanded, pure white, without dark spots. Snout-to-vent length about 2 inches.

Distribution.—Known only from Key West, Florida.

Habitat.—Trees and outbuildings; most abundant in coconut palms in the Navy Yard at Key West.

Leiocephalus carinatus virescens Stejneger
Bahamian Crested Lizard

General Appearance.—A medium-sized, rough-scaled lizard that often curls its tail over its back.

Distinguishing Characters.—Distinguished by the big keeled scales which number about 51-55 from occiput to base of tail and by the lack of femoral pores. The live animal is conspicuous in its striking habit of curling the long thin tail above the body.

Description.—Scales large, keeled, pointed, the rows convergent posteriorly; vertebral scale row on tail enlarged and, like mid-dorsal row on body, heavily keeled. Ground color gray to brown, the sides somewhat darker than the upper surface. Vertebral scales more or less dark-bordered; below a dorsal light area there may be a dark band or row of dark spots. Tail more or less banded, head irregularly marked with black. Light below with irregular spots on throat; belly immaculate or dimly speckled. Adult length about 3½ inches.

General Distribution.—Green Cay, Bahamas, and the Miami (Florida) area.

Florida Range.—Introduced in Miami and vicinity and perhaps established there.

Habitat.—Open woods, strand vegetation; limestone terrain, on sand, rocks, or logs.

Sceloporus undulatus undulatus (Latreille)
Southern Fence Lizard

General Appearance.—A medium-sized, rough-scaled lizard sitting on a log.

Distinguishing Characters.—This fence lizard may be recognized by its large, spiny, overlapping scales of which there are 31-40 (average 34) from occiput to base of tail (more than 40 in *woodi*) and by the lack of a well-defined dark lateral stripe.

Description.—Scales around mid-body 35-46, average 40; femoral pores 11-18. Color grayish, brownish or nearly black in males, the sides usually darker than back, without a clear-cut lateral band. Sides and back with about 8 (6-10) transverse bars (more distinct in females); tail vaguely ringed with dark and light; male with blue patches, broadly edged with black, on throat and sides of belly; these are less distinct in females and the gular patches of the females are surrounded by white and not black. Maximum length about 3 inches (snout-to-vent length).

General Distribution.—Southeastern coastal plain from South Carolina to eastern Louisiana.

Florida Range.—Northern Florida and the panhandle southward to Orange County.

Habitat.—Open woods, especially dry or upland hammocks and high pine and turkey oak.

Sceloporus woodi Stejneger
Scrub Pine Lizard

General Appearance.—A rough-scaled, brownish lizard of medium size.

Distinguishing Characters.—The Scrub Pine Lizard is known by its rough, overlapping scales, which usually number 40 or more from occiput to base of tail, and by its clear-cut dark lateral stripe. It superficially resembles the Bahamian Crested Lizard, but this species has no femoral pores, while *woodi* has.

Description.—Dorsal scales 36-45 from occiput to base of tail, keeled and overlapping; scales around mid-body 40-47. Femoral pores 14-20. Color usually brownish, with a conspicuous and definitely delimited dark band on side from neck to base of tail, and the back above this often marked with a series of 8-10 more or less distinct wavy vertical bars, those of the two sides separated by an unmarked mid-dorsal area. These vertical markings are stronger in females than in males. Males with a conspicuous blue patch, heavily bordered with black on each side of the throat, and a similar blue area with less heavy black border on each side of belly. Females generally white below except for weaker blue patches like those of males. Usual snout-to-vent length about 1¾ inches.

General Distribution.—Restricted to Florida.

Florida Range.—Peninsular Florida, discontinuously distributed in scattered sand pine and rosemary scrub areas from Marion and Putnam counties southward to Dade County.

Habitat.—Rosemary scrub and associated types, and cultural modifications of these.

Phrynosoma cornutum (Harlan)
Texas Horned Lizard

General Appearance.—A medium-sized thorny lizard with horns on its head and a wide flat body.

Distinguishing Characters.—The occipital horns and the broad flat spine-edged body distinguish this introduced species from any other lizard in Florida.

Description.—Dorsal scales mostly tiny; enlarged spines irregularly scattered on back; eye with a supraorbital ridge ending behind with a short, thick spine; occiput with a very large spine on each side; 3 temporal spines present, the 2 posterior the largest. Tympanum evident. Ground color yellowish or tan to brownish-red, with a dark blotch on each side of neck and upper shoulder; about four rows of black spots on back beside a light mid-dorsal stripe. Belly whitish or cream, sometimes thinly spotted.

General Distribution.—Kansas (and possibly Arkansas) through Texas into New Mexico and westward into southeastern Arizona.

Florida Range.—This western lizard has been released in various parts of the state and has been collected in Escambia, Lake, Orange, Putnam, Duval, and Dade counties.

Habitat.—On the ground in open country.

Ophisaurus ventralis Linnaeus
Common Glass Snake (Plate 52)

General Appearance.—A shiny, stiff-looking, speckled lizard with no legs.

Distinguishing Characters.—This form may be known by the lack of legs, the presence of eyes with lids, the occurrence of white spots on the posterior edges of the dorsal scales, and the lack of a mid-dorsal stripe.

Description.—Body wider than deep; dorsal scales slightly convex, not keeled; ventrals flat; ear opening oval, larger than nostril; dorsal scales in 14 longitudinal rows; frontonasal single. Coloration checkered, the middle of each scale brown and the ground color tan. On rows 4-7 (counting from above) there is white on the posterior part of each scale, and the resulting general pattern may be 3 irregular dark brown stripes running through the middle of the scales they traverse, and separated by 2 rows of narrow white spots. Belly white in young and yellow in mature individuals. Snout-to-vent length about 8½ inches. Tail usually not more than 2¼ times the body length.

General Distribution.—Coastal plain from North Carolina through eastern Louisiana.

Florida Range.—Throughout the state.

Habitat.—Fields, flatwoods, and hammock margins.

Ophisaurus attenuatus longicaudus McConkey
Eastern Long-tailed Glass Snake (Plate 53)

General Appearance.—A long-tailed, shiny, stiff-looking lizard with no legs.

Distinguishing Characters.—The lack of legs and the presence of eyes with lids show this to be a glass snake; and from related forms it may be distinguished by its coloration, by the fact that the white marks on the scales occupy the middle of the scales, and by the single frontonasal scale.

Description.—Dorsal scales in 14 rows; labials separated from the orbit by lorilabials. Adults with conspicuous dorsal crossbars which are 2 scales wide and separated from one another by 5 scale rows; each crossbar is a narrow white band bordered before and behind by a dark brown one; some of the bars cross the back, some are interrupted; none extends ventrally past the third scale row (counting down from above), and they fade on the tail. A mid-dorsal stripe or row of spots present. Lateral pattern of 3 brown stripes separated by white stripes. These stripes are specially prominent in young, which may lack the crossbars completely. Snout-to-vent length about 8 inches. Tail, unless regenerated, 2⅖ times snout-to-vent length or more.

General Distribution.—Southern states from Virginia to Kentucky, Mississippi, and Florida.

Florida Range.—Widely distributed; apparently lacking only in the southern part of the peninsula.

Habitat.—Old fields and dry open woods, especially turkey oak ridges.

Ophisaurus compressus Cope
Coastal Glass Snake (*Plate 53*)

General Appearance.—A long-tailed, shiny, stiff-looking lizard with no legs.

Distinguishing Characters.—Distinguished by the absence of legs, by the presence of eyes with lids, by the fact that at least one of the lower labials enters the orbit (not excluded by lorilabials as in other glass snakes in its range), and by the (usually) two frontonasal scales.

Description.—Anterior part of body heavily marked with white, the white markings comprising a usually single irregular spot near the edge of each scale. Side with a brown stripe from about mid-body onto tail, occupying lower half of fourth and upper part of fifth rows. Dorsal area between stripes tan, usually without pattern or with very vague mid-dorsal stripe. Color below the lateral stripes yellowish-white, like that of ventral surface, with no markings below the stripe in the back half of the body. Snout-to-vent length about 7½ inches. Tail between 2¼ and 3 times body length.

General Distribution.—South Carolina to Florida near the coast.

Florida Range.—Peninsular Florida.

Habitat.—Dune terrain; pioneer communities along the coast and coastal islands; rosemary scrub; occasional in flatwoods.

Cnemidophorus sexlineatus (Linnaeus)
Six-lined Racerunner (*Plate 52*)

General Appearance.—A slim, fast, athletic, ground-dwelling lizard with a bright eye and stripes.

Distinguishing Characters.—Easily recognized by the velvety, fine-scaled skin, the 6 narrow, clear-cut stripes, the 8 rows of large ventral scales, and the elongate body and tail.

Description.—Dorsal scales minute, 76-93 across back between outer ventrals at mid body. Two gular folds present. Ground color dark above with 6 well-defined, light, narrow, longitudinal stripes in young and in females, the lowest of these sometimes vague or lacking in males. Belly white, washed with blue in males. The largest specimens are about 3 inches in snout-to-vent length.

General Distribution.—Eastern half of the United States from Wyoming and Texas eastward to Maryland and Florida.

Florida Range.—Found throughout the state from Pensacola to the Keys.

Habitat.—Open places, digging burrows and remaining inactive underground in cold weather.

Lygosoma laterale (Say)

Brown Skink

General Appearance.—A very small, shiny brown lizard.

Distinguishing Characters.—Easily recognized by the small size, the absence of light stripes on the back, the lack of supranasals, and the "window" in the lower eyelid.

Description.—Scales 26-32 around body, smooth, rounded, and flat. Lower eyelid with a transparent patch, median subcaudals slightly enlarged. Color brown, light above, and with a broad dark brown band from tip of snout along side, which is clearly defined above but fades into lighter brown below except on neck and head. Belly light.

General Distribution.—Eastern United States from New Jersey to Kansas, southward to the Gulf of Mexico.

Florida Range.—Throughout the state.

Habitat.—Hammocks and other closed or nearly closed woods.

Eumeces egregius (Baird)

Striped Red-tailed Skink *(Plate 54)*

General Appearance.—A small, shiny lizard with a reddish tail.

Distinguishing Characters.—The reddish (pink to orange) tail distinguishes this form from all other eastern lizards except *onocrepis,* and from that the present species differs in its continuous light stripes (not fading at mid-body) and its two rows of enlarged mid-dorsal scales.

Description.—Scales 20-22 around middle of body. Postnasal lacking; supralabials 6 or 7; supraoculars 3. Ear opening largely concealed by a big scale. Median pair of scale rows distinctly wider than adjacent rows. Grayish to brown above, with a light stripe running along middle of second scale row from snout to base of tail, this line bordered above by a dark brown stripe. Ground color of sides bordered below by a somewhat vague lateral light stripe from snout along labials and on fifth or sixth scale rows to base of tail. Belly whitish or cream. Tail pink to orange. Snout-to-vent length about 2 inches.

General Distribution.—Extreme southeastern United States.

Florida Range.—As now defined the species is discontinuously distributed, occurring in northern Florida and the panhandle southward to Marion County and in the Florida Keys. There are obviously two forms involved, but they have not been separated taxonomically.

Habitat.—Sandy areas. Most abundant near salt water.

Eumeces onocrepis (Cope)
Brown Red-tailed Skink

General Appearance.—A small, shiny, red-tailed lizard.

Distinguishing Characters.—Distinguished by the red tail, the few (18-22) scale rows, incomplete stripes on the side of the body, and the unenlarged scales of the mid-dorsal pair of rows.

Description.—Scales big, shiny, 18-22 (usually 20) around the body, the two median rows of scales no larger than adjacent rows or only slightly so. Ground color yellowish-brown, lighter posteriorly. Shoulder with a dark-edged light stripe coming from rostral; this fades on the back third of the body. No median lines on head or body. Belly whitish, usually finely speckled. Tail pink to orange. Maximum snout-to-vent length about 2¼ inches.

General Distribution.—Restricted to Florida.

Florida Range.—Peninsular Florida, from Lake County southward to Dade County.

Habitat.—Dry hammocks and old dune terrain, rosemary scrub, high pine, and their cultural equivalents; found mainly underground.

Eumeces laticeps (Schneider)
Greater Five-lined Skink *(Plate 54)*

General Appearance.—A fair-sized, sometimes very big-headed, shiny lizard with an undeservedly sinister look.

Distinguishing Characters.—Recognized by this combination of features: 5 or 7 light lines or none; 1 postnasal; postlabials lacking or much reduced; the widened median row of scales under the tail; the relatively large size.

Description.—Supralabials 7 or 8; a postnasal and 2 postmentals present; postlabials lacking or single, or 2 and much reduced; scales 28-34 around body (usually 30-32). Intercalary row of lateral scales on fourth toe entering third phalanx. Juvenile coloration like that of *fasciatus* except that there may be an additional, usually vague, light line from axilla to groin. The fading of the color pattern in mature specimens is more extensive than in either *fasciatus* or *inexpectatus*. Maximum snout-to-vent length about 5 inches; in males this long, the head is red and very wide and swollen.

General Distribution.—Illinois, Missouri, and Texas southward to the Gulf and eastward to the Atlantic.

Florida Range.—North Florida and the panhandle southward to Marion County.

Habitat.—Woods; most frequent in mesic hammock.

Eumeces inexpectatus Taylor
Florida Five-lined Skink *(Plate 54)*

General Appearance.—A medium-sized often striped, and sometimes blue-tailed lizard.

Distinguishing Characters.—The combination of a postnasal scale, 5 stripes (if any), and the unwidened median row of subcaudal scales distinguish this from all other skinks.

Description.—Supralabials 7 or 8; postlabials 2, of good size. Scales 29-36 (usually 30-32) around body. Intercalary scale row on side of fourth toe not reaching third phalanx. Median subcaudals not (or very slightly) wider than adjacent rows. Juvenile coloration black with 5 distinct light lines, and below these, on each side, a less well defined light stripe. The dorsolateral line occupies the fifth scale row or parts of the fourth and fifth. Tail blue above. This pattern fades with age and old males become red-headed. Maximum snout-to-vent length 3½ inches.

General Distribution.—Southeastern states from Virginia to Louisiana.

Florida Range.—All Florida, including the Keys.

Habitat.—Open woods and scrub lands. Often abundant near salt water. Less arboreal than *laticeps*.

Eumeces fasciatus (Linnaeus)
Common Five-lined Skink

General Appearance.—A medium-sized, shiny lizard often with stripes and a blue tail.

Distinguishing Characters.—The combination of a body either with 5 lines or without lines; a single postnasal; broadened median scales under the tail (if not regenerated); 2 large postlabials; and the short intercalary row of scales on the fourth toe (on first 2 phalanges only) will distinguish this lizard.

Description.—Supralabials 7. Scales 25-31 around the body (usually 28-30). In young, ground color of body black, with 5 narrow light lines, the middle one dividing on the nuchals, passing along the edges of the frontal and reuniting on the rostral. The lateral light line extending from side of head through ear above base of foreleg and just above insertion of hind leg. Between these 2 light stripes there is on each side a dark stripe covering 1 full and 2 half rows of scales. Tail blue above. This coloration fades in old females and may disappear in old males, which may show only a brown lateral stripe; and may become red-headed. Snout-to-vent length about 3 inches (maximum 3⅛ inches).

General Distribution.—Eastern North America from southeastern South Dakota, Oklahoma, and central Texas eastward through southern Ontario to the Atlantic states, where it ranges from southeastern New England to Florida.

Florida Range.—Known only from Calhoun County.

Habitat.—Woods with debris, rock piles, or rotting logs.

Neoseps reynoldsi Stejneger
Florida Sand Skink *(Plate 54)*

General Appearance.—A small, shiny, burrowing lizard with hardly any toes.

Distinguishing Characters.—Easily recognized by the very weak limbs (the anterior almost completely lacking); the few shiny scales; and the reduced eyes protected by a lower eyelid with a translucent "window" in its center.

Description.—Scales smooth, overlapping, in 16 rows around the body; the dorsal pair of rows enlarged. Belly concave with a keel on either side. Ear opening hidden. Snout sharp, flattened. Foreleg more reduced than rear, its length little or no greater than distance from eye to nostril; foreleg one-clawed, hind leg two-clawed. Ground color grayish to brown, with a spot on each of the scales in the 2 enlarged mid-dorsal rows. Second and third scale rows marked by a vague longitudinal stripe. Side of head with a dark band from snout through eye, fading into a dark area on the side of the body. Snout-to-vent length about 2⅜ inches.

General Distribution.—Restricted to Florida.

Florida Range.—Central Florida; known from Alachua, Lake, Highlands, and Polk counties. Perhaps introduced into Dade County.

Habitat.—Old dune terrain in light sand; rosemary scrub, high pine, and their cultural modifications, burrowing and coming to the surface beneath logs.

Rhineura floridana (Baird)
Florida Worm Lizard *(Plate 52)*

General Appearance.—A lizard that looks like an earthworm.

Distinguishing Characters.—Easily known by the absence of limbs and eyes and by the ringed, wormlike body.

Description.—Body with about 250 rings of scales, largest below and smallest above, with 25-36 scales in each ring. Rostral and nasals located ventrally, the snout formed by a single big scale. Ear openings absent. Tail short, flattened, and covered above with tubercular scales. Color whitish, pinkish, or pale lavender. Maximum length a little less than a foot.

General Distribution.—Restricted to Florida.

Florida Range.—Central and northeastern Florida, from Columbia and Alachua counties southward to Highlands County.

Habitat.—Well-drained sandy soil, often found just beneath a leaf-mold layer, but also common in ploughed fields.

Carphophis amoena amoena Say
Worm Snake

General Appearance.—A small, glossy brown snake with a short, sharp-pointed tail.

Distinguishing Characters.—Known by the combination of a wormlike head not distinct from the neck, 13 rows of smooth scales, a loreal, and 5 upper labials.

Description.—Scales smooth, in 13 rows; ventrals average about 118 in males, in females about 124; subcaudals average 35 in males, 27 in females. Two internasals present, nasal plate not divided, no preoculars, loreal reaching the orbit, upper labials 5, lower labials 6. Color above uniform opalescent brown, belly bright pink. Rarely reaching a length of a foot, usually less than 10 inches. The tail is short, about ⅙ or less of the total length, tapering to a sharp point.

General Distribution.—From Connecticut and New York southward to central Florida and westward into the Appalachian Mountains.

Florida Range.—Northern Florida southward to Pinellas County.

Habitat.—Usually found under stones, or logs, or in rotting wood in moist forested areas.

Abastor erythrogrammus (Latreille)
Rainbow Snake *(Plate 56)*

General Appearance.—A large, heavy-bodied, shiny, gaudily-striped snake.

Distinguishing Characters.—Scales in 19 rows at mid-body, nearly all smooth. No preoculars; loreal present, reaching eye; two internasals.

Description.—Scales smooth and burnished except a few on the back near the tail which are weakly keeled. Scales in 19 rows at mid-body. Ventrals about 180; subcaudals 36-41. Tip of tail with a horny spine. Two internasals; no preoculars; loreal present, with postfrontal forming anterior margin of orbit; 2 postoculars. Upper labials 7; lower labials 8-10. Ground color bluish-black, with 3 narrow red dorsal stripes, and on each side a yellow to reddish stripe on first and second (lowermost), and part of third, rows of scales. Belly red, each ventral with a blue-black blotch near each end; most of them with a blotch near the middle also. Adults average about 4 feet in length.

General Distribution.—From Charles County, Maryland, southward to Florida and Alabama.

Florida Range.—Northern and north-central Florida southward to Marion County.

Habitat.—Swampy situations, spring runs, calcareous streams; often underground.

Farancia abacura abacura (Holbrook)
Horn Snake

General Appearance.—A large, shiny, black-and-red snake with a short tail.

Distinguishing Characters.—No pit between eye and nostril; a single internasal, no preoculars, loreal reaching eye; upper labials 7-8, lower labials 8-10. Each side of body with 53 or more red markings which on the neck come to within 3-4 rows of each other.

Description.—Scales in 19 rows, smooth except a few keeled on back near the tail; ventrals about 172, subcaudals 47. A single internasal; loreal present, with prefrontal forming anterior margin of orbit; no preoculars; 2 postoculars. Ground color bluish-black to black, sides with usually 53 or more somewhat triangular red markings which in the neck region are separated from those on the other side by no more than the width of 3-4 scale rows. Belly red, the color continuous with red of markings on sides. Black markings on sides extending onto belly. Said to reach a length of 6 feet but average only about 4 feet.

General Distribution.—Florida and eastern Alabama northward through Georgia in the coastal regions to south-central Virginia.

Florida Range.—Throughout the state except for the extreme western part of the panhandle.

Habitat.—Marshes, swamps, drainage ditches, and sloughs.

Farancia abacura reinwardti Schlegel
Western Horn Snake

General Appearance.—A big, shiny, black-and-red snake with a short tail.

Distinguishing Characters.—Like *F. a. abacura*, except that the red markings on the sides are usually 52 or fewer and not so pointed dorsally, and that those of the two sides in the neck region are separated by 8 or 9 scale rows.

General Distribution.—Extreme western Florida, westward along the Gulf Coast into eastern Texas, northward in low lands to southeastern Missouri and southern Indiana.

Florida Range.—Extreme western part of the panhandle.

Habitat.—Marshes, swamps, drainage ditches, and sloughs.

Diadophis punctatus punctatus (Linnaeus)
Southern Ring-necked Snake (*Plate 55*)

General Appearance.—A very small, black snake with a yellow neck ring.

Distinguishing Characters.—May be identified easily by the small size, the black back, yellow to orange belly and the yellow ring, often broken medially, around the neck, and the presence of a loreal plate.

Description.—Scales in 15 rows, smooth. Anterior temporal single; 2 internasals, 2 preoculars, and 2 postoculars; loreal present. Upper labials 8, lower labials 8. Anal divided. The back is a uniform dark gray to shiny black except for a yellow neck ring which is about the width of 2 scales. The belly is yellow to orange with a row of large semicircular black spots down the center. Average adult about a foot long, but reaches a maximum length of 18-20 inches.

General Distribution.—The southeastern states northward as far as northern North Carolina.

Florida Range.—Distributed throughout the entire state.

Habitat.—Usually in moist situations; often near water, under logs, bark, and in the less water-logged sphagnum beds.

Rhadinaea flavilata (Cope)

Yellow-lipped Snake (*Plate 55*)

General Appearance.—A small, smooth-scaled, brown snake.

Distinguishing Characters.—May be distinguished by the uniform rich reddish or golden-brown color above, the unmarked yellow belly and the yellow lips.

Description.—Scales in 17 rows, smooth. Ventrals about 126; subcaudals about 77. Two internasals; loreal present; one preocular; 2 postoculars. Upper labials 7, lower labials 9. The color above is usually reddish-brown to golden-brown with a velvety iridescence and sometimes with a suggestion of a narrow median dark stripe. There is a dark band from the eye to the corner of the mouth. Lips and belly yellow, a few black spots on some of the labials. Reaches a maximum length of at least 15½ inches, but most adults average about a foot in length.

General Distribution.—From Carteret County, North Carolina, southward along the coast to central Florida; westward to Louisiana.

Florida Range.—Northern and central Florida southward to Indian River County.

Habitat.—Damp situations in flatwoods and hammocks, under logs, loose bark, or other debris. Ideally, flatwoods at the borders of cypress ponds.

Heterodon platyrhinos Latreille

Common Hog-nosed Snake

General Appearance.—A very stout-bodied, blotched or black snake with an upturned nose.

Distinguishing Characters.—*Heterodon* may be distinguished from other genera by the upturned, keeled rostral plate. This species of hog-nosed snake has no group of small scales separating the prefrontals, while in *H. simus* such scales are present.

Description.—Scales in 25 rows, keeled except the lower 2 or 3 rows which may be smooth or very weakly keeled. Ventrals 123 to 148; sub-caudals 39-56. Rostral plate upturned and with transverse keel, making a shovel-like snout. The two internasals and the anterior part of prefrontals usually separated by the narrow azygous (sometimes rudimentary or wanting in south Florida individuals). Loreal present. Eye bordered (except above) by numerous small oculars (usually about 9). Upper labials 8, lower labials 11. Anal divided. Ground color gray, yellow, or even reddish. Pattern intricate and variable, usually consisting of a main series of about 28 quadrate dorsal blotches on the body, and one or more series of smaller lateral blotches. Some individuals are almost solid black above. Belly greenish-yellow with indistinct dark blotches; sometimes solid black; underside of tail lighter than belly. Average length about 2 feet, but occasionally reaching 3½ feet.

General Distribution.—New Hampshire southward through Florida and westward to Minnesota, Oklahoma, and Texas.

Florida Range.—Throughout the entire state except on the Keys.

Habitat.—High pine and upland hammock.

Heterodon simus (Linnaeus)
Southern Hog-nosed Snake

General Appearance.—A small, very stout-bodied, blotched snake with conspicuously upturned nose.

Distinguishing Characters.—The very much upturned, keeled rostral plate distinguishes *Heterodon* from other Florida genera. The prefrontal plates are separated by a group of small scales and the under surface of the tail is similar in color to the belly; these characters distinguish *simus* from *platyrhinos*.

Description.—Structurally much like *H. platyrhinos*, but stouter and shorter and much less inclined to play dead. The azygous plate is encircled posteriorly by a group of small scales not found in *platyrhinos*. The head is broader and shorter than in that form with the rostral more upturned. The color is usually pale, never nearly black, and the ventral surfaces of both tail and body are unmarked white. Usually less than 18 inches long.

General Distribution.—North Carolina southward to Florida; up the Mississippi Valley to Indiana.

Florida Range.—Northern Florida southward into the peninsula as far as Pinellas County.

Habitat.—Upland hammocks; dry floodplains of rivers; wire grass flatwoods; fields and groves.

Opheodrys aestivus (Linnaeus)
Rough Green Snake

General Appearance.—A small, very slender, bright green snake.

Distinguishing Characters.—Can be identified by its slender form, keeled scales, and bright green color (which may become blue in preservative).

Description.—Scales keeled, in 17 rows. Ventrals 154 to 163; subcaudals 111 to 135. Internasals 2; loreal present; usually 1 preocular. Upper labials 7, lower labials 8. Color above uniform light green, below whitish or yellow. May reach a length of 3½ feet; averages about 28 inches.

General Distribution.—Connecticut southward to Florida and the Gulf states and northward in the Mississippi Valley to Kansas, Illinois, and Ohio.

Florida Range.—Found throughout the state.

Habitat.—Hammocks; high pine and flatwoods; in bushes and trees.

Coluber constrictor paludicolus Auffenberg and Babbitt
Everglades Racer

General Appearance.—A slim, blue-gray racer of medium size.

Distinguishing Characters.—Similar to the Southern Black Racer in dentition, body form, and scalation, but differing in the much lighter dorsal color and the usually white or very dilute blue belly.

Description.—As in *priapus* there are 17 rows of smooth scales, reduced to 15 rows posteriorly. The ventrals range from 177-190, average 184; the subcaudals range from 99-117, average 107. Total length divided by tail length is 3⅕-3⅘. Color above bluish-gray to olive and rarely tan. Belly white, yellowish or bluish-white, sometimes with bluish or brown blotches. Chin usually white. Eyes most frequently red, sometimes amber or yellow. Young with 42-65 reddish-brown dorsal saddles alternating with reddish, rounded lateral spots, and with the belly pinkish or pinkish-white, with or without scattered spots. Adults about 45 inches long; extreme length about 5½ feet.

Range.—Florida, in two discontinuously placed populations. One of these occurs on Cape Canaveral, Brevard County. The other inhabits the Everglades from Hendry County eastward to central Palm Beach County, westward to Cape Sable.

Habitat.—Most frequently seen in limestone flatwoods.

Coluber constrictor priapus Dunn and Wood
Southern Black Racer

General Appearance.—A good-sized, slim, black snake.

Distinguishing Characters.—Readily recognizable by the slim active body, 17 rows of smooth scales, evenly and velvety black unmarked dorsal surface and slaty venter, and the 15 scales around the posterior end of the body.

Description.—Scales unkeeled, in 17 rows (reduced to 15 rows before vent). Ventrals about 178 (154-199); subcaudals 67-119. Upper labials 6-9, usually 7; lower labials 7-10, usually 8. Preoculars 2, or rarely 3; postoculars 2 or 3. Loreal present, longer than high. Temporals often 2+2+2. Uniform black above with a satiny luster. Throat and a variable expanse of the anterior venter usually white. Eyes brownish or reddish. Young marked with 47-73 brownish-red saddles along the back, and alternating with these a series of lateral spots; the belly is also spotted. Usual length about 3 feet, maximum length 58 inches.

General Distribution.—Southeastern coastal plain.

Florida Range.—All Florida, including the Keys, except the Everglades and Cape Canaveral, where another subspecies occurs.

Habitat.—Widely distributed. Usually most numerous in forest borders or fence row thickets through open fields.

Coluber flagellum flagellum (Shaw)
Eastern Coachwhip (Plate 57)

General Appearance.—A long, slim, whiplike, and very fast-moving snake.

Distinguishing Characters.—Adults readily recognized by the two-color body, the front part being black and the back part tan; the young may be known by the 17 rows of smooth scales, reduced to 11-13 at back end of body, and the dark brown crossbands on light brown ground color, distinct on anterior part of body and fading posteriorly.

Description.—Scales smooth, in 17 rows, reduced to 13, 12, or rarely 11 posteriorly. Ventrals 188-201; subcaudals 96-119. Upper labials usually 8; lower labials 9-11, usually 10. Preoculars 2, the lower very small; postoculars 2; temporals 2+2+2; loreal present, much higher than long. Color very dark brown anteriorly, the head almost black; posteriorly the dark brown gradually fades, and the hind third is light brown. Young with a variable number of distinct dark crossbands, each from 1 to 3 scales wide, separated by light bands 1 to 2 scales wide. Usual size of adults about 6 feet, with the maximum length about 8 feet.

General Distribution.—Southeastern United States from North Carolina to Kansas and Texas.

Florida Range.—Throughout Florida except for the Keys.

Habitat.—Most frequently seen in high pine-turkey oak; but found in nearly any open country with well-drained soil. Partial to gopher holes as a retreat.

Drymarchon corais couperi (Holbrook)
Indigo Snake *(Plate 56)*

General Appearance.—A large, rather thick-bodied, smooth, blue-black snake.

Distinguishing Characters.—May be recognized by the plain blue-black color, the single anal plate, and the 17 rows of smooth scales.

Description.—Scales smooth, glassy, in 17 rows. Ventrals about 190; subcaudals 60. Internasals 2; loreal present; preoculars 2; postoculars 2. Anal plate undivided. Color above a uniform blue-black; below, an unmarked slate-blue except for some reddish sometimes on the throat, chin, and sides of head. One of our largest snakes with a recorded maximum length of 7 feet 9 inches; although the average adult is only about 5 feet long.

General Distribution.—South Carolina southward to Florida and westward to Louisiana.

Florida Range.—Throughout the entire state.

Habitat.—High pine land in north and central Florida; dry glades, tropical hammocks, and muckland fields in south Florida; flatwoods.

Elaphe guttata guttata (Linnaeus)
Corn Snake *(Plate 58)*

General Appearance.—A medium-sized, gaily-colored snake with red-brown blotches.

Distinguishing Characters.—Strikingly set off by the 40 red, black-edged dorsal blotches, the spear-shaped blotch between the eyes, the black-checkered belly, the 2 rows of smaller spots on each side, the slightly keeled dorsal and unkeeled lower lateral scales, and the divided anal.

Description.—Scales weakly keeled to smooth, usually in 25-27-25-23-21-19 rows, as counted from neck region to region of the vent. Ventrals 207-235; subcaudals 65-71. Upper labials 8; lower labials 11. Loreal slightly longer than high; 1 preocular, 2 postoculars. Temporals usually 2+3+4. Ground color above reddish-brown to grayish with a series of 37-48 dorsal red blotches. These are black-edged and, on the front end of the body especially, have their corners extended anteriorly and posteriorly so as to meet, or almost meet, adjacent markings. Each side with 2 series of light reddish or orange spots, black-edged and irregular in shape, and smaller than the dorsal markings and alternating with them. Belly strongly marked with black-and-white checkering, the black blocks larger anteriorly. Top of head with a spear-shaped mark. Adults average about 3 feet in length.

General Distribution.—Southern New Jersey southward through Florida, westward to the Blue Ridge, and through Tennessee into Arkansas and Louisiana.

Florida Range.—Throughout mainland Florida.

Habitat.—Widely distributed; hammocks, deep sand pinelands, and flatwoods; fields and buildings.

Elaphe guttata rosacea (Cope)
Pink Rat Snake *(Plate 58)*

General Appearance.—A medium-sized, pinkish, blotched snake.

Distinguishing Characters.—Very similar to *E. g. guttata,* from which its less intense dorsal color pattern and plain, or nearly plain, yellowish belly distinguish it. The ground color is cream to buff, much lighter than the corn snake, and the spots are pink to vermilion, with the lateral series often nearly obsolete. The belly varies from yellow to orange, and while often marked anteriorly with a suggestion of the checkering of *guttata*, this is usually faint and is nearly or quite lacking posteriorly. Usual adult length 3½ to 4 feet.

General Distribution.—Restricted to Florida.

Florida Range.—The Florida Keys and the Marquesas Keys.

Habitat.—Hammocks, cultivated areas, and buildings.

Elaphe obsoleta deckerti Brady
Deckert's Rat Snake *(Plate 59)*

General Appearance.—A medium-sized, yellowish, striped snake.

Distinguishing Characters.—Very similar to *E. o. quadrivittata*, from which it differs in having a yellow chin and throat, a usually pinkish belly, and a pink to red iris; from *E. o. rossalleni* it differs in having narrow, well-defined longitudinal stripes, a pink instead of orange belly, a black tongue, and a dull yellowish-brown or olive overcast on the dorsum instead of a bright orange bloom. No structural differences between *deckerti*, *rossalleni*, and *quadrivittata* have been found. While live specimens of *deckerti* are usually recognizable, a short time in preservative tends to weaken or obliterate the color features that characterize the race.

General Distribution.—Restricted to Florida.

Florida Range.—Southernmost Florida from Miami to Cape Sable and Key Largo.

Habitat.—Widely distributed. Hammocks and fields; in and around buildings.

Elaphe obsoleta quadrivittata (Holbrook)
Yellow Rat Snake *(Plate 59)*

General Appearance.—A medium-sized, tan, brown-striped snake.

Distinguishing Characters.—Easily recognized by the presence of 4 dark brown longitudinal stripes on tan dorsal ground color; no blotches above except in juveniles. Blotched young may be recognized by the narrow, broken postorbital line.

Description.—Scale rows 27 at mid-body; 5-8 median rows keeled. Ventrals 225-242, average 235; subcaudals 85-100, average about 91. Upper labials 8, lower labials 10; loreal present, longer than high. Dorsal coloration olive to tan or brown, with 4 longitudinal stripes each covering 1 row of scales and half of each adjacent row. Space between dorsal and lateral bands involving 4 whole and 2 half rows; space between dorsal bands involving 3 whole and 2 half rows. Young with a series of dorsal blotches (like those of *spiloides* and *williamsi*) which later become connnected by the longitudinal stripes and finally are lost. Maximum length about 7 feet.

General Distribution.—Cape Hatteras, North Carolina, southward into Florida.

Florida Range.—Peninsular Florida, possibly extending westward to Madison County in the north, and ranging southward to Lake Okeechobee (except for the Levy County territory occupied by *williamsi*), where it is gradually replaced by *rossalleni*.

Habitat.—Widely distributed. Open woods, common in and around buildings.

Elaphe obsoleta rossalleni Neill
Everglades Rat Snake *(Plate 59)*

General Appearance.—A medium-sized snake with bright orange ground color.

Distinguishing Characters.—Very similar to *E. o. quadrivittata* and *E. o. deckerti* in scalation and body form and in having 4 longitudinal stripes. Distinguished by the bright orange dorsal ground color; the red tongue; the usually orange belly and throat; and by the fact that the dark stripes are usually diffuse, vague, or nearly lacking. The characters of the race are striking in life but scarcely discernible in preserved material.

General Distribution.—Restricted to Florida.

Florida Range.—Northern Dade and Monroe counties northward to Palm Beach, Glades, and Charlotte counties, and perhaps occurring occasionally in the rat snake populations of Sarasota and Martin counties.

Habitat.—Swampy or wooded areas, glade-land, prairies, and salt marshes. Somewhat arboreal.

Elaphe obsoleta spiloides (Duméril, Bibron and Duméril)
Whiteoak Snake

General Appearance.—A medium-sized, blotched, grayish or whitish snake.

Distinguishing Characters.—Recognized by the weakly keeled scales, with some of the lower rows unkeeled, the divided anal, the gray dorsal ground color, and series of dark dorsal blotches alternating with smaller lateral spots which are not connected by longitudinal stripes.

Description.—Scales in 25 rows at mid-body, the median 11 rows keeled, the rest smooth. Ventrals 234-250, average 238; subcaudals 70-89, average 81. Loreal small, longer than high; preocular 1, postoculars 2. Ground color gray to orange. Above with 30-35 dark chocolate-brown, faintly black-margined blotches on body and 12 on tail. Sides with 2 rows of smaller alternating blotches. Belly yellowish-white, more or less blotched with black except the foremost part which may be immaculate. Side of head with a black stripe from back of orbit to angle of mouth. Maximum length about 6 feet.

General Distribution.—The Florida panhandle northward to central Georgia, western Tennessee, and eastern Arkansas.

Florida Range.—The panhandle, eastward to Leon County and perhaps to Union County.

Habitat.—Open woods and fields.

Elaphe obsoleta williamsi Barbour and Carr
Gulf Hammock Whiteoak Snake

General Appearance.—A medium-sized, striped and blotched snake.

Distinguishing Characters.—Closely similar to *quadrivittata* and *spiloides* in scalation and body proportions but differing from both in its coloration, which includes gray to white ground color and longitudinal stripes connecting a series of dorsal and lateral blotches. It has the stripes of *quadrivittata* and the blotches and whitish ground color of *spiloides* and is thus directly intermediate between the two, and it intergrades completely with their populations in neighboring areas. That the *williamsi* pattern is stable throughout a considerable, well-marked range in the western part of the peninsula, however, seems to us ample basis for retention of the name despite an absence of structural differences.

General Distribution.—Restricted to Florida.

Florida Range.—Levy County, principally in the Gulf Hammock region.

Habitat.—Wooded areas generally. Partly arboreal.

Pituophis melanoleucus mugitus Barbour
Florida Pine Snake *(Plate 60)*

General Appearance.—A large, rusty brown, blotched snake with a bad temper and an awful hiss.

Distinguishing Characters.—May be distinguished by the usual presence of 4 prefrontals, the 27-31 rows of scales, some of which are keeled, and the undivided anal plate.

Description.—Scales in 27-31 rows, the 4 outer rows smooth, the fifth through seventh weakly keeled, the rest keeled. Ventrals 218-235, subcaudals 53-67; 2 internasals; usually 4 prefrontals; 1 preocular; 3 postoculars. Anal plate undivided. Ground color rusty brown, with 3 series of darker brown blotches, often indistinct, especially on anterior part of body. Adults average about 5 feet, but lengths up to 6 feet 6 inches have been recorded.

General Distribution.—Florida and extreme southern Georgia.

Florida Range.—Known almost throughout Florida, from Escambia County southward to Palm Beach County.

Habitat.—High pinelands; sandy places.

Lampropeltis doliata doliata (Linnaeus)
Scarlet King Snake *(Plate 60)*

General Appearance.—A small, gaudy snake with bright yellow, red, and black rings.

Distinguishing Characters.—Scales in 19 rows; the pattern of red, yellow, and black rings more or less encircling the body; snout reddish to the tip (black in the poisonous coral snake).

Description.—Scales smooth, usually in 19 rows; ventrals average about 175 (152-193); subcaudals 32-48. Anal single. Upper labials 7, lower labials 8. One preocular, usually 2 postoculars; loreal present; internasals 2. Pattern consists of 15 to 25 pairs of black rings encircling the body, and enclosing narrow rings of yellow. Black pairs separated by broad red rings; black rings sometimes are broken on the belly; red and yellow rings sometimes blotched with black on the belly. Posterior part of head crossed by a black band but the nose is plain reddish, never marked with black. Adults average about 15 inches in length with the maximum about 23½ inches.

General Distribution.—Central Kentucky and North Carolina southward through Louisiana and Florida.

Florida Range.—Distributed throughout the state.

Habitat.—High pine; upland and mesophytic hammock; under logs and loose bark—especially that of pine.

Lampropeltis calligaster rhombomaculata (Holbrook)
Brown King Snake

General Appearance.—A smooth, brown, dark-blotched snake.

Distinguishing Characters.—Scales smooth, in 21 or 23 rows; anal undivided. Body pattern of black-edged brownish blotches that do not extend onto belly.

Description.—Scales smooth, in 21 or 23 rows at mid-body; ventrals 191-213; subcaudals 31-55; anal plate undivided. Upper labials 7, lower labials 8 or 9; 1 preocular; 2 postoculars; loreal present; 2 internasals. Head small, not much wider than neck. Body pattern of 48 to 68 mid-dorsal blotches, reddish-brown with narrow black border, and an alternating row of irregular smaller blotches on the sides. Ground color a lighter brown, yellowish on lower sides. In some adults, pattern so obscure as to leave a nearly uniform brown color above. Belly white to yellowish, checked with dark brown. Average length about 3 feet; longest known specimen 3 feet, 9 inches.

General Distribution.—Maryland to central Florida, southeastern Mississippi, and eastern Tennessee.

Florida Range.—Northern Florida, southward in the peninsula as far as Lake County.

Habitat.—Little is known of the habits and habitat of this species beyond the fact that it is a burrower, being most often captured when dug up accidentally.

Lampropeltis getulus getulus (Linnaeus)
Common King Snake

General Appearance.—A medium-sized, smooth, black snake with narrow white or yellow crossbands.

Distinguishing Characters.—Scales smooth, in 21 or 23 rows; anal plate undivided. Body black with 23-52 narrow, pale crossbands that fork on lower sides and unite with adjacent bands to form a chain-like pattern.

Description.—Scales smooth, in 21 or 23 rows. Ventrals 203 to 224; subcaudals 38 to 58, anal undivided. Upper labials 7; lower labials 9; 1 preocular; 2 postoculars; 2 internasals; loreal present. Body generally black, with 23 to 52 narrow crossbands of white or yellow. These divide on the lower sides and join a series of quadrate spots of the same color. Other dorsal scales in the dark areas may have a light central spot. Belly checkered with black or brown and white or yellow.

Average adult size about 3½ feet, but lengths up to 5 feet, 9 inches have been recorded.

General Distribution.—Central New Jersey, southward east of the Alleghenies to central Florida and westward to southeastern Alabama.

Florida Range.—Northern Florida southward to Orange and Lake counties.

Habitat.—Generally distributed; most often in the vicinity of water; upland hammocks.

Lampropeltis getulus floridana Blanchard

Florida King Snake *(Plate 64)*

General Appearance.—A good-sized, dark snake, speckled and obscurely crossbanded.

Distinguishing Characters.—Similar to *L. g. getulus* except for the color pattern. In this form there are more crossbands (46 to 85, average 66) and the bands do not fork on the sides. There is a lateral series of light vertical spots alternating with the crossbands. The ground color is dark brown or blackish, but each scale has a light white or yellowish spot which tends to obscure the banding. This subspecies intergrades with *L. g. getulus* in northern and central Florida and with *L. g. brooksi* south of Lake Okeechobee.

General Distribution.—Restricted to Florida.

Florida Range.—Central and southern Florida except for the extreme southern tip of the peninsula.

Habitat.—Generally similar to that of *L. g. getulus.* Numerous around cypress ponds, in savannah lands and prairies.

Lampropeltis getulus brooksi Barbour

Brooks' King Snake *(Plate 64)*

General Appearance.—A good-sized, dull yellow snake, speckled with dark brown.

Distinguishing Characters.—Similar to *L. g. floridana* in form and scalation but differing in coloration. Color dull yellow, the scales being light in color and the dark ground color restricted to a small area on the tip of each scale. The pattern of bands is but slightly or not at all apparent. This form intergrades in the northern part of its range with *L. g. floridana.*

General Distribution.—Restricted to Florida.

Florida Range.—Extreme southern Florida in Collier, Dade, and Monroe counties.

Habitat.—Tropical hammocks, limestone flatwoods, glade-land; fields and edificarian situations.

Lampropeltis getulus goini Neill and Allen
Chipola King Snake

General Appearance.—A medium-sized, dark brown snake with wide, light crossbands.

Distinguishing Characters.—Generally similar to *L. g. getulus* but with fewer and wider crossbands—21 usually, instead of 25-50. It also may be more slender and usually has 21 rows of scales. Crossbands covering 4 to 8 scales, still wider low on sides. Scales of light crossbands yellow-white with posterior half of each black. Scales of dark parts a rich brown, each with a vaguely defined light spot. Belly brown with yellow streaks.

General Distribution.—Restricted to Florida.

Florida Range.—Known only from the valleys of the Chipola and Apalachicola rivers in Gulf and Calhoun counties, Florida.

Habitat.—Unknown, but probably the same as that of *L. g. getulus.*

Stilosoma extenuatum Brown
Short-tailed Snake (*Plate* 58)

General Appearance.—A small, slim snake with a very short tail.

Distinguishing Characters.—A slender, very short-tailed snake with 70 to 80 brown blotches on a gray background above, and with the belly marked with dark blotches that extend onto the sides.

Description.—Scales smooth, in 19 rows. Ventrals 235-260; subcaudals 40-44. Body very slender, tail very short. Preocular and loreal lacking, prefrontals and third upper labial forming anterior border of orbit. Silvery-gray above with about 60 black-bordered brown spots from head to vent and about a dozen more on the tail; belly silvery-gray with black blotches that extend upward across the 3 rows of scales, opposite the intervals between the dorsal dark blotches.

General Distribution.—Peninsular Florida.

Florida Range.—The central part of the peninsula. Known from Alachua, Marion, Citrus, Lake, Seminole, Orange, Hernando, Pinellas, and Polk counties.

Habitat.—Longleaf pine—turkey-oak ridges; rosemary—sand-pine scrub; upland hammocks.

Cemophora coccinea (Blumenbach)
Scarlet Snake

General Appearance.—A small, slim snake with bright red, yellow, and black crossbands, a pink nose, and a plain belly.

Distinguishing Characters.—Distinguished by the presence of a loreal; the red, yellow, and black pattern; the interrupting of the crossbands below by the plain white of the belly; the pink, pointed snout, and by the fact that the red bands are much wider than the black ones. Although superficially similar to the poisonous coral snake, this snake is easily recognized by its plain white belly and red snout.

Description.—Scales smooth, in 19 rows. In Florida specimens, ventrals range from 153-182 in males, 163-185 in females; subcaudals 41-52 in males, 38-48 in females. Anal single. Loreal and a single preorbital present. Upper labials 6, lower labials 8, the fifth the largest. Pattern of red, black, and yellow crossbars that do not continue around the belly, which is plain white or yellow; snout pointed, it and the top of the head before the eyes red. Average length about 16 inches.

General Distribution.—New Jersey to Florida, Louisiana, and Oklahoma.

Florida Range.—Found throughout mainland Florida.

Habitat.—Widely distributed, usually found burrowing in leaf mold, rotten logs, moist loam, or even muck and peat soil; under bark of dead trees.

Natrix sipedon fasciata (Linnaeus)
Banded Water Snake

General Appearance.—A heavy-bodied dark snake with crossbands along the entire length of the body.

Distinguishing Characters.—No pit between the eye and nostril, rostral normal, anal plate divided, scales strongly keeled, in 21-25 rows. Dorsal surface with 19-33 crossbands, belly with conspicuous squarish spots.

Description.—This water snake has heavily keeled scales in 21-25 rows; 126-137 ventrals; subcaudals about 68. There are generally 3 postoculars but only 1 preocular. Loreal present; 2 internasals and a normal rostral. Upper labials usually 8, lower usually 10. The entire length of the body is marked with crossbands of brown; these are broad on the back, much more narrow on the sides. The bands vary in number from 19 to 33, and in mature individuals may become obscure, the back being a uniform dark brown to black, but on the lower sides there will usually be seen triangular areas of the lighter ground color which normally separates the bands. The belly is yellowish, conspicuously marked with quadrate reddish spots. Average length 3 feet, maximum 4 feet.

General Distribution.—From North Carolina to southeastern Louisiana on the coastal plain except peninsular Florida.

Florida Range.—Northern Florida reaching into the peninsula as far as Marion County. Replaced by *clarki* along the Gulf.

Habitat.—Nearly any aquatic situation.

Natrix sipedon pictiventris Cope
Florida Banded Water Snake (*Plate 61*)

General Appearance.—A brownish snake with crossbands along the full length of the body.

Distinguishing Characters.—Like *N. s. fasciata* from which it may be separated by its ventral pattern of transverse blotches, often enclosing oval light spots (solid squarish spots in *fasciata*).

Description.—Generally like *N. s. fasciata*. Scale rows usually 25, ventrals 120-129. The dorsal bands average 29 (24-35). The ventrals are often bordered with red or black which may form transverse blotches, sometimes enclosing a light oval spot. Ground color above light brown, below yellow or white. Average length 32 inches, maximum 4 feet.

General Distribution.—Confined to Florida.

Florida Range.—Peninsular Florida except where replaced by *compressicauda* and *taeniata*.

Habitat.—Aquatic situations, seeming to prefer small marshes and bodies of water rather than the larger rivers and lakes.

Natrix sipedon clarki (Baird and Girard)
Clark's Water Snake (*Plate 61*)

General Appearance.—A rough-scaled snake striped above and below.

Distinguishing Characters.—Similar to *N. s. fasciata*, from which its stripes separate it. Distinguished from *taeniata* by having unbroken stripes and from other striped water snakes by having 21-23 rows of scales instead of only 19.

Description.—Scalation much as in *N. s. fasciata*. The body posteriorly and first third of tail somewhat compressed. The head is dirty brown and blackish; the body pattern consists of 4 longitudinal brown stripes, each 2 scales wide, separated by brown to grayish areas of about equal width. Ventrally the pattern includes 2 dark stripes, dark brown to brick red, separated by a yellow stripe, the latter not extending onto the tail. Adult specimens average about 2 feet in length.

General Distribution.—Gulf Coast from Corpus Christi, Texas, to Florida.

Florida Range.—Gulf Coast of Florida from Cedar Keys westward. South of Cedar Keys it intergrades with *N. s. compressicauda*.

Habitat.—Found only in brackish and salt marshes, mangrove swamps, and on coastal island beaches.

Natrix sipedon compressicauda (Kennicott)
Flat-tailed Water Snake

General Appearance.—A rough, medium-sized snake, somewhat compressed posteriorly, with variable pattern, the most consistent feature of which is the dark belly with a mid-ventral row of light spots.

Distinguishing Characters.—Distinguished from other water snakes by having the posterior part of the body and first third of the tail somewhat compressed, sub-triangular in cross section, higher than wide; and from *N. s. clarki* and *N. s. taeniata* by having no continuous dorsal stripes.

Description.—In scalation similar to *N. s. fasciata*. The color pattern is extremely variable, usually comprising a series of about 30 dark, ill-defined crossbands so shaped as often to run together to form vague longitudinal stripes. The belly is dark with a median row of light spots, one on each scute. Some specimens are entirely without markings and may be black, reddish, or even straw-colored above. Average length 2 feet; maximum, 32 inches.

General Distribution.—Coastal regions of the southern half of peninsular Florida and adjacent coast of Cuba.

Florida Range.—Coastal regions south of Pasco and Volusia counties; the Keys.

Habitat.—Salt marshes, mangrove swamps, bays, estuaries, salt and brackish water canals and ditches; sea beaches.

Natrix sipedon taeniata Cope
East Coast Striped Water Snake

General Appearance.—A small, rough-scaled, slender, striped snake.

Distinguishing Characters.—Similar to *N. s. clarki*, from which it is separated easily by the breaking of the lateral stripes into a series of blotches.

Description.—In scalation like *N. s. clarki*. The color pattern is distinct, the stripes being always more or less interrupted or broken. The mid-dorsal olive stripe is broken occasionally by bars connecting the two dorsolateral dark stripes which show a tendency to break into blotches posteriorly. The lateral stripes are broken into a series of roughly diamond-shaped blotches. The belly is black with a median row of cream-colored, broadly lanceolate spots. Ventral surface of tail black, except for the inner ends of the subcaudal scutes which are light. The largest individuals taken so far have all been less than 2 feet in length.

General Distribution.—The East Coast of Florida.

Florida Range.—Known only from Volusia and Indian River counties, Florida.

Habitat.—Tidal flats and sloughs.

Natrix cyclopion cyclopion (Duméril and Bibron)
Green Water Snake

General Appearance.—A rough-scaled, heavy-bodied, dark greenish to olive snake with a poorly defined color pattern.

Distinguishing Characters.—May be distinguished from other water snakes (except *N. c. floridana*) by the presence of one or more small scales separating the eye from the upper labials[*] and from other genera of snakes by the absence of a pit between eye and nostril, and by having a normal rostral, divided anal plate, and strongly keeled scales. Differs from *N. c. floridana* in ventral color pattern and in average scale counts.

Description.—Scales usually in 27 rows in males, 29 in females; the first row smooth, the second on each side weakly and all others strongly keeled. Ventrals average about 142 (136 to 148); subcaudals 68-78 in males, 57-70 in females. Preocular 1, postoculars 2, and suboculars 2 or 3. Upper labials 8, lower labials 10-13. The dorsal color pattern, often indistinct in larger individuals, consists of a series of about 50

---

[*] These subocular scales are very rarely found in *N. taxispilota* too.

mid-dorsal dark bars alternating with a lateral series on a greenish to brownish ground color. Belly yellowish anteriorly, the posterior two-thirds dark brown marked with semicircles of white or yellow on each scute. Average length 3 feet; maximum 4 feet, 2 inches.

General Distribution.—Lowlands of the Mississippi Valley from southern Illinois southward to the Gulf, from Texas eastward to west Florida.

Florida Range.—Escambia and Leon counties in the western panhandle.

Habitat.—Lakes, marshes, rivers, usually in quiet waters.

Natrix cyclopion floridana Goff
Florida Green Water Snake

General Appearance.—A heavy-bodied, dark greenish to brown snake with a whitish belly and a usually poorly developed pattern.

Distinguishing Characters.—Very near *N. c. cyclopion*, from which it may be separated by the different ventral color pattern, which is whitish with small dark spots along edges in this subspecies while in *cyclopion* it is yellowish on the anterior third of the belly and dark brown marked with numerous semicircles of white or yellow on the posterior two-thirds.

Description.—Scales usually in 29 rows in males, 31 in females. Ventrals average about 137 (132 to 142); subcaudals 80-84 in males, 69-78 in females. Lower labials 7-14. Sides with about 52 dark bars (*cyclopion* has about 45). Average length about 3 feet, though it may reach a length of 5 feet.

General Distribution.—Coastal region of South Carolina, southern Georgia, and Florida east and south of Tallahassee.

Florida Range.—Northeastern and peninsular Florida, from Leon County eastward and southward.

Habitat.—Shores of larger lakes; marshes; quiet waters generally.

Natrix erythrogaster erythrogaster (Forster)
Red-bellied Water Snake

General Appearance.—A dark, heavy-bodied, rough-scaled snake with an orange belly.

Distinguishing Characters.—Much the same in most characters as *N. s. fasciata*, from which it may be easily separated by the unmarked reddish-orange belly and plain dorsal color.

Description.—Scales in 23-25 rows, strongly keeled; ventrals about 152; subcaudals 64-85. One or 2 preoculars separate the large loreal from the eye; lower labials usually 10; postoculars 3. Color above usually a uniform black to reddish-brown, rarely exhibiting faint cross-barring. Very young individuals display a pattern of dark dorsal blotches with a row of smaller alternating lateral spots. Both young and old have an almost unmarked reddish-orange belly. Average length, 3 feet; maximum 4 feet 8 inches.

General Distribution.—Maryland, southward to Florida and Alabama.

Florida Range.—Occurs very rarely, and only in northern Florida southward to Alachua County.

Habitat.—Near water but possibly less aquatic than most water snakes. Apparently most frequent near rivers.

Natrix taxispilota (Holbrook)
Brown Water Snake *(Plate 62)*

General Appearance.—A heavy-bodied, rough, blotched, brown snake.

Distinguishing Characters.—No pit between eye and nostril; two postoculars, lower labials usually 11 to 13. All dorsal body scales strongly keeled, in 27-33 rows. Head subtriangular, posteriorly much wider than neck. A mid-dorsal row of about 25 squarish dark spots on the body.

Description.—Scales strongly keeled, in 27-33 rows; ventrals 139-151; subcaudals 70-99. Two anterior temporals; 1 preocular, 2 postoculars; loreal present, not reaching eye. Lower labials 11-13; upper labials 8. Anal divided. The ground color is reddish-brown. There is a mid-dorsal row of 25 squarish, blackish blotches on the body. Below, on each side, there is a row of similar but smaller blotches, well separated from and alternating with the mid-dorsal row. Belly usually yellow, heavily blotched with dark brown or black. This is the largest of our water snakes, reaching an alleged length of nearly 6 feet and averaging about 3½ feet.

General Distribution.—Coastal regions from Virginia to central Florida and westward possibly to Louisiana.

Florida Range.—Northern and central Florida, southward to Lake and Lee counties.

Habitat.—Rivers, creeks, alluvial swamps, and lakes.

Natrix rigida (Say)
Striped Water Snake

General Appearance.—A small, rough-scaled, striped snake.

Distinguishing Characters.—Separated from other Florida water snakes by having only 19 rows of scales at mid-body and no light stripe on lower sides. Differs from other snakes by these and the following characters: no pit between eye and nostril, 2 postoculars, 2 preoculars, anal divided, 2 internasals.

Description.—Scales keeled except for lower row on each side, in 19 rows at mid-body; ventrals about 135; subcaudals about 52-58. Loreal present; upper labials 7; lower labials 11. Ground color olive-brown above, paler on the sides, with 2 dark brown stripes along the back. Belly yellow with 2 rows of black or brown spots which may join to form 2 lines running the length of the body near the mid-line Tail unmarked underneath or with 1 irregular median stripe. Adults average about 16 inches; maximum length about 29 inches.

General Distribution.—Coastal plain of Virginia southward into northern Florida; westward to Louisiana.

Florida Range.—Northern Florida southward into the peninsula as far as Marion County.

Habitat.—Alluvial swamps, burrowing in the mud.

Natrix septemvittata (Say)
Queen Snake

General Appearance.—A slender, brownish, rough-scaled, striped snake.

Distinguishing Characters.—Shares many of its characters with N. *rigida* from which it is easily separated by the presence of a narrow yellow stripe along each side.

Description.—Dorsal scales heavily keeled, in 19 rows at mid-body; ventrals average about 144 (136-150) in males, 142 (135-148) in females; subcaudals, males 64-84 (average 78), in females 61-72 (average 68). Loreal present; 2 preoculars, usually 2 postoculars; upper labials 7, lower labials usually 10; 2 internasals. Anal divided. Ground color above chocolate-brown to chestnut with sometimes (usually in smaller specimens) 3 dark stripes down the back. In most adults these stripes are obsolete but all have a yellow stripe 1½ scales wide along each side on the first and second rows of scales; this is bordered below by a chestnut-brown band on lower half of first row of scales and edges of ventral scutes. Belly yellowish, with 2 rows of gray to brown spots forming 2 stripes, which join to form a single mid-ventral stripe under throat and for a short distance in front of vent and under tail. Adults average about 20 inches in length—maximum about 33 inches.

General Distribution.—Pennsylvania, Ohio, Michigan, and Wisconsin southward through Alabama and Georgia into Florida.

Florida Range.—The Apalachicola drainage. Known from Jackson and Liberty counties.

Habitat.—Stream and pond borders.

Seminatrix pygaea pygaea (Cope)
Black Swamp Snake *(Plate 62)*

General Appearance.—A small, black snake with a red belly.

Distinguishing Characters.—The combination of 17 rows of scales, all smooth except for a few on the tail, the loreal separated from the eye by a preocular, and a divided anal plate distinguish this species from all others. It may be distinguished from *S. p. cyclas* by an average difference in ventral numbers and also by the ventral pattern (see descriptions).

Description.—A small relative of the water snakes having 17 rows of scales which are smooth except for a few on the tail; 113-126 ventrals (mean about 120); 46-56 caudals in males, 36-46 in females. Loreal present, separated from the eye by a usually single preorbital. Body color above uniformly dark, almost black, but some scales (most often the lower rows on each side) may have a thin pale line through their centers. The belly is red with a variable pattern of dark markings. Some individuals having almost none, while some have a series of irregular lateral spots, 2 to a ventral, usually near its anterior edge. In others the dark color of the upper surface extends inward on both sides along the anterior edge of each ventral for about a third of its length. These extensions have the form of narrow bars, the posterior margins of which are usually curved. Maximum length about 16½ inches.

General Distribution.—South Georgia and northern peninsular Florida to the middle panhandle.

Florida Range.—Northern Florida from Jackson and Gulf counties eastward and southward almost to Tampa and Orlando and into Brevard County.

Habitat.—Cypress swamps, wet prairies, ponds, and ditches; usually associated with water hyacinths.

Seminatrix pygaea cyclas Dowling
South Florida Swamp Snake

General Appearance.—A small, black snake with a red belly.

Distinguishing Characters.—Similar to *S. p. pygaea*, from which it may be separated by the ventral pattern (see descriptions) and by usually having more ventrals.

Description.—The ventrals range in number from 112-121, with the mean about 116. The ventral pattern consists of short triangular dark markings on the outer anterior margins of the ventrals. These usually extend inward about ¼ the length of the ventral and have relatively straighter posterior edges and broader bases than the dark bars of *pygaea pygaea*. Maximum length about 16½ inches.

General Distribution.—Restricted to Florida.

Florida Range.—Southern Florida from Polk County southward to the tip of the peninsula.

Habitat.—Cypress swamps, wet prairies, ponds, and ditches, especially those with water hyacinths.

Storeria dekayi wrightorum Trapido
Wright's Brown Snake

General Appearance.—A small, brownish, crossbarred snake.

Distinguishing Characters.—Distinguished by the 17 rows of keeled scales without apical pits, the small size and distinct head, and the crossbarred back.

Description.—Scales strongly keeled, in 17 rows. No apical pits. Ventrals 122-130, average 125, in males; 127-134, average 131, in females; subcaudals 52-61, average 57, in males; 43-56, average 49, in females. Head scales normal; preocular single, about twice as high as broad; postoculars 1 or 2, rarely 3. Color brownish above with about 75 black crossbands, each about ½ scale wide and extending to the sixth scale row. Vague lateral spots alternating with the crossbars. Whitish below with scattered dark specks at the outer edges of the ventrals. A small snake, with the maximum length 16 inches.

General Distribution.—Atlantic coastal plain from Virginia to the Mississippi Basin, including only the northernmost part of Florida.

Florida Range.—The panhandle; known from Gadsden, Liberty and Escambia counties.

Habitat.—Frequent near water, under stones or debris.

Storeria dekayi victa Hay
Florida Brown Snake (Plate 63)

General Appearance.—A small, brownish snake with a more or less spotted back.

Distinguishing Characters.—Recognized by the 15 rows of keeled, unpitted scales, the divided anal, the brownish color and spotted back, and the crossbanded nape.

Description.—Scales strongly keeled, in 15 rows. Ventrals 131-142 in males, 130-148 in females; subcaudals 52-69 in males, 46-64 in females. Head scales normal. One preocular, twice as high as broad; postoculars usually 2; anterior temporal single, posterior temporals usually 2. Upper labials 7; lower labials usually 7. Ground color brown or tan with a variable amount of spotting of the scales of the sixth row. Back of head with a light crossband followed by a dark crossband on the occiput. Belly whitish, often with a black spot on the outer end of each ventral. A small snake, usually under 16 inches in length.

General Distribution.—Southeastern Georgia southward throughout the peninsula of Florida.

Florida Range.—From northern Florida southward to Cape Sable; replaced by another race, *S. d. wrightorum*, in the panhandle.

Habitat.—Marshes; ponds and ditches; under debris or logs, and frequently found among water hyacinths.

Storeria occipitomaculata obscura Trapido
Florida Red-bellied Snake

General Appearance.—A tiny, black snake with a red or pinkish belly not regularly spotted.

Distinguishing Characters.—Readily known by the small size, the black dorsal color, and red or pink belly, and the 15 rows of keeled, pitless scales.

Description.—Dorsal scales in 15 rows, keeled, without apical pits. Ventrals 114-116, average 114.7, in males; 111-126, average 119 in females; subcaudals 46-56, average 51 in males; 42-48, average 44.6 in females. Color black above, with a light neck ring; belly red or pink. Total length usually less than 7 inches.

General Distribution.—Georgia in the coastal plain and Florida southward to the middle of the peninsula.

Florida Range.—Northern Florida southward to Marion County and possibly to Charlotte County. Intergrades with *S. o. occipitomaculata* in the western panhandle.

Habitat.—Woods, in leaf mold; gardens and flower beds, in light loam or debris.

Haldea valeriae valeriae (Baird and Girard)
Eastern Ground Snake

General Appearance.—A tiny, brown snake with a narrow head.

Distinguishing Characters.—In the small size, the absence of the preocular, and in other features, this species agrees with *H. striatula*, but differs in having 15 rows of smooth scales (sometimes a few keeled on the posterior part of the body), usually 6 (instead of 5) upper labials and a slightly lower number of ventrals (115-132), and of subcaudals (23-38).

Description.—Scales smooth except for a few at the rear end of the body, usually in 15 rows. Ventrals 115-121 (average 117) in males; 120-132 (average 123) in females. Subcaudals 31-38 (average 36) in males; 23-31 (average 27) in females. Upper and lower labials usually 6; preocular lacking, loreal and prefrontal entering eye. Brown or grayish above, sometimes with 4 longitudinal rows of black dots; belly whitish. Average length about 8 inches; maximum length a foot or less.

General Distribution.—New Jersey to Florida, Alabama, and southern Ohio.

Florida Range.—Northern Florida, southward to Alachua County.

Habitat.—Leaf mold in hammocks; in and under logs in various types of situations.

Haldea striatula (Linnaeus)
Rough Ground Snake *(Plate 63)*

General Appearance.—A tiny, brown snake with a narrow head.

Distinguishing Characters.—Recognized by the absence of the preocular, the usually single internasal, the 17 rows of keeled scales and the small size.

Description.—Scales all keeled, in 17 rows. Ventrals 119-131 (average 125) in males; 119-136 (average 127) in females. Subcaudals 40-50 (average 44) in males, 34-40 (average 38) in females. No preocular, prefrontal and loreal entering the eye; one internasal (rarely double); one postocular; 5 upper labials. Brown or grayish above, sometimes with a vague light band across back of head; belly yellowish to pink. Maximum size less than 12 inches.

General Distribution.—Virginia to Florida, eastern Oklahoma, and Texas.

Florida Range.—Northern Florida southward to Alachua County.

Habitat.—Acid flatwoods, under logs about cypress ponds and bay-heads.

Liodytes alleni alleni (Garman)
Allen's Swamp Snake

General Appearance.—A small-headed, brown, dark-striped snake.

Distinguishing Characters.—Recognized by the smooth scales (except for a few keeled ones above vent), the single internasal, the divided anal, the 5 longitudinal stripes and the plain or casually spotted belly. Distinguished from *L. a. lineapiatus* by the absence of a regular mid-ventral dark line or row of spots.

Description.—Scales in 19 rows, smooth except on posterior part of body and anterior part of tail, where they are strongly keeled. Ventrals 110-133 (average 122); subcaudals 49-63 (average 57). One internasal; loreal present, in contact with prefrontal. One preocular, 3 or 4 postoculars. Upper labials 8, lower 11. Dorsal pattern of longitudinal stripes including a broad, dark-brown, mid-dorsal band 5 or 6 scales wide, a pale yellowish or olive stripe below this, another brown stripe under this, and lower still, on the bottom 3 rows of scales, a yellow or olive band. Belly uniform yellowish, with or without scattered dusky patches, sometimes tending toward linear median arrangement. Average length about 16 inches.

General Distribution.—Florida and southern Georgia.

Florida Range.—Northeastern Florida southward through the peninsula to the Okeechobee area, where it intergrades with *L. a. lineapiatus.*

Habitat.—Marshes and swamps; sloughs and sphagnum bogs. Lakes and streams with dense beds of water hyacinths.

Liodytes alleni lineapiatus Auffenberg
Everglades Swamp Snake

General Appearance.—A small-headed, brown, dark-striped snake.

Distinguishing Characters.—Scales smooth except for a few on top of the tail which are keeled; anal divided, internasal single; body with 5 longitudinal stripes. This subspecies is distinguished from the related *L. a. alleni* by the presence of a distinct mid-ventral row of black spots or vague mid-ventral line. In other features of its form, structure, and coloration this subspecies is like the more widely distributed *alleni*. Maximum size about 21 inches.

General Distribution.—South Florida.

Florida Range.—Central Glades County southward through the southern tip of the peninsula. Apparently not on the Florida Keys.

Habitat.—Marshes and shallow lakes with organic bottom and much floating or emergent vegetation.

Thamnophis sauritus sackeni (Kennicott)
Southern Ribbon Snake *(Plate 57)*

General Appearance.—A very slim, dull brown snake with a yellowish stripe on each side.

Distinguishing Characters.—Set apart by its undivided anal plate, sharply keeled scales, and unmarked belly.

Description.—This very slender, long-tailed snake, like other garter snakes, has very heavily keeled scales. It has 19 rows of dorsal scales, 154-171 ventrals, and 109-134 caudals. There are 2 nasals and a loreal. Color above dull brown to olive with a bright yellow stripe on each side on third and fourth rows of scales. Belly yellowish-white, unmarked. Adults average about 2 feet in length, of which $\frac{1}{4}$ to $\frac{1}{3}$ is tail.

General Distribution.—Coastal and lowland regions from Charleston, South Carolina, to the Mississippi River.

Florida Range.—Found throughout the state except for the Keys.

Habitat.—Partly aquatic; generally found near bodies of water, in marsh borders and wet meadows.

Thamnophis sirtalis sirtalis (Linnaeus)
Common Garter Snake

General Appearance.—A medium-sized snake, olive to brownish in color with 3 distinct longitudinal yellowish stripes.

Distinguishing Characters.—Scales conspicuously keeled; ventral plate undivided; small black markings on edges of ventrals near their ends.

Description.—Scales sharply keeled, in 19 rows. Ventrals 137-167; caudals 54-84. Upper labials usually 7, nasals 2; loreal present. Ventral plate undivided. This snake shows considerable variation in color and some in details of the spotting and checkerboard pattern to be seen on the dorsal surface between 3 distinct stripes, one of which runs down the middle of the back and one along each side on second and third rows of scales. Belly greenish-white to yellowish, with narrow black edging near ends of plates. Reaches a length of about 2½ feet.

General Distribution.—Ranges from southern Canada, north of Lake Superior, to Nova Scotia, and southward throughout the United States east of the Mississippi River.

Florida Range.—Found throughout the state.

Habitat.—While this species favors open moist situations, it is found in practically every type of environment within its range.

Tantilla coronata coronata Baird and Girard
Crowned Snake

General Appearance.—A tiny, tan snake with a black head.

Distinguishing Characters.—A very small, rear-fanged snake with 15 rows of smooth scales, an undivided anal, no loreal, and 2 internasals. Differs from *T. c. wagneri* in its higher ventral and subcaudal count and in the more well-defined light band on back of head.

Description.—Scales smooth, opalescent, in 15 rows. Ventrals 131-144, average 135, in males; 139-148, average 143, in females; subcaudals 42-51, average 46 in males; 41-46, average 44 in females. One preorbital in contact with postfrontals, which extend down to labials. Upper labials 7. Body uniformly pale reddish-brown to tan, lighter below. Top of head with a black cap bordered behind by a distinct light crossband that crosses the tips of the parietals and is bordered behind by a black band on the nape. Maximum length 13 inches.

General Distribution.—Virginia to Louisiana and western Kentucky.

Florida Range.—The panhandle.

Habitat.—Loose soil or leaf mold, under rocks and logs.

Tantilla coronata wagneri (Jan)
Florida Crowned Snake

General Appearance.—A tiny, tan snake with a black head.

Distinguishing Characters.—This small, rear-fanged snake may be distinguished by the smooth scales in 15 rows, the divided anal plate, the 2 internasals and the absence of the loreal. The ventral and subcaudal scale counts are lower than in *T. c. coronata* and the light band on back of head is much less definite.

Description.—Scales smooth, opalescent, in 15 rows. Ventrals in the males 119-129, in females 123-145. Subcaudals vary from 50-67 in males and from 41-59 in females. Anal plate divided; loreal absent.

One preorbital is in contact with the postfrontals which extend down to labials. Upper labials 7. Body uniformly pale reddish-brown to tan, lighter beneath. The head is dark, almost black, with an obscure light crossband followed by a narrow dark band on the nape. Not known to exceed 10 inches in length.

General Distribution.—The peninsula of Florida.

Florida Range.—The peninsula of Florida.

Habitat.—Most often found under stones and other objects not too deeply imbedded in friable soil in open woods or fields.

Micrurus fulvius barbouri Schmidt
South Florida Coral Snake

General Appearance.—A small snake with a gaudy, stick-candy pattern of red, yellow, and black rings and a black nose.

Distinguishing Characters.—Distinguished as a coral snake by the black nose, the red, yellow, and black rings completely encircling the body, and the short, fixed fangs in the upper jaw. The only difference between this race and the common coral snake is the absence in this form of black pigment in the red rings on the dorsal side of the body.

General Distribution.—Southern Florida.

Florida Range.—Not well defined. Known only from the vicinity of Paradise Key in the Everglades National Park, Dade County.

Habitat.—Hammock and glade-land.

Micrurus fulvius fulvius (Linnaeus)
Common Coral Snake *(Plate 67)*

General Appearance.—A small snake with a gaudy, stick-candy pattern of red, yellow, and black rings, and a black nose.

Distinguishing Characters.—The coral snake is easily recognized by the combination of a black nose, a pattern of rings of red, yellow, and black completely encircling the body, and a pair of short, fixed fangs in the upper jaw. This subspecies is distinguished from the south Florida race, *barbouri,* by the presence of black pigment in the red rings dorsally.

Description.—Scales smooth, in 15 rows. Ventrals 202-238; subcaudals 25-45; anal divided. Loreal lacking, 1 preocular, 2 postoculars. Upper and lower labials 7. Head oval as seen from above, the snout short and rounded. Color pattern of broad black rings each bordered by narrow yellow rings and separated from the next yellow-bordered black ring by a broad red ring. Top of head and snout black. Red rings blotched with black pigment dorsally. Average length, 2 feet; maximum recorded length, 43 inches.

General Distribution.—North Carolina westward to the Mississippi.

Florida Range.—All Florida except the southern tip of the peninsula.

Habitat.—Woodlands generally; perhaps most abundant about wooded lake margins.

Ancistrodon piscivorus piscivorus Lacépède
Cottonmouth Moccasin *(Plate 65)*

General Appearance.—A thick-bodied, broad-headed snake with a dark band on the side of the head and no rattle on the tail.

Distinguishing Characters.—Recognized by the facial pit between eye and nostril, the broad head and thin neck, the lack of a rattle on the tail, and the absence of a loreal, which is present in the closely similar copperhead.

Description.—Scales keeled, in 25 rows. Ventrals, 130-150; subcaudals 38-50, some single, some divided. Anal single. Preoculars 2 or 3; postoculars 2 or 3; loreal lacking. Side of head with a pit midway between and a little below level of eye and nostril. Pattern of 10-15 wide, dark crossbands on brown or olive-brown ground color, old individuals nearly uniform brownish-black. Belly yellowish, dark-mottled. Side of head with a broad dark band from eye to angle of jaw. Average length about 3 feet.

General Distribution.—Virginia to the Gulf states, Arkansas, and Illinois.

Florida Range.—Found throughout mainland Florida.

Habitat.—Woodland ponds and tree-bordered marshes; river swamps.

Ancistrodon contortrix contortrix (Linnaeus)
Southern Copperhead *(Plate 65)*

General Appearance.—A thick-bodied, broad-headed, medium-sized snake with broad, brown crossbands and no rattle.

Distinguishing Characters.—The copperhead may be distinguished by the combination of a facial pit between eye and nostril, a broad head and slim neck, the lack of a rattle on the tail, and the presence of a loreal, which is lacking in the similar cottonmouth moccasin.

Description.—Scales keeled, in 23 rows. Ventrals, 147-154 (average 151); subcaudals not divided, 45-51 (average 47) in males; 43-

45 (average 44) in females. Anal entire. Loreal present; 3 preoculars; postoculars 4 or 5. Pit located midway between, and somewhat below level of eye and nostril. Coloration pale, including pastel shades of tan, buff, or pinkish. There are about 20 (16-21) dark brown, hourglass-shaped crossbands, some so constricted in the middle that they fail to meet. Belly pale with desultory mottling. Average length about 2½ feet.

General Distribution.—Central Maryland to Florida, Illinois, Arkansas, and eastern Texas.

Florida Range.—Known only from the Apalachicola drainage in Gadsden and Liberty counties.

Habitat.—Hammocks and floodplain forests; fields.

Sistrurus miliarius barbouri Gloyd
Florida Ground Rattlesnake (*Plate 66*)

General Appearance.—A small, blotched, hot-tempered rattlesnake.

Distinguishing Characters.—Known by the rattle on the tail, the presence of large plates (instead of small scales) on top of the head and the dorsal and lateral pattern of dark blotches.

Description.—Scales keeled, in 25-23-17 rows. Ventrals 128-144 in males, 132-148 in females; subcaudals 31-39 in males, 26-36 in females. Loreal large, separating preoculars from postnasal. Upper edge of snout sharp. Ground color brownish-gray above. Pattern a median dorsal row of 27-45 dark spots and 3 lateral rows of smaller spots. A bright brown mid-dorsal stripe from nape backward, sometimes to base of tail. Belly light, blotched with gray or black. Average mature length about 2 feet.

General Distribution.—Southeastern South Carolina to southeastern Mississippi.

Florida Range.—Found throughout the state.

Habitat.—Flatwoods; most abundant near lakes and marshes.

Crotalus adamanteus Beauvois
Eastern Diamondback Rattlesnake (*Plate 67*)

General Appearance.—A huge, heavy rattlesnake with a dorsal pattern of diamond-shaped markings.

Distinguishing Characters.—This snake is easily recognized at all ages by the rattle on the tail, the lack of large plates on top of the head back of the eyes and the striking dorsal pattern of light-centered, dark diamonds with yellow borders.

Description.—Scales keeled, in 29 rows. Ventrals, males 165-175; females, 174-182; subcaudals, males 27-32; females 22-26. Upper labials 12-17; lower labials 15-21. Ground color brown or dusky, with 26-34 black or dark brown, diamond-shaped figures, wider than long, each lighter in the center and bordered by a row of light yellowish scales. Head dark above, marked with light lines on sides; rostral usually edged with white; posterior edge of prenasals and supranasals with a vertical light line. The largest North American poisonous snake and one of the heaviest in the world. Average mature length about 5 feet; maximum recorded length (probably in error) 8 feet, 9 inches.

General Distribution.—North Carolina westward in the coastal plain to southeastern Louisiana.

Florida Range.—Found throughout the state.

Habitat.—Widely distributed. Perhaps most abundant in open prairie with clumps of saw palmetto.

Crotalus horridus atricaudatus Latreille
Canebrake Rattlesnake *(Plate 66)*

General Appearance.—A big, crossbanded rattlesnake.

Distinguishing Characters.—This snake is readily recognized by the rattle on the tail, the lack of large plates on top of the head back of the eyes, the pattern of dark crossbands on a lighter background and the mid-dorsal stripe on the fore part of the body.

Description.—Scales keeled, usually in 25 rows. Ventrals 164-179 in males, 168-181 in females; subcaudals 24-31 in males, 20-28 in females. Divided subcaudals 1-6, usually 1-3. Upper labials 12-16, usually 14 or 15; lower labials 13-18, usually 15 or 16. Ground color grayish-brown to pinkish-buff. Head with a conspicuous brown band from eye to beyond angle of mouth. Back with a series of 23-32 dark blotches divided at the mid-line and more or less confluent at their outer edges. Side with a series of narrow black streaks alternating with another series of larger blotches along the lower side. A varyingly conspicuous mid-dorsal stripe extends from nape to tail. Length of adult about 4½ feet, reaching lengths above 6 feet.

General Distribution.—North Carolina to Texas in the coastal plain, northward in the Mississippi Valley to southernmost Illinois.

Florida Range.—Northern Florida southward to Alachua County.

Habitat.—Flatwoods; river bottoms and hammocks.

PLATE 41

CONANT

Upper, Florida Mud Turtle, *Kinosternon subrubrum steindachneri;* 4 miles southwest of Wauchula, Hardee County. Middle, Florida Snapping Turtle, *Chelydra serpentina osceola;* Everglades National Park. Lower, Florida Box Turtle, *Terrapene carolina bauri;* Gainesville, Alachua County.

PLATE 42

CONANT

Upper, Florida Diamondback Terrapin, *Malaclemys terrapin macrospilota* (female above, male below); Cedar Key, Levy County. Lower, Chicken Turtle, *Deirochelys reticularia*; 6 miles east of Gainesville, Alachua County.

PLATE 43

CONANT

Upper, Mobile Turtle, *Pseudemys floridana mobilensis* (young). Middle, Yellow-bellied Turtle, *Pseudemys scripta scripta* (young). Lower, Barbour's Sawback Turtle, *Graptemys barbouri* (young). All from Chipola River, Jackson County.

PLATE 44

CONANT

Upper, Mobile Turtle, *Pseudemys floridana mobilensis* (young) (ventral view); Chipola River, Jackson County. Lower, Yellow-bellied Turtle, *Pseudemys scripta scripta* (young) (ventral view); Chipola River, Jackson County.

PLATE 45

CONANT

Upper, Barbour's Sawback Turtle, *Graptemys barbouri* (adult female); Chipola River, Jackson County. Middle, Yellow-bellied Turtle, *Pseudemys scripta scripta* (adult male); Gainesville, Alachua County. Lower, Florida Red-bellied Turtle, *Pseudemys nelsoni*; Alachua County.

PLATE 46

CONANT

Peninsular Turtle, *Pseudemys floridana peninsularis;* 20 miles south of Ocala, Marion County.

CONANT

Peninsular Turtle, *Pseudemys floridana peninsularis* (ventral view of same).

PLATE 47

CONANT

Upper, Atlantic Green Turtle, *Chelonia mydas mydas;* specimen in Key West Aquarium. Lower, Atlantic Hawksbill Turtle, *Eretmochelys imbricata imbricata;* specimen in Key West Aquarium.

PLATE 48

CONANT

Upper, Atlantic Ridley, *Lepidochelys kempi*; specimen in Key West Aquarium.
Lower, Atlantic Loggerhead Turtle, *Caretta caretta caretta;* specimen in
Key West Aquarium.

PLATE 49

Southern Soft-shelled Turtle, *Amyda ferox ferox;* 2 miles south of Gainesville, Alachua County; photo by John S. Mecham.

American Crocodile, *Crocodylus acutus*; Whitewater Bay, Monroe County; photo by J. C. Dickinson.

PLATE 50

CONANT

Upper, Ashy Gecko, *Sphaerodactylus cinereus* (young); Key West, Monroe County. Lower, Ashy Gecko, *Sphaerodactylus cinereus* (adult); Key West, Monroe County.

CONANT

Upper, Reef Gecko, *Sphaerodactylus notatus* (spotted phase); Key West, Monroe County. Lower, Reef Gecko, *Sphaerodactylus notatus* (striped phase); Key West, Monroe County.

PLATE 51

CONANT

Upper, Yellow-headed Gecko, *Gonatodes fuscus* (male); Key West, Monroe County. Lower, Yellow-headed Gecko, *Gonatodes fuscus* (female); Key West, Monroe County.

CONANT

Upper, Brickell Hammock Anole, *Anolis distichus floridanus*; Miami, Dade County. Lower, Warty Gecko, *Hemidactylus turcicus turcicus*; Key West, Monroe County.

PLATE 52

CONANT

Upper, Key Anole, *Anolis sagrei stejnegeri;* Key West, Monroe County. Lower, Six-lined Racerunner, *Cnemidophorus sexlineatus;* Key West, Monroe County.

CONANT

Upper, Florida Worm Lizard, *Rhineura floridana;* Gainesville, Alachua County. Lower, Common Glass Snake, *Ophisaurus ventralis;* 6 miles east of Gainesville, Alachua County.

PLATE 53

Upper, Coastal Glass Snake, *Ophisaurus compressus;* Marion County; photo by John S. Mecham. Lower, Eastern Long-tailed Glass Snake, *Ophisaurus attenuatus longicaudus* near Chiefland, Levy County; photo by Mark Mooney, Jr., courtesy of the Zoological Society of Philadelphia.

PLATE 54

CONANT

Upper, Striped Red-tailed Skink, *Eumeces egregius;* Cedar Key, Levy County. Lower, Florida Five-lined Skink, *Eumeces inexpectatus;* Everglades National Park.

CONANT

Upper, Florida Sand Skink, *Neoseps reynoldsi;* Polk County. Lower, Greater Five-lined Skink, *Eumeces laticeps* (adult); Micanopy, Alachua County.

PLATE 55

CONANT

Yellow-lipped Snake, *Rhadinaea flavilata;* Burbank, Marion County.

CONANT

Southern Ring-necked Snake, *Diadophis punctatus punctatus;* Placida, Charlotte County.

PLATE 56

CONANT

Indigo Snake, *Drymarchon corais couperi;* Monroe County.

CONANT

Rainbow Snake, *Abastor erythrogrammus;* Santa Fe River, Gilchrist County.

PLATE 57

CONANT

Eastern Coachwhip, *Coluber flagellum flagellum;* Ross Allen's Reptile Institute.

CONANT

Southern Ribbon Snake, *Thamnophis sauritus sackeni;* Monroe County.

PLATE 58

CONANT

Upper, Short-tailed Snake, *Stilosoma extenuatum;* Ocala, Marion County. Middle, Pink Rat Snake, *Elaphe guttata rosacea;* Lower Matecumbe Key, Monroe County. Lower, Corn Snake, *Elaphe guttata guttata;* Gainesville, Alachua County.

PLATE 59

CONANT

Upper, Deckert's Rat Snake, *Elaphe obsoleta deckerti;* Lower Matecumbe Key, Monroe County. Middle, Everglades Rat Snake, *Elaphe obsoleta rossalleni;* Ross Allen's Reptile Institute. Lower, Yellow Rat Snake, *Elaphe obsoleta quadrivittata;* Ross Allen's Reptile Institute.

PLATE 60

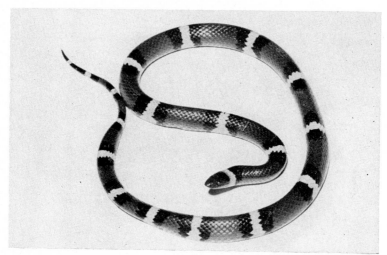

CONANT

Scarlet King Snake, *Lampropeltis doliata doliata;* Ross Allen's Reptile Institute.

CONANT

Florida Pine Snake, *Pituophis melanoleucus mugitus;* Ross Allen's Reptile Institute.

PLATE 61

CONANT

Clark's Water Snake, *Natrix sipedon clarki;* Cedar Key, Levy County.

CONANT

Florida Banded Water Snake, *Natrix sipedon pictiventris;* Clewiston, Hendry County.

PLATE 62

CONANT

Brown Water Snake, *Natrix taxispilota;* Okefinokee Swamp Canal, Georgia.

CONANT

Black Swamp Snake, *Seminatrix pygaea pygaea;* Payne's Prairie, Alachua County.

PLATE 63

CONANT

Rough Ground Snake, *Haldea striatula;* Lynchburg, Texas.

CONANT

Florida Brown Snake, *Storeria dekayi victa;* Payne's Prairie, Alachua County.

PLATE 64

CONANT

Florida King Snake, *Lampropeltis getulus floridana;* Ross Allen's Reptile Institute.

CONANT

Brooks' King Snake, *Lampropeltis getulus brooksi;* Miami Serpentarium.

PLATE 65

CONANT

Upper, Southern Copperhead, *Ancistrodon contortrix contortrix;* Camp Sea Gull, Craven County, North Carolina. Middle, Cottonmouth Moccasin, *Ancistrodon piscivorus piscivorus* (young); Ross Allen's Reptile Institute. Lower, Cottonmouth Moccasin, *Ancistrodon piscivorus piscivorus* (adult); Everglades National Park.

PLATE 66

CONANT

Florida Ground Rattlesnake, *Sistrurus miliarius barbouri;* Everglades National Park.

CONANT

Canebrake Rattlesnake, *Crotalus horridus atricaudatus;* Pecan Island, Port Arthur, Jefferson County, Texas.

PLATE 67

CONANT

Eastern Diamondback Rattlesnake, *Crotalus adamanteus;* Ross Allen's Reptile Institute.

CONANT

Common Coral Snake, *Micrurus fulvius fulvius*; Ross Allen's Reptile Institute

APPENDIX

First-Aid Treatment of Snake Bite

The Following Account is compiled from recent authoritative articles on the treatment of bites of poisonous snakes. We describe here only *first-aid* treatment, since, in the event of a bite, a competent physician should invariably be consulted at the earliest possible moment. The following snakes occurring naturally in Florida are known to be dangerously poisonous and a person bitten by any one of them should have immediate first-aid treatment, followed as soon as possible by a physician's care.

    Eastern Diamondback Rattlesnake—*Crotalus adamanteus*
    Canebrake Rattlesnake—*Crotalus horridus atricaudatus*
    Florida Ground Rattlesnake—*Sistrurus miliarus barbouri*
    Cottonmouth Moccasin—*Ancistrodon piscivorus piscivorus*
    Southern Copperhead—*Ancistrodon contortrix contortrix*
    Common Coral Snake—*Micrurus fulvius fulvius*
    South Florida Coral Snake—*Micrurus fulvius barbouri*

The most important first aid in any case is the prevention of bites. It cannot be emphasized too strongly that the catching or handling of poisonous snakes is nothing less than foolhardy, unless practiced by an expert; and even then it usually leads to eventual accident.

The treatment for the bite of a poisonous snake consists of four major steps:

(1) Prevention and treatment of shock.
(2) Prevention of spread of poison.
(3) Extraction of poison.
(4) Neutralization of poison.

The first three of these steps may come under the category of first aid; the fourth had best be left to a physician.

It is impossible to tell from inspection how serious a bite may be; hence indiscriminate hacking and cutting should be avoided, since more damage may result from this than from the bite itself. Many drugstores stock snake-bite kits, consisting of a tourniquet, a razor blade or similar cutting implement, suction cups, and an antiseptic. Such a kit should be kept readily available to persons who frequent areas in which they may encounter poisonous snakes.

Immediately upon being bitten, apply a tourniquet several inches

above the bite (between the bite and the heart). If a rubber tourniquet from a snake-bite kit is not available, a necktie, belt, or handker-
chief will serve. This should be loose enough so that a finger can be
forced between it and the skin. *A tourniquet that is too tight may
cause serious damage* and THE TOURNIQUET MUST BE RE-
LEASED FOR ABOUT FIVE MINUTES EVERY FIFTEEN MIN-
UTES.

Keep the patient comfortable, warm, and calm and take steps to
obtain medical aid. Under no circumstances allow the patient to run
or to take strong stimulants such as whiskey, since these simply in-
crease the rate of spread of the poison. Avoid panic. It may be con-
soling to know that probably over 75 per cent of bites by poisonous
snakes are not fatal in any case and that perhaps 98 per cent or more
cases recover if adequate treatment is given.

It is well to keep the bitten part below the general level of the body
since this tends to slow down the spread of the poison.

If the snake has injected any appreciable amount of poison, swelling and/or agonizing pain may develop in the region of the bite within five or ten minutes. After swelling or pain develops, make small
incisions (not more than a quarter of an inch deep and a quarter of
an inch across) in the vicinity of the bite and start suction. Suction
can be produced either by the suction cup from a snake-bite kit or by
the mouth (snake poison is harmless to healthy tissues of the mouth
and stomach). If the aid of a physician has not been obtained within
fifteen minutes, release the tourniquet for about five minutes, then
replace it a couple of inches above the line of swelling, making additional incisions in the region of the swelling and applying suction to
these new cuts. Release the tourniquet for about five minutes once
every fifteen minutes. If the swelling advances, continue to make incisions and apply suction until a doctor is reached.

SELECTED REFERENCES

FISHES

BREDER, CHARLES M. JR.
  1929—Field Book of Marine Fishes of the Atlantic Coast. G. P. Putnam's, New York, xxxvii+332, illus.
LA MONTE, FRANCESCA
  1945—North American Game Fishes. Doubleday, Doran, New York, xiv+202, illus.
SCHRENKEISEN, RAY
  1938—Field Book of Fresh-Water Fishes of North America. G. P. Putnam's, New York, xii+312, illus.
SCHULTZ, LEONARD P., and EDITH M. STERN
  1948—The Ways of Fishes. Van Nostrand, New York, xii+264, illus.

AMPHIBIANS AND REPTILES

BARBOUR, THOMAS
  1934—Reptiles and Amphibians, Their Habits and Adaptations. Revised edition. Houghton Mifflin, Boston, xx+129, illus.
BISHOP, SHERMAN CHAUNCEY
  1943—Handbook of Salamanders. Comstock, Ithaca, xiv+555, illus.
CARR, ARCHIE
  1952—Handbook of Turtles. Comstock, Ithaca, xv+542, illus.
SCHMIDT, KARL PATTERSON, and D. DWIGHT DAVIS
  1941—Field Book of Snakes. G. P. Putnam's, New York, xiii+365, illus.
SMITH, HOBART MUIR
  1946—Handbook of Lizards. Comstock, Ithaca, xxi+557, illus.
WRIGHT, ALBERT HAZEN, and ANNA ALLEN WRIGHT
  1949—Handbook of Frogs and Toads. Comstock, Ithaca, xii+640, illus.

INDEX